North American Species
of
HYGROPHORUS

L. R. Hesler
The University of Tennessee

Alexander H. Smith
The University of Michigan

THE UNIVERSITY OF TENNESSEE PRESS

KNOXVILLE

Preface

Since Fries' treatment of *Hygrophorus* in *Epicrisis Systematis Mycologici* (pp. 320–333) in 1838, there has been less confusion over species concepts in this genus than in most other genera of agarics. This situation is due in part at least to the fact that field characters are often critically diagnostic, and the differences between species are often striking.

In North America, once a reasonable sample of the *Hygrophorus* flora had been studied, it was found that most of the apparent confusion here was caused by our attempt to "force" American *Hygrophorus* populations into previously described species where they did not belong. True, there are confusing situations in this genus just as in any other sizable genus of plants, but the various complexes, for instance, do not approach in complexity those which Smith and Singer[1] have encountered among the species of *Galerina*.

The point of greatest difference between various investigators hinges on what constitutes a discontinuity of generic magnitude. Although we held a conservative point of view in our early work, we have given serious consideration since then to the recognition of the genera as Singer (1951) has outlined them. In fact at one time we were almost ready to accept them. We finally returned to our original point of view because we felt that those erecting new genera were simply doing it on the basis of single outstanding characters of odd species, i.e., *Hygroaster*, *Neohygrophorus*, and *Humidicutis*. There is better evidence for recognizing *Hygrotrama* as a genus, but we believe this group connects too clearly with the series *Hygrocybe* to justify generic separation. On last analysis, however, this matter will probably continue to remain one of opinion, as it has in the past. Certainly each investigator may exercise his right of opinion, based on the material he has seen. One point, however, which we would like to make, is that it is to us more realistic to try to arrange the species of *Hygrophorus* in a natural classification within a large genus than to distribute them among a number of genera, and thus create the impression of a degree of discontinuity which we believe does not actually exist.

---

[1] Unpublished studies.

v

Acknowledgments

In a study of this scope, the best can be achieved only with the generous assistance of others. Institutions and individuals have been most helpful in these studies through loans, gifts, and exchanges of collections.

Invaluable beyond estimation has been the loan of type collections. We have been privileged to borrow and to examine fully the types of all available North American *Hygrophorus* species. We acknowledge with thanks these loans from the several institutions and persons listed herewith: The University of Florida, Gainesville (Murrill's Florida types), Dr. Erdman West; Iowa State College, Ames; The University of Massachusetts, Amherst, Dr. Howard E. Bigelow; The New York Botanical Garden, New York City (Murrill's types), Dr. Clark T. Rogerson; The New York State Museum, Albany (Peck's types), Dr. E. C. Ogden and Mr. Stanley Jay Smith; The University of North Carolina, Chapel Hill (Coker's types), Dr. John N. Couch.

Our desire to study Friesian and other European species of *Hygrophorus* has been satisfied to some extent by the gift, loan, or exchange of collections from abroad. Material has thus been made available to us by Dr. Meinhard Moser, Bodenbiologisches Institut, Imst, Austria; Dr. P. Heinemann, Institut Agronomique, Gembloux, Belgium; Dr. Morten Lange, The University of Copenhagen, and Mr. J. P. Jensen, Copenhagen, Denmark; Dr. G. Taylor, Dr. R. W. G. Dennis, and Dr. Derek A. Reid, Royal Botanic Garden, Kew, England; Dr. Marcel Josserand, Lyon, and Dr. G. Métrod, Champagnole, France; Dr. M. A. Donk, Dr. R. A. Maas Geesteranus, and Dr. C. Bas, The University of Leiden, Netherlands; Dr. H. S. C. Huijsman, Cernier, Switzerland.

In addition to loans and gifts of authentic exsiccati, we are deeply indebted to the National Science Foundation for generous grants in support of our field and laboratory studies; and especially to the Office of Science Information Service, Support of Scientific Publications, for a special grant covering the cost of composition, printing, and binding of this volume.

Finally, the entire manuscript has been read with great care by Dr. A. J. Sharp, Professor of Botany, University of Tennessee. Without his sharp-eyed professional criticisms many deficiencies in writing would have been unsparingly imposed on the reader. The original drawings were prepared by the senior author, and the plates were then traced for reproduction by Mrs. Romance Carrier. The photographs were made by us, with a few exceptions noted. To these individuals, for their indispensable help, we offer our thanks in grateful acknowledgment.

L. R. HESLER
The University of Tennessee
Knoxville

ALEXANDER H. SMITH
The University of Michigan
Ann Arbor

Table of Contents

ILLUSTRATIONS

North American Species
of
H Y G R O P H O R U S

Introduction

HISTORY

The history of *Hygrophorus* as a genus may be said actually to date from the treatment given it by Fries in *Epicrisis Systematis Mycologici*, pp. 320–333, 1838. The name was actually published by Fries in 1835 and only a short diagnosis given (see Donk, 1949). Previously, the species were distributed through the genus *Agaricus*. In *Systema Mycologicum I* (Fries, 1821), we find a significant number of those now grouped in section *Hygrocybe* included in the subtribe *Hygrocybi* of tribe *Clitocybe*. Such well-known species as *H. unguinosus, H. psittacinus, H. laetus, H. ceraceus, H. conicus, H. puniceus,* and *H. miniatus* were included among others. In the subtribe *Camarophylli* of tribe *Clitocybe* he included *H. camarophyllus, H. nemoreus, H. pratensis,* and *H. virgineus.* Thus, in the light of later anatomical studies, the confusion between the tribe *Limacium* (*Systema I*, p. 31) and *Camarophyllus* began. In tribe *Limacium* of the *Systema*, Fries included *H. ligatus, H. chrysodon, H. erubescens, H. eburneus, H. discoideus,* and many others. When brought together under the genus *Hygrophorus* in the *Epicrisis* there were twenty species recognized in "Tribe" *Limacium*, sixteen of which are included in the present work. In "Tribe" *Camarophyllus* twelve species were included, three of which have been subsequently placed in section *Hygrophorus* because of their bilateral gill trama. Five of the remainder we have been able to recognize in North America. In "Tribe" *Hygrocybe* the first two species listed are now placed in *Cantharellus.* Of the remaining sixteen we have recognized eleven here in North America. It is readily apparent from this situation that the species known from Europe are for the most part also present in North America. Though many species have since been described both from Europe and North America, it is still true that by far the majority of the well-established (as pertains to our knowledge of them) European species also occur in our flora.

The history of the genus from 1838 to the present has been remarkably uninteresting. Fewer changes have been suggested than in many other agaric genera, and yet the genus is based primarily on a subjective character, the waxy hymenophore. Such changes as have been suggested up until recently merely involved spelling the name differently (see *Hydrophorus* Quélet), or simply involved raising the "Tribes" of the treatment in *Epicrisis* to generic rank. Kummer (1871) was apparently the first to do this; though both Wünsche (1877) and Karsten (1879) accepted these rankings, they were not recognized by many investigators until comparatively recent times, and even now there still exists a difference of opinion. The family *Hygrophoraceae* (as *Hygrophores*) was proposed by Roze (1876), and most recently was taken up by Singer (1951) in which treatment he recognized five genera: *Hygrophorus* for species with bilateral gill trama (Fries *Limacium* and part of *Camarophyllus*), *Camarophyllus* for those with interwoven hymenophoral trama, *Hygrocybe* with "parallel" trama in the hymenophore, and *Bertrandia* Heim, characterized by species with a latex and pseudocystidia. Heim (1957) has since added the genus *Bertrandiella* and *Hodophilus*. *Neohygrophorus* was erected to care for *Hygrophorus angelesianus* Smith, an *Hygrophorus*-like fungus with amyloid spores. Singer (1958) himself, in his studies of the genus, has also proposed a number of segregates. *Hygrotrama* was erected for species intermediate between *Hygrocybe* and *Camarophyllus* but having an hymeniform epicutis over the pileus. *Humidicutis* (Singer, 1958, p. 225) was proposed for certain species of *Hygrocybe* which lacked clamp connections on the hyphae of the carpophore and which possessed unstable pigments in the presence of 10% KOH. *Hygroaster* was proposed by Singer (1955) for the nodulose-spored *Hygrophorus nodulisporus* Dennis. These constitute the bulk of the names used for *Hygrophori*. Mention should be made of the fact, however, that the name *Godfrinia* Maire was applied to *Hygrophorus conicus* Fr. (Maire, 1902), that Murrill used the spelling "*Hydrocybe*" in the *North American Flora*, vol. 9, 1916, following Karsten's misspelling of the name in 1879. *Hydrocybe* is a name generally associated with the genus *Cortinarius*. Also, the name *Hydrophorus* Earle (1909), attributed to Battarea, with *H. coccineus* as type has been proposed. In spite of all the names that have been proposed there has been relatively little variation in the concept that these waxy-gilled, white-spored agarics represented a readily recognizable phylogenetic group.

Fries (1874) was the first, so far as we have ascertained, to suggest groupings below the rank of section (tribes). He proposed five subheadings based on color of the pileus for *Limacium*: "*Albi l. albolutescentes*" for the white to yellowish species, "*Rubentes*" for *H. erubescens* and related species, "*Fulventes l. flavi*" for the brown to tan or bright yellow ones, "*Olivaceoumbrini*" for the olivaceous ones, and "*Fuscocinerei l. lividi*" for the gray to blackish species. We have retained much of this terminology in our recognition of subsections and series in the present work. In *Camarophyllus* and *Hygrocybe* his sub-headings were more of the nature of headings in a text key. Fayod (1889) used the following groupings under the genus *Hygrocybe: Coccineae, Puniceae, Conicae,* and *Mycenae.* He did not assign infrageneric status to them, but in our classification they would be at the series level. Bataille's (1910) classification is the clearest for infrageneric nomenclature which we have seen to date. He recognized *Hygrophorus:* subgenera *Limacium, Camarophyllus,* and *Hygrocybe. Limacium* is divided into sections as follows: *Candidi* and *Colorati.* Section *Candidi* is subdivided into *Ligati* and *Eburnei.* Section *Colorati* is divided into subsections *Pudorini, Aurei, Discoidei, Olivaceoumbrini,* and *Tephroleuci.* Subsection *Pudorini* is divided into series *Exannulati* and *Subannulati.*

The subgenus *Camarophyllus* is divided by Bataille into subsections *Rutili, Virginei, Fornicati, Ovini, Cinerei, Subradiati,* and *Caprini.* Bataille did not specifically designate the rank of his infrageneric categories here, but from the way the text is set up it is reasonable to infer that *Camarophyllus* contained only one section and that the categories mentioned above were at the next lowest level which we interpret to be subsections.

In *Hygrocybe* he recognized section *Laeti* with subsections *Psittacini, Coccinei, Squamulosi, Campanulati* (with two series, *Nigrescentes* and *Laeticolores*), and *Convexi.* Section *Tristes* included subsection *Inolentes* divided into series *Viscosi* and *Sicci,* and subsection *Olidi.*

Lange (1940) recognized *Limacium* as a genus divided into sections (apparently) *Peronata* and *Nudipedia* with the latter further divided into *Tephroleuca* and *Laeticoloria. Camarophyllus* he divided into *Subturbinata* and *Emarginati. Hygrocybe* he divided into *Emarginato-subliberae* and *Adnato-decurrentes*—names clearly intended to be divisions of a text key.

Smith and Hesler (1939) divided *Hygrophorus* into subgenus *Limacium* which was further divided into section *Eu-Hygrophorus* and *Clitocyboides. Eu-Hygrophorus* was further divided into subsections *Albidi, Lutei, Fuliginei,* and *Brunnei.* Section *Clitocyboides* contained subsections *Pallidi, Fulvoincarnati, Erubescentes,* and *Atrocinerei.*

The same authors (1942) established the subgenus *Pseudohygrophorus* containing a single species. Subgenus *Camarophyllus* was divided into section *Microspora* which was further divided into subsections *Impoliti, Odorati, Hymenocephali,* and *Pelliculosi.* Section *Eu-Camarophyllus* was further divided into subsections *Viscidi, Subaquosi,* and *Impoliti*. They divided subgenus *Hygrocybe* into section *Pseudo-camarophyllus* which was further divided into *Laevi* and *Squamulosi*. Section *Eu-Hygrocybe* was divided into *Conici* and *Obtusi*. Section *Viscidipedes* was divided into *Laeti* and *Obscuri*.

Singer (1951) attempted to bring order out of this maze of infrageneric categories and recognized the following: *Hygrophorus sensu stricto* (*Limacium* Fries) divided into section *Candidi* which was further subdivided into subsections *Chrysodontini*, *Pallidini*, and *Eburnei*. Section *Pudorini* he divided into subsections *Erubescentes* and *Fulvoincarnati*. Section *Discoidei* was not subdivided. Section *Colorati* he divided into subsection *Olivaceoumbrini* and *Tephroleuci*. The genus *Camarophyllus* he did not subdivide. *Hygrocybe* was divided into section *Tristes*, section *Coccineae* with subsections *Coccineae*, *Squamulosae*, and *Inopodes;* section *Conicae* with subsections *Conicae* and *Obtusae;* section *Subglutinosae;* and section *Laetae* with subsections *Laetinae* and *Obscurinae*.

A PROPOSED SYNOPSIS

In the present work, for the first time we have given serious thought to the establishment of infrageneric categories in conformity with the International Rules of Botanical Nomenclature. This necessitates some changes due to the Rules having been changed since Singer (1951) published his classification, and other changes because the arrangement we are proposing here differs from previous classifications. Early authors, such as Fayod and Bataille, did not indicate the infrageneric category for most of their groups. We have attempted to use the earliest names and have recognized them at a level which we believe to be consistent with their classification in which they were proposed. The following is an outline of our classification:

Hygrophorus Fries (1835)
Type species: *H. eburneus* Fr.

I. Subgenus *Pseudohygrophorus* Sm. & Hes. (1942)
　　Type species: *H. angelesianus* Sm. & Hes.
II. Subgenus *Hygrophorus*
　　1. Section *Camarophyllopsis* Hes. & Sm.
　　　　Type species: *H. pratensis* Fr.
　　　a. Subsection *Camarophyllopsis*
　　　　(1) Series *Virginei*
　　　　　　Type species: *H. virgineus* (Fr.) Fr.
　　　　(2) Series *Viscidi*
　　　　　　Type species: *H. subviolaceus* Pk.

(3) Series *Camarophyllopsis*

    b. Subsection *Microspori* Sm. & Hes. (1942)

        Type species: *H. microsporus* Sm. & Hes.

    (1) Series *Microspori*

    (2) Series *Pelliculosi*

        Type species: *H. pallidus* Pk.

2. Section *Hygrotrama* (Singer) Hes. & Sm.

3. Section *Hygrocybe* Fr. (1838)

    Type species: *H. miniatus* (Fr.) Fr.

    a. Subsection *Hygrocybe*

    (1) Series *Conici* (Fayod)

        Type species: *H. conicus* Fr.

    (2) Series *Hygrocybe*

    (3) Series *Coccinei* (Fayod)

        Type species: *H. coccineus* (Fr.) Fr.

    b. Subsection *Punicei* (Fayod)

        Type species: *H. puniceus* Fr.

    (1) Series *Punicei*

    (2) (see series *Conici*)

    c. Subsection *Psittacini* Bataille

    (1) Series *Psittacini*

    (2) Series *Obscuri*

        Type species: *H. unguinosus* (Fr.) Fr.

    (3) Series *Puri*

        Type species: *H. purus* Pk.

4. Section *Hygroaster* (Singer) Hes. & Sm.

    Type species: *H. nodulisporus* Dennis

5. Section *Amylohygrocybe* Hes. & Sm.

    Type species: *H. metapodius* Fr.

6. Section *Hygrophorus*

    Type species: *H. eburneus* (Fr.) Fr.

    a. Subsection *Hygrophorus*

    (1) Series *Hygrophorus*

    (2) Series *Chrysodontini*

        Type species: *H. chrysodon* (Fr.) Fr.

    (3) Series *Discoidei*

        Type species: *H. discoideus* (Fr.) Fr.

    (4) Series *Aurei*

        Type species: *H. aureus* Fr.

    (5) Series *Olivaceoumbrini*

        Type species: *H. olivaceoalbus* (Fr.) Fr.

b. Subsection *Camarophylli*

Type species: *H. camarophyllus* (Fr.) Dumée

(1) Series *Clitocyboides*

Type species: *H. sordidus* Pk.

(2) Series *Pudorini*

Type species: *H. pudorinus* Fr.

(3) Series *Rubentes*

Type species: *H. erubescens* Fr.

(4) Series *Fulventes*

Type species: *H. arbustivus* Fr.

(5) Series *Camarophylli*

General Considerations

MACROSCOPIC CHARACTERS

PILEUS

COLOR—Color has assumed an importance in the classification of *Hygrophorus* at the levels of subsection and below since the time of Fries and is reflected in the names used for subgenera and series in the present work. It is thus important to have accurate data on color and a consistent nomenclature for it. To accomplish this we have used Ridgway (1912). All who have used this volume are aware that it is out of print and not easy to acquire; moreover, when it is available, the problem of matching colors is at times difficult. In addition, when attempting to match colors in the gray series especially, one may find this work less than satisfactory. However, it was the best available when we started our studies.

Color, in *Hygrophorus,* is caused chiefly by pigments dissolved in the cell sap and to a lesser extent by incrustations on, or pigment in, the cell wall. These pigments have a tendency to be broken down by intense light so that it is not at all uncommon to find a species with a red pileus bleaching out to orange and finally to yellow. In addition to bleaching there is the usual change from a moist to a dry and faded condition which is covered under the term hygrophanous; this situation applies particularly to the section *Humidicutis.* It is very important to note the colors of fresh young caps, mature ones, old ones, and faded ones in ascertaining the color range of a given species. In *H. psittacinus* for instance, the young caps are parrot green at first, fade to yellow, and become pinkish-vinaceous in age or on drying. The best way to learn about the color range of any species is to observe it when the species is fruiting prolifically and when fruiting bodies in all stages of development are present.

In addition to ascertaining the color range of a species by observation of prolific fruitings, the problem in *Hygrophorus* is further complicated by albinism, or at least white forms of a species which, from field data, appear genetically constant. Such a situation is illustrated by the whitish variant of *H. laetus.* It is at times difficult in species, such as *H. nitidus,* to be sure one has a faded specimen or a white variant.

Color changes on bruising which result in oxidation caused by released enzymes are very important characters, as for instance the change to black in *H. conicus* and its variants, *H. singeri,* and to some extent *H. tahquamenonensis.* In the *Rubentes* of section *Hygrophorus* these reactions may be slow to develop but show up as spots on the gills by the time the fruiting body is mature; or from gills which are white at first there may be a progression to dark vinaceous red in age. Other species may show a color change to green on some part in age or on bruising.

A chemical study of the pigments in *Hygrophorus* would be interesting, but we have not ventured in this direction. The problem is difficult because there are so many components in many of the species, and simple tests as to whether a pigment is destroyed or not by strong bases is not carrying the problem far enough, though the information may have some value in differentiating arbitrarily between certain species.

SIZE AND SHAPE—In nearly all genera of the *Agaricales* there is a tremendous range in size of the fruiting bodies between those with the largest and those with the smallest pilei, and nutritional differences may account for great variation within many species. Within broad limits, however, size of pileus has some taxonomic significance. In many *Hygrophori* the pilei vary from 2–5 cm in diameter and in a few they measure 3–12 mm. Going in the other direction, in *H. sordidus* and *H. pudorinus* var. *fragrans* the pilei may measure 20 cm or more broad, and a number of species have a range between 8–15 cm, i.e., *H. russula, H. subsalmonius, H. purpurascens* (occasionally 20 cm or more broad), *H. ponderatus,* and *H. tennesseensis.* In general the species with large pilei are found in section *Hygrophorus.*

The shape of the pileus, especially at maturity, is often of taxonomic value. Generally in the larger species the pileus is convex but gradually expands to plane or merely plano-convex. In a few species the disc is depressed to umbilicate or the cap may become infundibuliform. In some species it may remain umbonate. In some the pileus is sharply conic when young and merely expands to broadly conic or plane with a sharp conic umbo in age. In those species in which the pileus is notably depressed, or acutely umbonate to conic, taxonomic use is made of the character. The separation of series *Conici* in *Hygrocybe* is an example of such use.

SURFACE CHARACTERS—The characters of the pileus surface which are, or may be, of importance in species diagnosis include whether or not the cap is glabrous, fibrillose, or scaly; whether it is dry, moist and hygrophanous, lubricous, viscid, or slimy; whether the margin is even or striate; and whether veil remnants are visible along the edge.

The question of whether a pileus is glabrous or not is usually determined with the naked eye or with the aid of a hand lens and simply means that no debris from a broken veil is present anywhere, and no scales, loose or attached, are present. Bald is the common term which might be regarded as a synonym of glabrous. In some species, such as those in the series *Hygrocybe*, especially *H. miniatus*, the young pileus may appear glabrous or at the most appressed fibrillose. At maturity, however, the epicutis of the pileus loosens, the individual fibrils aggregating into fascicles attached to the cap at the base but with the free ends projecting. Under a lens such a cap appears to have small scales and is described as squamulose. The tips of the squamules may assume a color not in evidence anywhere else on the pileus. Such color differences should be noted.

In a few species of the section *Hygrophorus* the pileus surface is more or less glabrous but is radiately-streaked usually by appressed fibrils of a different color. This condition is described as virgate and is found in such species as *H. virgatulus*, *H. olivaceoalbus*, and *H. camarophyllus*. This condition may occur under a thick coating of slime. If no such coating is present and the ends of the fibrils curl up so as to be free, we have the condition described as fibrillose-squamulose.

Throughout the genus we find species in which the epicutis of the pileus is formed by a layer of hyphae chemically different from those of the context because their walls gelatinize. This causes the pileus surface to be slippery, sticky, or slimy (gelatinous), depending on the thickness of the epicutis and how far the gelatinization has proceeded. In wet weather this change is accentuated to the point where a pileus may actually have puddles of slime on it, or in continued wet weather the layer may be washed away completely. If the opposite conditions prevail and the weather is dry, such an epicutis drying down to a hard shiny layer causes the pileus to appear as if varnished. Under these circumstances the pileus is dry to the touch. The most reliable manner to ascertain if an epicutis is made up of gelatinous hyphae is to section it and mount the sections in water (for fresh material) or 3% KOH (for material that has been dried). If the hyphae of the epicutis are gelatinous the layer has a translucence quite different from the context beneath it. The greatest hazard to guard against in sectioning a gelatinous layer is that the layer does not stick to the razor blade. To avoid this hazard hold the piece of tissue in such a way that the cut is through the epicutis into the pileus context.

In most species of *Hygrophorus* the pileus margin is even. In about a dozen of those with thin flesh, however, the gills show through the moist cap as radiating lines or *striae,* and such a cap is described as translucent-striate when moist. These lines are usually not visible on faded specimens. This difference, taken together with the change in color from the moist to the dry and faded condition, produces a marked change in the appearance of the cap. In interpreting the character of striation one must also guard against the effect of excessive soaking by constant rain, as badly water-soaked specimens may show the character to some extent in species not ordinarily having it.

CHARACTERS OF THE CONTEXT—The context exhibits a number of important characters though not as many as the pileus surface. The color may be important but is usually a paler shade of the prevailing color of the pileus. It is especially important if it differs markedly from the pileus color. Often the context is white to pallid at first and slowly takes on the color of the pileus. More important are marked color changes when the context is injured. It may blacken, turn red, brown, or occasionally olive. These changes are often used as key characters. In both *H. conicus* and *H. singeri* the flesh blackens on bruising; in *H. olivascens* it stains brownish; and in *H. ovinus* it soon becomes reddish. Certain characters not yet adequately recorded for North American species are those associated with contact of the context with certain chemicals, such as potassium hydroxide, ferrous sulphate, and Melzer's reagent.

Odor of the context is important if it departs from the normal which is mild or a slight "fungus" odor. There are several specific odors, each distinctive for one or a few species in a series. In *H. westii* and *H. subfuscescens* var. *odora* it is disagreeable—a rather generalized category. In *H. saxatilis* it resembles dried peaches. In *H. agathosmus, H. monticola,* and others it reminds one of cherry pits or bitter almonds. In *H. tennesseensis* it resembles raw potatoes; in *H. foetens,* chloride of lime; in *H. rainierensis,* freshly husked green corn. In *H. nitratus* it is nitrous, raphanoid in *H. spadiceus* var. *odorus,* and mephitic in *H. mephiticus* and *H. auratocephalus.* As can be seen the problem of odor is difficult as to nomenclature as well as the chemistry involved.

TASTE—Taste, another chemical character, presents the same difficulties as does odor, or more so because of various taste factors in the human population. Bitter is a common category in agarics generally, and one not too difficult to deal with, but with some people it fails to register. A few *Hygrophori* have it, namely *H. reai* and *H. pallidus.* Farinaceous, a flavor very common in some genera such as *Lyophyllum,* is rare in *Hygrophorus.* Both the odor and the taste must be determined from fresh specimens, preferably those not yet completely mature to avoid any odors caused by yeast or bacterial infection, and a number of collections should be tested. When specimens are collected and wrapped in waxed paper packages at the time of collection, the time to check for the presence of a characteristic odor is when the package is unwrapped. It is useless to check the odor after the specimens have been in a refrigerator for any length of time, as too many variables are thus introduced. The greatest source of error in the matter of checking the taste is that one is likely not to chew the material long enough. Some flavors develop rather tardily. Taste is very likely to be altered by the process of drying the specimens; any original characteristic odor may be lost, though in some agarics special odors develop as a result of drying the specimens. As yet we have not found this true for *Hygrophorus*.

LAMELLAE

In *Hygrophorus* gill attachment exhibits a wide range of conditions from species to species. The lamellae may be adnate in one species, decurrent in another, and in still others adnate at first and become decurrent in age. Sometimes they secede in a characteristic manner, as in *H. squamulosus*. In species with sharply conic caps they are likely to be ascending-adnate and to secede readily if the cap expands further to plano-umbonate. Species with depressed pilei are likely to have the gills become decurrent if they are not attached in this manner from the beginning.

The terms applied to the spacing of the gills are relative, but with a little experience the collector will have no difficulty in recognizing the spacing referred to as crowded, close, subdistant, and distant. Crowded applies to a condition in which the lamellae are so close together that they seem to be almost in contact with each other. The term close indicates a spacing where, as the term implies, the gills are not far apart, but still it is evident that there is space between them. Distant may be defined simply as a spacing in which the lamellae are far apart, and subdistant a spacing halfway between close and distant. Variation within a species will usually cover two of these categories, i.e., crowded to close, close to subdistant, or subdistant to distant, and one must be sure to make comparisons between mature fruiting bodies, as the spacing may change somewhat from youth to age. Crowded gills are shown for *H. russula* (Fig. 108); close for *H. erubescens* var. *erubescens* (Fig. 110); and distant for *H. pacificus* (Fig. 113).

Color and color change, if any, of the lamellae may be of considerable taxonomic importance. In perhaps a majority of the species they are white to pallid at first, becoming cream-tinted at maturity. There are, however, many species in which lamellae colors are distinctive, and the list of colors is long: deep yellow, bright orange, red, pink, blue, green, gray, brown, or various shades of these. In the *Rubentes* of section *Hygrophorus* they become reddish-spotted to entirely dark vinaceous red. In *H. paludosus* Peck they become spotted with green or olive. In most species the gills are pale at first and merely develop a flush of the color of the pileus, as in *H. pudorinus*. If brilliant when young, the gill color tends to fade out in age, but in *H. marginatus* var. *marginatus* the lamellae are bright orange, and this color usually persists, at least along the edges, long after the pileus has faded. Few species in *Hygrophorus*, however, regularly have the gill edges a different color than the faces, a condition referred to as marginate, and which characterizes a number of species in the related genus *Mycena*.

Color changes which occur from injury are as important on the gills as on the pileus and have already been discussed.

STIPE

The context of the stipe and pileus in *Hygrophorus* are continuous, and therefore the one organ is not easily separated from the other. The stipe is typically central in its attachment to the pileus, but occasional specimens with an eccentric stipe do occur in some species, *H. camarophyllus,* for instance. Characteristically it is solid or stuffed solid, the latter description applying when a pith can be distinguished from a cortex.

The surface features of the stipe are, however, important in the recognition of species. Color and color changes are important here, as they are for the pileus. The stipe may be practically the same color as the pileus, or the apex may be paler. The stipe is likely to be most heavily pigmented in the lower two-thirds of its length, except for the buried base which is likely to be pallid. The stipe may be white at first and become flushed with the color of the pileus later, as in *H. pudorinus*. In some there is a tendency for the base to change color to yellow (*H. pudorinus*) or some other color, and this change may not be in the category of a change due to bruising. We have found that where growing in deep moss, as in variants of *H. camarophyllus*, the pigment may fail to develop in the stipe causing it to appear pallid.

The most important color character, however, is that involved in the application of certain chemicals, such as ferrous sulphate, potassium hydroxide, Melzer's reagent, and other chemicals to the surface ornamentation. This is an area for future investigation as our data are incomplete for most species, but in the tests made to date some striking results have been obtained. In *H. pudorinus* for instance, the ornamentation at the apex of the stipe is instantly yellow to orange in KOH. In certain species, such as *H. tephroleucus* and *H. pustulatus*, the ornamentation of the stipe apex is white at first but slowly becomes ashy, the color change being limited to the elements of the ornamentation. In a few *Hygrophori* the ornamentation at the apex of the stipe consists of golden granules. If a veil is present, it may or may not be colored; but if colored, there is often a sharp difference in the color of the stipe between the covered and uncovered portions.

The surface ornamentation is important both for its color and morphology. The most unspecialized type is a smooth, glabrous to somewhat silky surface, up to the point of gill attachment. However, in most species the surface near the apex is powdery (pruinose) or covered with a slight roughness (scabrous), the elements of which may project as points and consist of fascicles of a primitive type of dermatocystidium usually not much different in shape from a simple hyphal tip. In some species the stipe apex is very rough.

As on the pileus, the outer layer of the stipe may be composed of gelatinous hyphae or these hyphae may be the remains of a veil; in the latter instance the stipe is not slimy above the point where the veil breaks. Either the presence of a gelatinous outer veil or a continuous outer gelatinous cortical layer is of great importance in the recognition of species. In section *Hygrophorus*, the only section in which a gelatinous veil is found, its presence or absence is the major character on which the section is subdivided. The gelatinous veil is an outer veil extending over the surface of the pileus and causing the latter to be slimy like the stipe. The character is an easy one to ascertain correctly if fruiting bodies in various stages of development are present, because the veil, as the cap expands, extends from the cap margin to the stipe. Below the point of attachment the surface is slimy like the pileus. There are two sources of possible error, however, which should be mentioned. If the stipe is short and the pileus large, the cap margin may approach the stipe surface near the base of the stipe, so that as the cap expands the greater part (or nearly all) of the stipe surface is dry. Observations on button stages are needed to properly resolve conditions of this kind. A situation in which a species lacks a veil, but has a slimy pileus and has some of the slime drip off onto the base of the stipe, may also be encountered. Again, observations on young fruiting bodies are essential to a correct interpretation of this character. In dry weather the slime dries rapidly and is greatly reduced in volume. On exposed specimens of this kind, a varnished appearance over the lower part of the stipe usually indicates that a gelatinous veil was originally present.

In a number of species a fibrillose "dry" veil is found between the gelatinous veil and the stipe surface. When such a veil breaks it may leave a rather persistent fibrillose annular zone on the upper part of the stipe. The European *H. ligatus* apparently has a fibrillose but not a gelatinous veil, as does our own *H. subalpinus. H. hypothejus* and *H. olivaceoalbus* have both types, and *H. fuligineus* has only the gelatinous veil. *H. speciosus* and its variants seem to be intermediate in that an inner veil is present in one variant along with the gelatinous veil. *H. laurae, H. variicolor,* and *H. subsalmonius* have the remains of the gelatinous veil only over the lower part or base of the stipe. In subsection *Camarophyllus,* by definition, the gelatinous outer veil is absent, though a fibrillose "dry" veil may be present.

In section *Camarophyllopsis* the stipe is typically dry and veils are lacking, but in section *Hygrocybe* the stipe may be very slimy to merely viscid from an outer gelatinous cortex of appressed hyphae or a structure termed an ixotrichodermium which is discussed in detail under microscopic characters. We have no data as to how this type of surface evolved, but it seems unlikely that this type of layer is derived from a veil.

The shape of the stipe and its diameter have taxonomic value within broad limits. The diameter, as given in our description, is taken near the apex, and shape is indicated from this point down, i.e., narrowed to a pointed base, clavate (means enlarged below) or fusiform, meaning enlarged in the middle and tapered both ways.

MICROSCOPIC CHARACTERS

Spores

Spore characters are now considered among the most fundamental of all those characters used in the classification of the *Basidiomycetes;* but because of remarkable homogeneity in *Hygrophorus,* they are not as important to the classification of its species, let us say, as the spores of *Inocybe* are to the arrangement of species in that genus.

Historically, spore size and shape, after the color of the spore deposit (which is typically white), were among the first features of the spores to be widely used and are still important in *Hygrophorus* at the species level. Spore size and shape should be determined from spores from a deposit since by definition these are mature. In practice, however, one frequently crushes a small piece of gill tissue from a mature cap. A deposit of spores from a pileus with 4-spored basidia, when the spores are measured, will give a simple, unimodal curve. In spores between 6 and 14 μ long the expected variation is a micron or two on either side of the peak, the variation being greater for the larger spores. Corner (1936), and later Dennis (1953), described an unusual situation in *H. firmus* and its variants, in which two sizes of basidia occur in the hymenium, and two distinct ranges of spore size are found, the small spores coming from small basidia and the large ones from large basidia. A cytological study of *H. firmus* to count chromosome numbers in the nuclei of each size of basidium might be most revealing.

This phenomenon is also known as the *Ascomycetes* (Kanouse, 1950). It is not to be confused with the production of occasional giant spores from occasional large basidia, a feature of many agarics. In the latter instances because so few spores are produced they are not taken into account in determining the size range. Occasional exceptionally small spores may also be found in deposits. The most commonly occurring situation which confuses the determination of spore size in *Hygrophorus* is the presence of 1-, 2-, 3- and 4-spored basidia in the hymenium of a single cap. The presence of just 2-spored and 4-spored basidia will produce a spore deposit giving spores which fall rather neatly into a bimodal curve as far as size is concerned, but the picture becomes very confused when all types are present. It seems to us that a more careful cytological study of this genus than any yet made might yield additional data of taxonomic importance. It is concluded that basically spore size is a constant and valuable aid in the definition of species in *Hygrophorus,* but that there are a number of factors which must be taken into account in its use.

Spore shape is rather monotonous in this genus, most spores being elliptic to oblong or globose. However, a few species have fusoid spores, and in a few others the spores in profile may be slightly curved. In a few species the spores are extremely narrow, and in others peanut-shaped (constricted in the middle). In *H. sphaerosporus* and *H. hymenocephalus*, with globose spores, there is a tendency for the spores to have one side flattened and hence appear obscurely angular under the microscope.

In his studies Bataille (1948) reports the spores of most species to be smooth. In a few, however, he finds them rough. According to him the spore wall is punctate in *H. caprinus* (*H. camarophyllus*), *H. discoideus, H. limacinus, H. marzuolus, H. olivaceoalbus, H. pudorinus,* and *H. russocoriaceus*. In *H. agathosmus* and *H. pratensis* he described them as subsmooth. We have found those in the above group occurring in North America to have smooth spores. Morten Lange (1954), Moser (1955), and Orton (1960) state that the spore wall in *H. schulzeri* is minutely punctate-warty. Dennis (1953) described *H. nodulisporus* with truly nodulose spores. Singer (1955) made this the type of the genus *Hygroaster*. In *H. schulzeri* we agree that the spore wall is minutely punctate-warty or at times slightly wrinkled-warty. In general, the spores of *Hygrophorus* are seldom ornamented. One artifact common to all thin-walled hyaline basidiospores is the accumulation of minute oil droplets (or other refractive material) against the inner surface of the spore wall, and under high dry objectives such spores appear minutely punctate.

Chemical reactions of the spore wall are often of significance in the delimitation of taxa at all levels in the *Hymenomycetes*, but, as with ornamentation, the spores of *Hygrophorus* offer little in this regard. One species related to *Camarophyllopsis* and two related to *Hygrocybe* have been found to give a positive amyloid reaction. KOH, which causes a color change on spores in some groups, notably the *Cortinariaceae*, has no effect in *Hygrophorus*.

BASIDIA

As already emphasized one of the important generic characters of *Hygrophorus* is the long basidia. In instances of a questionable generic identification, the final decision may rest on whether or not the basidia are narrow and elongated. A typical *Hygrophorus* basidium is about 40–52(60) × 6–8 μ. In more than half of the species studied we found the basidia to be uniformly 4-spored, and the sterigmata typically are prominent.

Throughout the genus however, according to the species, the size of the basidium and the number of spores borne on it deviate from the usual condition described above. In some species of section *Camarophyllopsis* relatively small basidia are found. For example, in *H. fallax*, *H. angustifolius, H. basidiosus, H. deceptivus,* and *H. microsporus* small basidia 30–40 × 4.5–6.3 μ are the rule. Examples of exceptionally large basidia are *H. inocybiformis,* 62–84 × 10–12 μ, and *H. amygdalinus,* 42–74 × 7–11 μ. Additional examples could be cited. There appears to be a general correlation between size of basidium and of spores in *Hygrophorus*. In *H. megasporus* the spores measure 12–18 × 7–9 μ and are borne on relatively large basidia, 55–71 × 7–11 μ. In *H. monticola* the spores are 10–14 × 5.5–7.5 μ, and the basidia are 56–82 × 7–11 μ. In several species related to *H. peckianus* the spores are about 4.5–6 × 3.5–4.7 μ, and the basidia are small.

It is desirable at this point to refer again to the dimorphism of the basidia in *H. firmus* var. *firmus* by Dennis (1953) and re-emphasize the desirability for critical cytological work and studies on the sexuality of fungi showing this phenomenon.

The number of spores borne on each basidium may vary with the species. In fact, variant-spored forms are common in *Hygrophorus*, as they are in *Mycena* (Smith, 1934), comprising about forty percent of the material we have studied. *H. subcaespitosus* was found to be consistently 2-spored. *H. acutoconicus*, 1-, 2-, 3- and 4-spored; *H. puniceus* mostly 4-spored. Maire (1902) based the genus *Godfrinia* on the 2-spored variant of *H. conicus*, but the genus has not been generally accepted by other authors.

We have not engaged in a critical study of the microchemical tests or staining reactions on the basidia, but there does not seem to be much promise in the way of valuable taxonomic data from such a course. KOH produced no significant color reactions such as are obtained in some *Cortinarii*. In view of the KOH reaction on the squamules at the apex of the stipe in such species as *H. pudorinus*, it was hoped that some significant reactions of the basidia might be found. Melzer's reagent has given the most valuable results. The yellowish to dark-brown granules observed for some species (see *H. microsporus*) are undoubtedly constant and distinctive, but their distribution and composition need further study.

As compared with other families of white-spored *Agaricales*, the basidia of *Hygrophorus* may be said to be relatively important in the classification of species though we have not tried to use their characters in our keys.

CYSTIDIA (Figs. 1 and 2)

A relatively small number of the *Hygrophori* we have studied have pleurocystidia and cheilocystidia. Examples are: *H. translucens* in section *Amylohygrocybe* (Fig. 2, i,j); *H. amygdalinus* in section *Hygrophorus* (Fig. 2, k,l); *H. turundus* (Fig. 1, e) and *H. calyptraeformis* in section *Hygrocybe* (Fig. 1, a,b). None was found in section *Camarophyllopsis*. As is usual for agarics, the pleurocystidia vary in size and shape with the species. They are voluminous in *H. calyptraeformis* (Fig. 1, a,b), very conspicuous in *H. subaustralis* (Fig. 2, e) and *H. subovinus* (Fig. 2, b,c), and more or less imbedded in the hymenium in *H. amygdalinus* (Fig. 2, k,l), *H. cuspidatus* (Fig. 1, c,d), *H. turundus* (Fig. 1, e), and *H. appalachianensis* (Fig. 1, h,i). In a few species cheilocystidia are present but pleurocystidia are absent—a situation which is quite routine throughout the agarics.

The pleurocystidia may be fusoid, ventricose, spathulate, cylindric, or clavate and are thin-walled, smooth, and hyaline; or if resembling basidioles, may have a somewhat colored content as revived in KOH. As to category, those we have studied would be classed as leptocystidia, but pseudocystidia have been reported for *H. ovinus* by Kühner (1936) and in *H. conico-palustris* by Haller (1953). Tramal cystidia are described for both *H. firmus* var. *stratiotes* and *H. hypohaemactus* (Corner, 1934 and 1936). In some species the cheilocystidia are merely

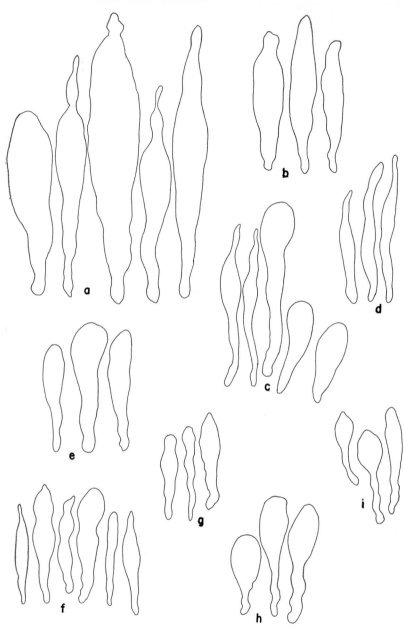

Fig. 1. Cystidia—*H. calyptraeformis:* a, pleurocystidia; b, cheilocystidia. *H. cuspidatus:* c, pleurocystidia; d, cheilocystidia. *H. turundus* var. *turundus:* e, pleurocystidia. *H. turundus* var. *sphagnophilus:* f, pleurocystidia; g, cheilocystidia. *H. appalachianensis:* h, pleurocystidia; i, cheilocystidia.

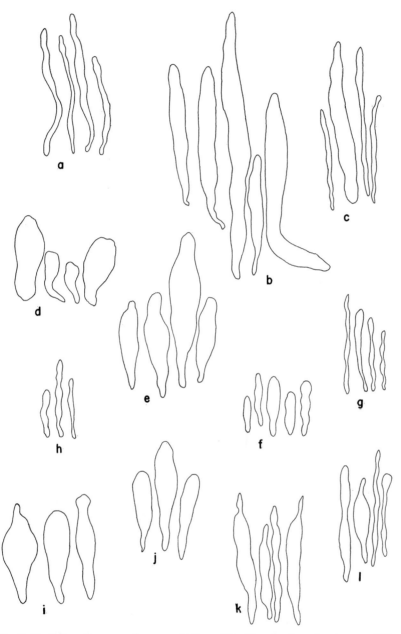

Fig. 2. Cystidia—*H. squamulosus:* a, cheilocystidia. *H. subovinus:* b, pleurocystidia; c, cheilocystidia. *H. flavoluteus:* d, cheilocystidia. *H. subaustralis:* e, pleurocystidia. *H. mycenoides:* f, cheilocystidia. *H. laetus:* g, cheilocystidia. *H. hondurensis:* h, cheilocystidia. *H. translucens:* i, pleurocystidia; j, cheilocystidia. *H. amygdalinus:* k, pleurocystidia; l, cheilocystidia.

gelatinous or non-gelatinous hyphal extensions. In general pilocystidia as such are very rare or absent in the genus *Hygrophorus*, and when present are more like a terminal hyphal cell. We have not found them to be of any significance taxonomically. In species which have the epicutis of the pileus in the form of a dry trichodermium the end cell of the epicuticular hyphal element may be cystidioid in shape; i.e., broadly clavate to somewhat fusoid-ventricose, but this kind of structure is tied up more with the development of the hymeniform type of pileus epicutis than with scattered true pilocystidia. Caulocystidia are also of a relatively undifferentiated type, mostly more or less resembling hyphal tips. Their chief claim to interest is that undoubtedly, in the fresh state, they will show some valuable color reactions with certain chemicals.

We regard it as curious that this genus shows so little in the way of cystidia when such genera as *Mycena* are noted for the presence of diverse cystidial types. Whether this argues for or against the connection we have regarded as existing between the two genera depends on one's interpretation of the situation. We assume that the cystidia as found in *Hygrophorus* represent a primitive condition, and it seems logical further to suppose that the diverse types of cystidia found in *Mycena* are derived from that primitive condition. But, it should also be remembered that cystidia are a feature of nearly all *Hymenomycetes*, and that these structures must have originated from basidia independently on numerous occasions.

Gill Trama (Figs. 3–6)

The arrangement of the hyphae forming the gill trama has for years been the basis on which *Hygrophorus* has been subdivided into three genera or three subgenera or sections, depending on the author. We have used it to delimit the sections of subgenus *Hygrophorus*.

1. In section *Hygrophorus* (Fig. 3) the hyphal arrangement is termed divergent or bilateral because the hyphae extend downward and outward from a thin central strand of somewhat interwoven to nearly parallel hyphae. The hyphae vary in diameter with the species but usually are 4–8 μ broad. They are thin-walled and mostly colorless. In age some of the component cells may inflate somewhat, but they do not become sphaerocyst-like. This hyphal arrangement is easily demonstrated by freehand sections cut from fresh material, but in revived material one sometimes encounters certain difficulties. Apparently in the process of drying, the hyphae in the area of divergence straighten out, and when sections are made from this dried material and revived in KOH, the hyphae do not assume their original arrange-

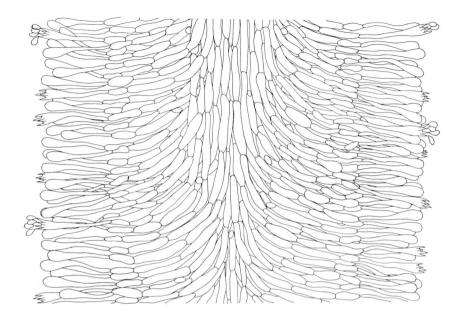

Fig. 3. Gill trama—divergent type, as found in *H. fuligineus*.

ment but instead appear parallel in the sections. We have encountered this situation to some extent in the trama of the type of *H. eburneiformis*, except that here some indications of divergence were observed, and the central strand was more interwoven than parallel. Consequently, it is important to section fresh material of *Hygrophorus* to be sure that one's interpretation of the hyphal arrangement of the gill trama is correct.

2. In section *Camarophyllopsis* (Fig. 4) typically the hyphae of the hymenophore are compactly as well as intricately interwoven and are narrow—usually 5–10 μ in diameter but range from about 2 to 14 μ depending on the species. In several species, however, there is a layer of subparallel hyphae next to the subhymenium (see *H. colemannianus*). We believe this tendency has some significance as far as the evolution of tramal types in *Hygrophorus* is concerned. Hesler has observed a peculiar situation in *H. bakeri* and *H. umbrinus* in which there is, in revived sections, a central strand of parallel hyphae flanked on either side by interwoven elements. This is the opposite of the *H. colemannianus* type. In *H. microsporus* the gill hyphae are only somewhat interwoven as viewed in mounts of revived material but definitely interwoven as seen on sections of fresh specimens.

3. In *Hygrotrama* the hyphal arrangement is more interwoven than parallel, but the species in other respects appear to be most closely related to those of section *Hygrocybe* on the characters of stature and epicutis of the pileus.

4. In section *Hygrocybe* (Fig. 5) the gill trama is composed of hyphae which are parallel to somewhat interwoven. In this type the width of the hyphae may be great (20 μ or more at times), and the individual cells are usually elongated. One of the most extreme examples of this type is found in *H. conicus* (Fig. 5). In others, as in *H. coccineus*, the tramal hyphae are more narrow and shorter (Fig. 6).

In summary, we have found from our studies that the arrangement of the hyphae in the trama of the hymenophore in *Hygrophorus* is a generally reliable character by which to distinguish sections of the subgenus *Hygrophorus*, but we are not convinced that the differences are of sufficient magnitude to justify recognizing the various sections as genera. We now believe that from a careful study of hyphal arrangement in the hymenophore on a large number of species in the fresh condition, it will be shown how one of these types originated from the other. It will then be possible truly to evaluate the meaning of the different arrangements in terms of a classification of the species and their phylogeny. In view of the difficulties with revived material, and the almost uniform poor condition of much of the older authentic materials as dried, we feel that a study made from such materials is too likely to prove misleading to justify the work being done in that manner.

PILEUS: CONTEXT AND CUTIS

The hyphae of the context are disposed generally in a direction radial to the stipe, but in relation to each other they may be loosely to compactly interwoven to subparallel or parallel. Usually only one hyphal system is evident, but in some species a distinct laticiferous system is also to be noted. The cells of the structural hyphae for the most part inflate as maturity is approached or passed in the enlargement of the pileus. In a few species peculiar brown granules are noted in the hyphae on mounts made in Melzer's reagent, but for the most part the microscopic structure of the context offers little of value to the taxonomist.

The surface layers (the cutis), however, offer many features of great taxonomic value and will be discussed in the approximate order of their complexity.

Type 1. The simple cutis (Fig. 7, a,b): In species with a dry glabrous pileus a section through the latter reveals no differentiation

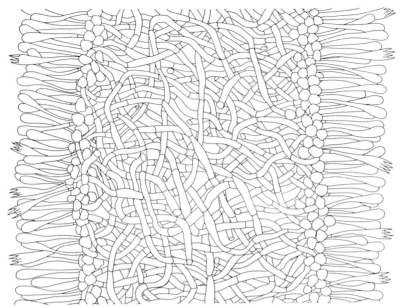

Fig. 4. Gill trama—interwoven type, as found in *H. pratensis*.

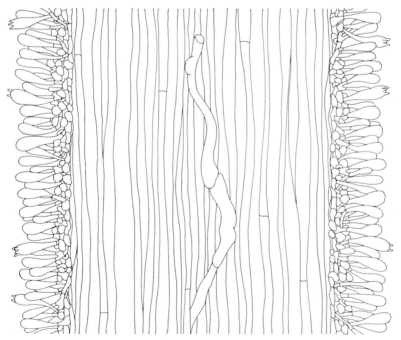

Fig. 5. Gill trama—parallel type, hyphal cells long and broad, as found in *H. coni-cus;* lactifer represented in the center. See also Fig. 6.

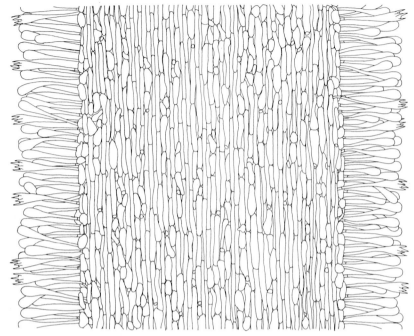

Fig. 6. Gill trama—parallel type, hyphal cells short and relatively narrow, as found in *H. coccineus*. See also Fig. 5.

between the context and the hyphae at the surface. The surface hyphae are repent and often extend in a periclinal direction. At times, even in so-called glabrous pilei, free hyphal ends may extend more or less upward (Fig. 7, e,g). Such an undifferentiated type is not uncommon in the section *Hygrocybe*, especially series *Coccinei*. A pileus with this type of surface-covering may be moist and hygrophanous, or appressed fibrillose. It becomes squamulose at times if exposed to bright sunlight or dry winds. Most members of the *Agaricales* showing a similar cutis structure behave according to this pattern. Examples of the simple cutis include: *H. aurantius, immutabilis, marginatus* var. *marginatus* (Fig. 7), and *subaustralis* (Fig. 7).

Type 2. Non-gelatinous but differentiated epicutis: The most important difference between this and Type 1 is that the hyphae forming the surface layer are narrower (often 1.5–4 μ diameter) and more compactly arranged, hence they do constitute a distinct layer as contrasted to the first type. The hyphal walls, as far as can be determined by observation in water, KOH, or Melzer's reagent, are of the same composition as those of the hyphae of the context. They do not swell up and gelatinize in KOH. A pileus with this type of surface has a

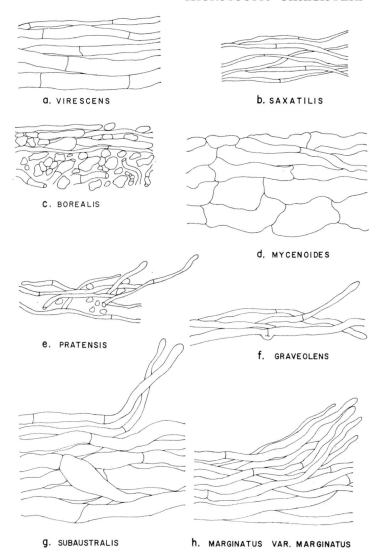

a. VIRESCENS

b. SAXATILIS

C. BOREALIS

d. MYCENOIDES

e. PRATENSIS

f. GRAVEOLENS

g. SUBAUSTRALIS

h. MARGINATUS VAR. MARGINATUS

Fig. 7. *Hygrophorus* cuticle types—a, *H. virescens:* simple dry cutis, hyphae repent, non-gelatinous, not sharply differentiated from the pileus trama; b, *H. saxatilis:* cutis, the surface hyphae repent, narrow, and loosely arranged. Since the hyphae are slightly gelatinous at first (but soon dry), this type of cuticle approaches an ixocutis; c, *H. borealis* f. *borealis:* cutis, some hyphae periclinally arranged, others radial (seen as cut-ends in a tangential view); d, *H. mycenoides:* cutis, the surface hyphae broad and the cells medium short, extending in a periclinal direction; e, *H. pratensis:* cutis, with a few uplifted hyphal ends, the surface hyphae both radial and periclinal in their direction; f, *H. graveolens:* cutis, with an occasional uplifted hyphal end; g, *H. subaustralis:* cutis, with few to many uplifted surface hyphae; when densely fibrillose, the cuticle is of a trichodermial type; h, *H. marginatus* var. *marginatus:* cutis, with an uplifted cluster of surface hyphae forming a squamule.

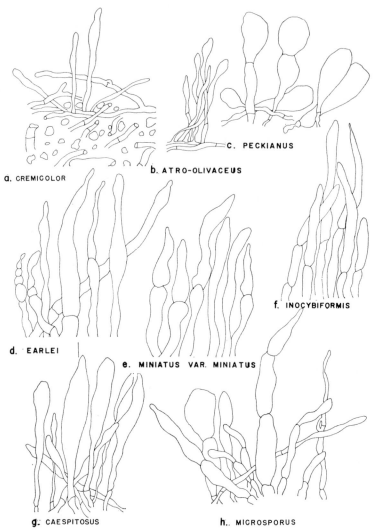

Fig. 8. *Hygrophorus* cuticle types—a, *H. cremicolor:* the cuticle of the trichodermium type; most hyphae loosely arranged radially; b, *H. atro-olivaceus:*
a trichodermium; the hyphal elements in fascicles, forming squamules; c, *H.
peckianus:* a trichodermium composed of fuscous hyphae, the end-cells of
which are pyriform, clavate, ovoid, or subglobose; this structure approaches an
hymeniform cuticle; d, *H. earlei:* a trichodermium in which the surface hyphae
are repent, or more rarely erect; e, *H. miniatus* var. *miniatus:* a trichodermium
in which the hyphae at first repent, but become more or less erect, septate,
and often constricted; f, *H. inocybiformis:* a trichodermium, the hyphae
smoky-tinted, and clustered to form squamules; g, *H. caespitosus:* a trichodermium, turf-like, the hyphae at times more or less repent, but more often
erect, the terminal elements variable in shape; h, *H. microsporus:* a trichodermium, composed of irregular, septate, fuscous, constricted hyphae, the
terminal elements cystidioid.

smoother appearance, especially when faded, than the pileus of Type 1. A great deal of intergradation occurs between these two types so that at times it is difficult to decide which category fits the best.

Type 3. The ixocutis (Fig. 10, a): This type is a progression from the previously described cutis in which the hyphal walls show that they are chemically different from the walls of the context hyphae by swelling up and gelatinizing in water or KOH. The gelatinized material gives a translucence to the layer which is in quite sharp contrast to the context. Gelatinized hyphae have a tendency to be only 1.5–3 μ in diameter, and the whole layer has considerable tenacity, for it can frequently be peeled from the cap as a film. This is what is meant by a separable pellicle which commonly occurs in section *Hygrocybe*. In some species the layer can be 50 μ or more thick and in others only 10–15 μ or even less. The extent to which gelatinization occurs determines how sticky or slimy the fresh pileus is when touched. Examples are found in *H. agathosmus, odoratus,* and *rainierensis* (Fig. 10).

Type 4. Trichodermium (Fig. 8): This is a totally different type from any of the first three. In a trichodermium the context hyphae or branches from them project upward or more or less perpendicular to the surface and become aggregated into small bundles, which to the naked eye appear as minute squamules. These projecting hyphae may be two- to several- or more-celled with the terminal cell at times somewhat cystidioid in shape, and the walls are not gelatinous. Several examples of this type are found in *Hygrocybe*, series *Hygrocybe* (*H. miniatus,* Fig. 8, e; *H. turundus,* etc.). A somewhat special type is represented by *H. rugulosus.* In it the cutis is a trichodermium in which the elements all terminate at the same level to produce an hymeniform epicutis of pedicellate-inflated to vesiculose elements. We believe that the epicutis in the species of section *Hygrotrama* originated by a shortening of the trichodermial hyphae to a point where these consisted of simply an apical cell with a single modified penultimate cell.

Type 5. The ixotrichodermium (Fig. 9): In many *Hygrophori* the epicutis of the pileus consists of a trichodermium of very narrow branched hyphae (1–3 μ diameter) covering the pileus surface like a turf, and are imbedded in a mass of slime. Such a surface is very slimy when fresh and wet, and has a varnished appearance when dry. This type of epicutis may not be as readily separable as in Type 3. From this it is evident that viscidity of the pileus is based on two different anatomical types of epicuticular structure. Actually, from the standpoint of the shape of the epicuticular elements two subtypes can be recognized in Type 5: (1) one in which the hyphae stand erect,

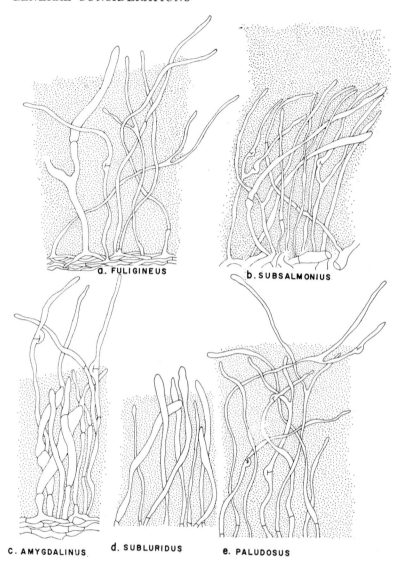

Fig. 9. *Hygrophorus* cuticle types—a, *H. fuligineus:* an ixotrichodermium, with a thick zone of slender, erect, pale hyphae imbedded in a gelatinous matrix (represented by stippling)—all resting on an hypodermium; b, *H. sub-salmonius:* an ixotrichodermium, a broad gelatinous zone (stippled), the upper portion of clear gelatinous substance, the lower portion a turf, or ixotrichodermial palisade, of slender hyphae; c, *H. amygdalinus:* an ixotrichodermium, the hyphae fuscous, at times branched, resting on an hypodermium; d, *H. subluridus:* an ixotrichodermial turf, or palisade, with slender, cylindric-clavate hyphae; e, *H. paludosus:* an ixotrichodermium, similar to that in *H. fuligineus,* but in the former the epicuticular hyphae are pale fuscous—all resting on an hypodermium.

rather close together in an hymeniform arrangement—an ixotrichodermial palisade, as in *H. subsalmonius* (Fig. 9) and *H. amygdalinus*
(Fig. 9), and (2) one in which the hyphae may be more or less erect
but not in a palisade, a simple ixotrichodermium (see *H. fuligineus,*
Fig. 9; *H. paludosus,* Fig. 9; *H. flavodiscus,* Fig. 10; and others).
Such a layer may vary from 20 μ to 500 μ in thickness, according to
the species.

Type 6. The epithelium (Fig. 10, b,c): The feature of this layer
is that it appears pseudoparenchymatous if one focuses down on the
pileus with a sufficiently high magnifying system. There are two
types, based on the manner of origin of the component cells. In one
the radial surface hyphae become divided into short cells by the for-
mation of numerous septa, and the individual cells finally assume a
vesiculose shape and are approximately isodiametric.

The second type consists of a palisade of clavate-pedicellate cells
arranged perpendicularly to the cap surface and so crowded as to be
misshapen from mutual pressure in their enlarged part. This is the
type on which Heim (1957) established the genus *Hodophilus,* based
on *H. foetens* (Fig. 10, c) and *H. atropunctus.* Unfortunately the name
is not valid since no Latin description accompanied its publication.
We regard this type of epicutis to have been derived by a shortening
of the hyphae of a simple trichodermium, as previously stated. It is the
character on which Singer (1958) based the genus *Hygrotrama,* which
we are here recognizing as a section.

The hypodermium is a differentiated layer beneath the epicutis but
is generally regarded as part of the cutis in contrast to the context. It
is not present in many agarics. It is rare in section *Hygrocybe* and
Camarophyllopsis but present in some species of section *Hygrophorus.*
It usually consists of a highly colored layer, the hyphae often having
incrusted material on their walls, or the cells being enlarged differently than those of the context. A well-defined hypodermium has been
observed in *H. amygdalinus* (Fig. 9), *H. fuligineus* (Fig. 9), *H. paludosus, H. glutinosus, H. bakerensis, H. recurvatus, H. colemannianus,*
and others. In *Hygrophorus* it is apparently found only in species with
viscid to slimy pilei. More rarely a false hypodermium is found. In
H. fuscoalbus and in *H. elegantulus* there is a lower zone of somewhat
brownish hyphae, but they are neither parallel nor compact as in a
true hypodermium.

CLAMP CONNECTIONS

In our studies we have, in recent years, paid close attention to the
presence or absence of clamp connections on the hyphae of the fruiting

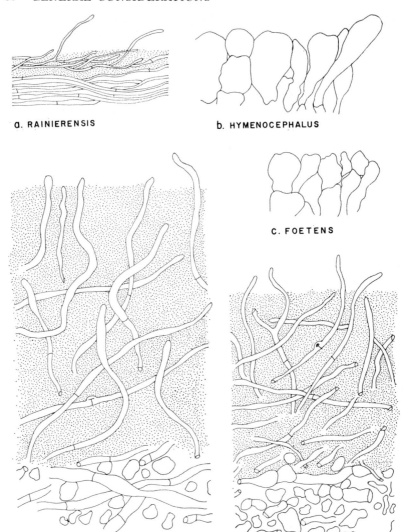

Fig. 10. *Hygrophorus* cuticle types—a, *H. rainierensis:* an ixotrichodermium in which the surface hyphae are at first more or less erect, then become elongated and repent; b, *H. hymenocephalus:* an epithelium, the surface composed of an irregular palisade of inflated cells; c, *H. foetens:* an epithelium, the surface layer a dense palisade of more or less upright pseudoparenchymatous elements; d, *H. flavodiscus:* an ixotrichodermium, a thick zone with loosely tangled hyphae inbedded in a glutinous substance; e, *H. piceae:* an ixotrichodermium, with loosely tangled, slender hyphae, some free ends extending above the gluten.

body. We have found that in section *Hygrophorus* they are almost always present (but are absent in *H. adiaphorus*). In *Camarophyllopsis*, *Hygrocybe*, and *Hygrotrama* they are frequently absent. We have not found them in *H. foetens, H. hymenocephalus, H. rugulosus, H. subfuscescens, H. fallax, H. paupertinus,* and *H. peckianus.*

In *Hygrocybe* they are absent in a number of species, *H. deceptivus, H. marginatus, H. atro-olivaceus,* etc. In some species we found them present but very difficult to locate, as in *H. immutabilis, H. caespitosus, H. ovinus, H. subovinus,* and *H. perplexus.* In other species we found them restricted to the subhymenium only, *H. calyptraeformis;* rare on cuticular hyphae, common on the stipe, *H. miniatus* var. *longipes;* pileus trama only, *H. turundus* var. *sphagnophilus;* on laticiferous hyphae only, *H. firmus* var. *militaris* and *H. westii.*

Our studies have convinced us that in *Hygrophorus* the presence or absence of clamps on the hyphae of the fruiting body is a good additional character to aid in delimiting species, but that it is extremely impracticable for the most part because of the irregular pattern of occurrence. We found ourselves differing as to whether clamps were absent in a number of species, and the answer too often turned out to be that if you look long enough you can find them. They seem to have dropped out of the genus here and there without regard to relationships of the species. Consequently we have de-emphasized their use in our classification even though previously we (1954) published a key to *Hygrophori* lacking them. The pattern of the occurrence of clamp connections in *Hygrophorus* is no different from that in most other genera. The proportion of clamped to clampless species varies greatly between genera. Critical studies on clamp connections based on experiments with appropriate material and by means of cultures should be undertaken. We do not really know what the absence of clamp connections on the hyphae of a fruiting body means in terms of nuclear behavior. It would also be interesting to know whether the mycelia which produce the clampless fruiting bodies have clamped hyphae.

CHEMICAL CHARACTERS

The use of chemical characters in the delimitation of species is nothing new. They have always been used as far as certain categories are concerned, such as odor and taste, different pigments, etc., but the features which have come into prominence in the last two decades mainly involve color reactions from the application of specific reagents, such as potassium hydroxide, ferrous or ferric sulphate, Melzer's reagent (see Singer, 1951).

It is now evident to us that some of these reagents produce color reactions of value in the recognition of species, and any future studies of the genus should pay close attention to the color changes on the apical ornamentation of the stipe when KOH is applied. Melzer's reagent has proven of value in a number of species by focusing attention on peculiar granules in the hyphal cells. We have used this reagent in all of our studies of dried material in recent years, but have been unable to recollect all the North American species to check color reactions on the fresh specimens.

From our limited experience, however, we believe that, in general, this type of feature will be about as monotonous as a character such as spore size. Since we believe by far the majority of species can be readily recognized on morphological characters, we feel that it is not desirable to postpone the publication of this monograph until all the problems of the chemical approach have been solved.

ECOLOGICAL CONSIDERATIONS

Insofar as distribution as to habitats-distribution can be ascertained by the fruiting bodies collected, *Hygrophorus* stands out as an unspecialized genus which exhibits tendencies toward habitat specialization in certain of the infrageneric categories. Primarily *Hygrophori* occur in forest or brushy situations, but they are known from pastures as well, and the edge of a wood lot is often a good hunting ground. Some of the forest-inhabiting species are very generalized, occurring under hardwoods and conifers alike, and seeming to need only a shady moist location. *H. psittacinus* and *H. pratensis* are examples. In fact the species of *Hygrocybe* generally exhibit more widely distributed habitats than *Camarophyllopsis* or *Hygrophorus* species. *H. conicus* grows "almost anywhere." *H. puniceus* fruits abundantly during very wet years in a variety of forest types, as does *H. flavescens*. Such species, on the basis of field evidence, would of necessity be regarded as saprophytes either without the ability to form mycorrhiza or with the ability to enter into this relationship with almost any rootlet in the vicinity of the mycelium. In either case the term unspecialized is appropriate.

At the other end of the spectrum we find species whose fruiting bodies have been collected only in the vicinity of certain species of seed plant. *Hygrophorus speciosus*, to our knowledge, fruits only in the vicinity of tamarack trees (species of *Larix*), and the type variety perhaps exclusively with *Larix occidentalis*. It is assumed, on the basis of many observations, that the fungus cannot produce fruiting bodies without benefit of the mycorrhizal relationship. To the mushroom collector, the relationship between the kind of tree and the mushroom fruiting body is very important.

Nearly all the species showing a probable mycorrhizal relationship are found in the section *Hygrophorus*. *H. hypothejus* is associated with 2- or 3-needle pines; *H. kauffmanii* apparently with oak; *H. pudorinus* with *Abies* and *Picea* (balsam and spruce); and *H. laricinus* with larch. There appears to be a true correlation between the degree of development of the slimy outer veil and ability to form mycorrhiza. *H. camarophyllus* and *H. pudorinus* are limited to conifers; and *H. agathosmus* appears to be most frequently associated with spruce. For many species the number of collections is not sufficient to allow accurate conclusions to be drawn from them. In the mixed conifer-hardwood forests of Northern Michigan, or in the Great Smoky Mountains National Park, it is often difficult or impossible to determine which forest plants might be involved.

Certain relationships between forest types and seasonal appearance have been evident to students of *Hygrophorus* for a long time. For instance, species of *Hygrocybe* would be expected to grow in July and August in hardwood forests, especially in copses. Species of section *Hygrophorus* would be sought in the conifer forests, and to some extent the hardwoods, after heavy autumn rains and the first frosts. This temperature relationship undoubtedly explains why our mountain conifer forests fairly "blossom" with species of section *Hygrophorus* when the fall rainy season sets in.

The species of *Hygrotrama* which we have observed seem to occur more frequently on naked, moist, but packed soil in what might be regarded as generally unfavorable habitats, but correlations are difficult to establish. On the basis of the habitat data to date we would be forced to conclude that *H. subfuscescens* has two forms, one occurring at the edge of wood lots under hardwoods and specifically associated with poison ivy, and the other on peat hummocks in cedar swamps. We doubt that this species is so restricted.

Sphagnum bogs are a good habitat for *Hygrophori*, especially the *H. miniatus—H. turundus* complex, *H. laetus*, and *H. nitidus*. But our luck in finding them has been best during hot, dry years when the water level of the bog was reduced and the habitat had warmed considerably. Cold, wet *Sphagnum* bogs are usually unfavorable for agarics until the autumn fruiting of mushrooms, especially species of section *Hygrophorus*.

Usually species of *Hygrophorus* grow in the leaf mold which covers the soil. It is, then, as Ramsbottom (1953) says, more logical to relate their occurrence and distribution to the nature of the humus rather than of the soil itself, and, of course, the kind of humus in turn is dependent on the vegetation which produced it. Thus it is useful to speak of vegetation types as habitats—deciduous woods, coniferous woods, mixed woods, or grasslands (lawns, meadows, pastures)—rather than soil-types.

Although animal dung provides a substratum for certain agarics, we know of no record of such habitation for any species of *Hygrophorus*.

GEOGRAPHIC CONSIDERATIONS

Any effort to present a comprehensive and precise picture of geographic distribution of agarics is beset with problems arising out of their erratic appearance. The occurrence of mushroom crops in any given area is so sporadic, unpredictable, and often brief that conclusions from reports are hazardous. There is also the problem of agreement as to species identity. Based on the records at hand, however, some tentative generalizations are offered.

Field studies undertaken in the tropics by Murrill (see 1916) and by Dennis (1953) have yielded collections of some species of *Hygrophorus* which, to date, have not been found in temperate North America. For example, *H. subpratensis,* found in Cuba and St. Johns, has not yet been reported for Canada or the continental United States. Dennis (1953) has reported *Hygrophorus* species from Trinidad, including *H. bakeri, buccinulus, cremeus, umbrinus, cinerascens, erinensis, firmus* (and its varieties *militaris, occidentalis, purpureus, trinitensis*), *luteistipes, papillatus,* and *troyanus.* None of these has as yet been reported for temperate North America. These, so far as we now know, are tropical species. It is quite within the realm of possibility that at least some of these so-called tropical species may yet be discovered in Canada or the United States. In this connection, it is interesting to observe that *H. cantharellus* occurs in eastern temperate North America, and also in Jamaica, Trinidad, and Venezuela. Murrill's *H. flavoluteus,* originally described from Jamaica, was subsequently collected in Mexico. The type of *H. hondurensis* was found in British Honduras, and is now known also from Florida, Michigan, Washington, and from Trinidad. *H. subaustralis,* the type from North Carolina, has been collected by Dennis in Trinidad. *Hygrophorus subflavidus,* the type from Jamaica, has been found in Michigan; *H. subminiatus*, also described from Jamaica, has appeared in North Carolina, Michigan, and Washington.

The known distribution pattern of certain *Hygrophori*, in the northern half of the United States and in southern Canada, may now be considered. Among these, species which are also known from Europe, we note the following: *H. camarophyllus, capreolarius, chrysodon, discoideus, eburneus, erubescens, fuscoalbus, hypothejus, olivaceoalbus, pudorinus*, and others of section *Hygrophorus*; in *Camarophyllus, H. borealis, niveus, pratensis, virgineus*; in *Hygrocybe, H. calyptraeformis, ceraceus, coccineus, flavescens, laetus, marginatus* var. *marginatus, miniatus* var. *miniatus, puniceus, reai*, and *unguinosus* var. *unguinosus*.

Certain species of *Hygrophorus*, according to current knowledge, are known only in the Pacific Northwest, including limited areas of the Rocky Mountains and California: *H. avellaneifolius, bakerensis, inocybiformis, megasporus, odoratus, saxatilis, vinicolor*—all in section *Hygrophorus*; in *Camarophyllus, H. graveolens*; and in *Hygrocybe, H. citrinopallidus, flavifolius*, and *laetissimus*.

Several species are thus far known only from the southeastern United States. Included in this category are: *H. eburneiformis, fulvosiformis, arnoldae, foliirubens, subluridus*, and *westii*. Some or all of these may, with critical searching, turn up at least in adjacent states. Murrill's *H. subsordidus*, first described from Florida, subsequently was found in Texas and Alabama; and *H. tennesseensis*, the type from Tennessee, has been found in Kentucky, North Carolina, and, more interestingly, in Massachusetts.

It seems clear that extending a known distribution, in some instances at any rate, depends on a diligent collector with a critical eye. It is noteworthy that a few of Peck's little-known *Hygrophori* have been re-discovered, and other such finds will surely be made.

Again, work on *Hygrophori* and other agarics in Japan, such as that of Imai and of Hongo, has revealed the occurrence there of *Hygrophorus* species which are found on the continent of North America. Included in these reports are: *H. capreolarius, virgineus, calyptraeformis, coccineus, conicus, flavescens, laetus, minutulus*, and *turundus* f. *sphagnophilus* (as *miniatus* f. *sphagnophilus* by Hongo, 1952a).

As would be expected, certain species which are widely known in North America and Europe have been reported from South America. It also seems certain that many species there are new to science, and are awaiting study and report.

SEASONAL OCCURRENCE

Every collector in the temperate zone is aware of the seasonal phenology of agarics. The influence of season on the fruiting of *Hygrophori*, in general, parallels that for the species of other mushrooms.

In temperate North America, most *Hygrophori* fruit in the summer and autumn. In some species fruiting may occur in the spring; in others, fruiting occurs in the winter; for some species the fruiting period extends from the autumn into the winter months, or from summer into autumn.

Relatively few species in the temperate zone of North America produce carpophores in late winter and spring. Our notes, however, do show spring collections of *H. occidentalis, purpurascens, subisabellinus,* and *acutoconicus;* in Europe, *H. marzuolus* appears in the early spring near snow-banks. But, fruiting of these species may also occur in the summer and autumn.

As already stated a majority of temperate species appears during the summer and autumn months, and for certain species of the United States the autumn fruiting period extends into the winter. From November to January, one finds many species of section *Hygrophorus,* notably *H. fragrans, fuligineus, hypothejus, ponderatus, roseibrunneus, subsordidus,* and *tephroleucus.*

In any season when certain species of *Hygrophorus* may be expected, appropriate rains are a determining factor. Experienced collectors are fully aware of the essential influence of at least normal rainfall in carpophore production. Field experience suggests that certain species which appear, for example, in the winter do not appear in other wet seasons of the year, in response to rain-periods. It is assumed, therefore, that for most species of *Hygrophorus* there are temperature factors as well as moisture factors which strongly influence fruiting.

It appears, as M. Lange (1948) has pointed out, that many agarics may properly be categorized as spring species, summer species, autumn species, or winter species—in the temperate zone—with allowance for some overlap of preceding and succeeding seasons.

One problem on which critical, extended observations are needed is that of the periodicity of fruiting. Our general observations indicate that a year of heavy fruiting may be followed by one or more years of light fruiting. Excellent collecting seasons come at intervals varying from two to ten years, depending on weather conditions and on the species. Apparently an agaric crop more or less exhausts a mycelial-system, and an extended time-interval is then necessary to produce another mycelium with fruiting-potential.

Rains are essential for fruiting. But rains are also required for normal development of a mycelium. It may be assumed that the time required for the development of a crop-producing mycelium varies with the species. When the mycelium has reached its carpophore-producing potential, then normal frequent rains rather than infrequent torrential downpours appear more favorable for fruiting.

PHYLOGENY AND CLASSIFICATION

In order to arrange the species of *Hygrophorus* in at least a somewhat natural sequence it is necessary to review briefly the species in related groups of gill fungi to see if it is possible to ascertain the origin and development of the characters which finally serve to distinguish the family and its principal genus, *Hygrophorus*. The characters which concern us most are the long, narrow basidia often with flexuous pedicels and the waxy hymenophore. The ordinarily rather thick lamellae tending to become venose in the interspaces are also important, as is the general tendency for the gills to be spaced far apart, i.e., distant or subdistant. We regard the parallel and bilateral arrangement of the hyphae in the trama of the hymenophore to be advanced characters and the interwoven arrangement to be primitive. This conclusion is based on our experience with agarics and on evaluation of the literature. If this assumption is accepted, we can add interwoven gill trama to the primitive characters to be expected in ancestral forms of the family.

A search of the *Agaricales* furnishes us with some relationships of the more specialized groups of *Hygrophorus*, such as *Hygrocybe* with such groups as the *Adonidae* of *Mycena*, and possibly a case can be made for relationships to *Clitocybe* and *Tricholoma*, though we do not wish to defend the possibility of these at present. The relationships, if they can be said to exist, all require more detailed study.

It is only when we turn to *Cantharellus* that we find species conspicuously possessing the characters which define the genus *Hygrophorus*. It is in this genus that we find the elongated basidia more or less of the "clavarioid" type. It is true that they are not as "clavarioid" in *Hygrophorus*, as in *Cantharellus*, but it is only in this genus that a significant relationship can be made on this character. The same can be said for the waxy hymenophore, but it must be admitted that this is a subjective character which many people find difficult to recognize in *Hygrophorus* itself. Consequently, some debate as to whether it is present in *Cantharellus* is to be expected. As two investigators who have observed these two groups over a period of many years, we are convinced that there is a true relationship between *Cantharellus* and *Hygrophorus* on this character also. We believe there is some significance to the fact that Fries (1838) placed *Cantharellus cinnabarinus* in section *Hygrocybe* of *Hygrophorus*. Thus, we believe that in *Cantharellus* we find the two major characters which define *Hygrophorus*. The latter differs from the former, however, in a number of important features. *Cantharellus* typically has blunt gill edges, whereas in *Hygrophorus* they are sharp. *Cantharellus* shows a tendency to have the lamellae narrower and more vein-like, whereas in *Hygrophorus* the gills are well formed and typically broad. In both there is a decided tendency for them to be distant. In *Cantharellus* the arrangement of the hyphae in the gill trama is typically loosely interwoven, a feature which, if accepted as primitive, could argue in favor of the species of *Camarophyllopsis* being most closely related to *Cantharellus*. Spore types in *Cantharellus* are more diverse than those found in *Hygrophorus*, a feature which aids in distinguishing *Cantharellus* as a genus.

It is known that in the *Clavariales* and in *Cantharellus*, in general, the basidium is a "stichobasidium" whereas in the *Agaricales* we find the "chiastobasidium." We would insist that in a measure this difference helps to distinguish *Cantharellus* from *Hygrophorus*, but that it does not mean that the latter could not have been derived from the former. We should like to see a cytological study of these two genera made by modern techniques to elucidate this situation since we believe there are fundamental similarities as far as nuclear behavior and other cytological features are concerned. Pending such a study, we would prefer not to emphasize cytological details in discussing this problem. We would for the present rest our case on the data presented in regard to the features which delimit *Hygrophorus*.

If we consider the evolution within *Hygrophorus* on the premise that the species of *Camarophyllopsis* are primitive and related to *Cantharellus*, what sort of picture do we get? In the first place, species of sections *Camarophyllopsis* and *Hygrophorus* are often impossible to place unless one actually examines the anatomy of the gills. This similarity in appearance is so great that it was found necessary to change the sectional name of the group with interwoven gill trama because the type species, *H. camarophyllus*, was actually found to have bilateral gill trama and therefore had to be transferred to section *Hygrophorus*. As far as section *Hygrophorus* is concerned we have also found, in *H. diaphanes*, that it is impossible at times to distinguish species of section *Hygrophorus* from those of section *Hygrocybe* on macroscopic characters. It is such similarities as this that have in part caused us not to recognize these sections as separate genera. Closely related genera separated by a single character are weak genera at best.

However, when most species of section *Hygrophorus* are compared with most of those in section *Hygrocybe* a number of obvious differences stand out as indicated in our taxonomic data. The problem of evolution and relationship is thus reduced to a discussion of how readily bilateral trama on the one hand and parallel trama on the other can be derived from the primitive interwoven type. We believe that this is not such a difficult change as may appear at first glance.

In the first place the term "interwoven hyphae" actually is not indicative of an homogeneous condition throughout *Camarophyllopsis*. In some species, such as *H. borealis*, the gill trama hyphae at maturity are up to 14 μ broad. In *H. cremicolor* these hyphae are very narrow (1.5–3 μ broad). For most species the hyphal cells are 4–12 μ in diameter and may be of equal diameter throughout or somewhat enlarged. In such species as *Hygrophorus colemannianus* the hyphae of the hymenopodial zone are actually subparallel, with the ramose subhymenium a narrow zone to the exterior on either side. All that is needed here to arrive at a type of hyphal arrangement very common in the hymenophore of an *Hygrocybe* is for the central interwoven body of the gill trama to become reduced in extent and the subparallel arrangement of the hymenopodial area to become better developed. No appreciable change in the genetic mechanism of the species need be postulated to produce such a change. From this point forward it is a simple progression to the typical kind of parallel gill trama such as that found in *H. conicus*, where the central strand has been obliterated and the subhymenium arises directly from the parallel hyphae of the hymenophoral tramal body. This appears to be a simple progression easily accounted for genetically, and it is not clear that "parallel" vs. "interwoven" gill trama can be a character sufficiently significant to base a genus on it. It is well known that hyphal diameters and hyphal arrangements change markedly from youth to old age in a single species so that at most the character is one in which considerable latitude in interpretation must be allowed for in all except the most distinctive types, i.e., such as the inverse type characterizing the *Volvariaceae*.

We may now examine the possible origin of the bilateral type of gill trama found in section *Hygrophorus*. In many species of section *Hygrophorus* it is possible to demonstrate that the hyphae diverge from a thin to a distinct strand of interwoven hyphae extending downward and finally toward the subhymenium. One of the problems of working with dried specimens is that in a few instances we have found that these hyphae straighten in the drying process, and when revived do not regain their original arrangement. The hyphal arrangement in such circumstances appears to be parallel except for the narrow, somewhat interwoven central strand. It seems to us that this observation could be significant in postulating the origin of the divergent arrangement in the first place. But regardless of significance, let us return to the hyphal arrangement observed in *H. colemannianus.* Here, all that is necessary for a primitive type of divergence to develop is for the hyphae toward the exterior of the hymenopodial area to grow out in a more orderly pattern through the subhymenium, and thus reduce the distinctness of that layer. This condition would constitute primitive divergence. The more this layer develops at the expense of the layers interior to it, the more prominent the character of "divergence" becomes. The more the interwoven central strand develops the more the divergence is reduced. The operation of this last principle is well exemplified by certain species of *Catathelasma* (*Armillaria ponderosa,* and its relatives). In this genus the hyphae of the hymenophoral trama is considered to be bilateral (divergent), but in *C. ventricosa* this characteristic can be observed only on immature gills, and the diverging hyphae are in the hymenopodial area. By the time the cap is fully expanded the development of the interwoven central area has progressed to the point of obliterating the original divergence and from simply observing sections of mature gills one would be forced to conclude that the hyphal arrangement of the gill trama was subparallel to somewhat interwoven. Smith checked this on Collection *60672* of *C. ventricosa* from central Idaho. In *Hygrophorus* we assume that the opposite tendency prevailed because in section *Hygrophorus,* in fresh material, the hyphae can be demonstrated to be clearly divergent, and the central strand of more or less interwoven hyphae is reduced in varying amounts depending on the species. Here again the genetic mechanism for controlling the hyphal arrangement need not undergo much of a change to produce the alterations in arrangement postulated.

Admittedly this subject of hyphal arrangement in the hymenophore of *Hygrophorus sensu lato* needs to be studied further in order to elucidate more fully the arrangement in the species which might be considered intermediate. It is by means of this procedure that the manner of origin of the bilateral type, with which we are here concerned, can best be elucidated. When such a study has been made on a large series of species, a more meaningful interpretation can be made relative to the importance of the character in the recognition of genera. In the meantime, and in view of the similarities of aspects in all three groups, we prefer the conservative point of view expressed by the use of hyphal arrangement in the hymenophore at the sectional level.

Assuming that species of *Camarophyllopsis* are primitive and resemble species of *Cantharellus* more closely than those of the various sections of *Hygrophorus*, we must accept the fact that gymnocarpic development is a more primitive condition in the *Hygrophoraceae* than the hemiangiocarpy displayed by a number of species in section *Hygrophorus*. This certainly "fits" the circumstances since *Cantharellus* is characterized by gymnocarpic development of the fruiting body. This line of reasoning would point to *H. olivaceoalbus* as perhaps the most advanced species in the section *Hygrophorus*—at least as far as those we have studied are concerned. As to the section *Hygrocybe*, the most specialized group would appear to be those with both a viscid stipe and pileus, subsection *Psittacini*. The members of section *Hygrotrama* appear to have been derived from the area of *Camarophyllopsis* nearest the series *Hygrocybe* of section *Hygrocybe* (the *H. miniatus* group). Our basis for this conclusion is that it is in this area that the epicutis of the pileus shows transitions from appressed fibrils to a true trichodermium, and by a shortening of the trichodermial hyphae the hymeniform type of epicutis is readily derived. As for certain other characters in the genus, the nodulose spores could have arisen *de novo* anywhere in the genus. This character has thus appeared in a number of groups of *Hymenomycetes*. The amyloid spores of a few species, a character taken by itself, can just as readily be interpreted on the same basis as the nodulose character of the spores. For this reason we do not place *Pseudohygrophorus* in the direct line from *Cantharellus* to *Camarophyllopsis*, and we recognize the section *Amylohygrocybe* largely as a taxonomic convenience. *Bertrandia* Heim appears to us, from accounts in the literature, to be amply distinct as a genus. We have examined no material and have nothing to offer as to its possible derivation.

Although our ideas of the evolution of the *Hygrophori* have been discussed only in the light of our own data on North American species, a survey of the literature, although not very enlightening, shows that approximately the same ideas have been expressed or implied by other investigators. Kühner and Romagnesi (1953) arrange *Hygrophorus* following *Cantharellus*, which is exactly the position we would assign to it, except that these authors treat *Hygrocybe* first (as a genus), *Camarophyllus* next, and *Limacium* last. Singer (1951) argues for the recognition of *Hygrophorus* (*Limacium*), *Camarophyllus*, and *Hygrocybe* as genera; but since the family *Hygrophoraceae* is the first group treated in his work it is not clear from what source he thought it derived. He said, "Hardly anything can be said about the origin of this family" (p. 142). His discussion is concerned more with separating the family from the *Tricholomataceae*.

As for phylogenetic relationships of the *Hygrophoraceae* to the *Tricholomataceae*, the section *Hygrocybe* seems to us to hold the best possibilities, especially through the section *Adonidae* of *Mycena*. In *Mycena* it is important to measure basidia for a length-to-width ratio, and compare this with the same ratio for basidia of the smaller species of section *Hygrocybe*. In *Mycena amabilissima* the hymenophore is waxy—a fact which indicates a breakdown of this character in the genus *Hygrophorus*. However, we do not find a similar relationship to *Laccaria*, or to *Clitocybe* or *Tricholoma*, and we concur with Singer (1951, p. 142) that such relationships are improbable. Nevertheless, as further studies of the *Tricholomataceae* are made, the possibility of such relationships should be kept in mind, for at this time it is unrealistic to believe that an inventory of the North American representatives of this family is near completion or that all known species have been studied carefully enough in this respect. We do not regard the peculiar *Clitocybe gomphidioides* as an established relationship of *Clitocybe* to species of section *Hygrophorus*, but rather as a singular species of uncertain relationship. Although the hymenophore is somewhat waxy in *Gomphidius*, its dark-colored spores and peculiar cystidia indicate that it is not related to the *Hygrophoraceae*, as Singer (1951) has pointed out.

In summary, we place *Hygrophorus* in a position intermediate between *Cantharellus* on the one hand and the *Tricholomataceae*, as defined by Singer, on the other. We recognize a number of lines of evolution in the genus leading to the highly specialized species and with one real possibility of a true connection to the *Tricholomataceae* through the genus *Mycena*.

MATERIALS STUDIED

It is impossible to state precisely the numbers of *Hygrophorus* collections we have studied in the course of our investigations on this genus, but the numbers of collections cited is approximately thirty-two hundred. As in any investigation of this sort, much more material is handled in the fresh condition than is finally filed in the herbarium. More important than the total number of collections cited is the number of plant associations from which the collections have been made. Since *Hygrophori* are primarily forest fungi, forest associations and shrub associations are most important. These are discussed under ecological considerations.

Specimens as preserved in most herbaria lack the necessary field data for proper identification. Hence, our studies in this respect have been mostly on the type specimens of species described by Atkinson, Coker, Kauffman, Murrill, and others. The purpose of such studies is to obtain data on microscopic characters which was not included in the original description.

Our own collections come from areas fairly well distributed over the United States and a few are from southern Canada. Since 1925, as time permitted, Hesler has collected agarics generally, and *Hygrophorus* in particular, in Tennessee and North Carolina, with more limited field work in Virginia, Kentucky, Georgia, South Carolina, Alabama, Mississippi, Louisiana, and Florida. Smith's collections are numerous from the Great Lakes region, from an area extending along a line from Ann Arbor to the tip of Whitefish Point in Lake Superior. Work was also done at Lake Timagami in Ontario, Canada, and at the Petawawa Experimental Forest near Deep River, in company with Dr. J. Walton Groves of the Canadian Department of Agriculture. One season was spent in Nova Scotia and one in the Adirondack Mountains of New York. His collections from the area west of the Great Plains constitute most of what is known about the genus from the western United States. In this region the important areas worked intensively are as follows: Priest Lake area, northern Idaho; central Idaho, south of the Salmon River; Medicine Bow Mountains of Wyoming; Trout Lake district, southwestern Colorado; the Mt. Baker National Forest in northern Washington; both Mt. Rainier and the Olympic Mountains National Parks; the Oregon and northern California coastal areas; and the Grants Pass area in southwestern Oregon. An important area not covered is the Coast Range south of San Francisco.

We wish it clearly understood that we do not claim to have exhausted the *Hygrophorus* flora of any area. We have approached the problem on a sampling basis. Anyone with experience in field work on agarics knows that about once in ten years, in most areas, a fruiting of fungi occurs which may be considered truly "fabulous," and during such a year one can still find species new to science in almost any genus he decides to study. We had a few such years, as 1940 in southern Michigan, 1951 in northern Michigan, and 1947 in the Mt. Hood National Forest, but for the most part only the usual "unusual" weather conditions were encountered. Dry weather seriously handicapped our efforts on a number of occasions, especially in the Southeast.

A limited number of collections of European material have been examined, but, though we both have visited in England and Hesler on the continent of Europe in addition, we do not claim to have made any real progress in comparing the European *Hydrophorus* flora with that of North America on a firsthand basis.

In the "Material Studied," for each species, we have indicated for each collection the name of the state or other political unit where the specimens originated, the name of the collector, and when available, the herbarium number or the collector's own number.

We have included in our study the *Hygrophori* reported by Dennis (1953) from Trinidad, cognizant that this island is regarded as belonging to South America. It is just possible that the species from Trinidad may subsequently be found in the West Indies proper or in Florida, or other Gulf States.

DOUBTFUL AND EXCLUDED SPECIES

Camarophyllus alboumbonatus Murr., Mycologia 3: 195. 1911.

This is a *Rhodophyllus* (*Entoloma*, perhaps *E. cuspidatum* Pk.). The spores of the type are 12–15 × 12–13 μ, angular, 4–5 sided. Murrill has, in sequence, placed it in *Hygrocybe,* then *Hygrophorus,* and finally *Camarophyllus* (see Murrill, 1916, p. 290).

Hygrophorus aurantiacoluteus B. & C., Ann. Mag. Nat. Hist. III (4): 293. 1859.

The type at Kew showed no spores and was unsatisfactory for study.

Hygrophorus bellus Massee, Jour. Bot. 30: 161. 1892.

We have been unable to study the type which was collected on the Island of St. Vincent, West Indies. Its colors and unusually large spores distinguish it. Murrill (1911) places it in *Hydrocybe.*

Hygrophorus fimbriatophyllus Kauff., Papers Mich. Acad. Sci., Arts and Letters 5: 131. 1925.

The type is of no value, and the name should be discarded. It is called *Tricholomopsis fimbriatophyllus* (Kauff.) Singer, in Lilloa 22: 196. 1951.

Hygrophorus graciae Sumstine, Mycologia 33: 19. 1941.

An examination of the type at the Carnegie Museum shows this to be *Entoloma cuspidatum* Pk.

Hygrophorus haematocephalus B. & C., Ann. Mag. Nat. Hist. II (12): 424. 1853.

We have not seen the type, but Murrill (1916) in his study of the type was unable to make a valid comparison. He states that it resembles *H. laetus,* but that the preserved specimens are old and faded.

Hygrophorus hudsonianus Jennings, Memoirs Carnegie Mus. III (Botany), 12: 2. 1936.

Bigelow has transferred this species to *Clitocybe hudsonianus* (Jenn.) Bigelow, Rhodora 62: 189. 1960.

Hygrophorus lactus Johnson, Minn. Acad. Sci. Bull. 1: 336. 1878.

In a communication to us dated November 23, 1959, it is stated that the type is not in the herbarium at the University of Minnesota.

Hygrophorus montanus Murr., Mycologia 3: 199. 1911.

A study of the type at the New York Botanical Garden shows that this is an *Hebeloma.*

Hygrophorus multifolius Kauff., Papers Mich. Acad. Sci., Arts and Letters 5: 131. 1925.

This is a species of *Lyophyllum.*

Hygrophorus ohiensis Mont., Syll. Crypt. p. 135. 1856.

Murrill (1916) says that the specimens at Paris are very poor, and are mixed with *Coprinus micaceus.* We have not seen the type.

Hygrophorus quelétii Bres., Fungi Trident. 1: 11. 1881.

Murrill (1916) says that this name was applied to a New York collection by Peck, but that later the specimens were referred to *H. pudorinus.* We have not seen Peck's material nor authentic specimens of Bresadola's species.

Hygrophorus serotinus Pk., N. Y. State Mus. Bull. 116: 32. 1907.

A study of the type at Albany, N. Y., shows that this is not an *Hygrophorus.*

Hygrophorus stenophyllus Mont., Syll. Crypt. p. 135. 1856.

Murrill (1916) states that the "specimens at Paris are too poor to compare successfully." We have not seen the type.

Hygrophorus variolosus Fr., Nova Acta Soc. Sci. Upsal. III (1): 29. 1851.

Murrill (1916) reports having been unable to find specimens of this species in Europe. He further states that Oersted, who collected it in Costa Rica, made colored drawings which suggest *Armillaria alphitophylla.* We have not seen the type.

Classification

Hygrophorus Fries

Gen. Hymen. p. 8. 1836

Limacium (Fr.) Kummer, Führ. in Pilzk., p. 118. 1871.
Camarophyllus (Fr.) Kummer, Führ. in Pilzk., p. 117. 1871.
Hygrocybe (Fr.) Kummer, Führ. in Pilzk., p. 111. 1871.
Hydrocybe (Karst.) Murrill, North Amer. Flora 9: 376. 1916.
Hygrotrama Singer, Sydowia 12: 221. 1958.
Humidicutis Singer, Sydowia 12: 225. 1958.
Godfrinia Maire, Rech. Cyt. Tax. Basidiomycetes, p. 116. 1902.
Hygroaster Singer, Sydowia 9: 370. 1955.
Hodophilus Heim, Les Champ. d'Europe, p. 219. 1957.

Hymenophore waxy, spores rarely ornamented, white in deposit; lamellae typically thick but with sharp edges, usually distant to subdistant and characteristically with a clean appearance; stipe confluent with pileus and nearly always centrally attached; basidia typically long and narrow as in species of *Cantharellus*.

Type species: *Hygrophorus eburneus* (Bull. ex Fr.) Fr.

Discussion: The waxy nature of the hymenophore is a difficult character to ascertain because it is to a large degree subjective. Because of this, certain aids in the accurate identification of the genus are pointed out at this time. If the gill edges are blunt, try *Cantharellus* first. In *Cantharellus* the hymenophore is somewhat waxy and clean in appearance. If a collection is at hand which has keyed out to *Clitocybe* and the basidia are long and narrow, it may be an *Hygrophorus*. *Mycena* and the smaller species of section *Hygrocybe* do intergrade, and some experience will be necessary with both genera before accurate assignments can be made. Fortunately, the number of such species is small and the fungi themselves are not very frequently collected.

KEY TO SUBGENERA

1. Hymenophoral trama of interwoven hyphae, reddish in KOH; spores amyloid..................Subgenera *Pseudohygrophorus*, p. 47
1. Not with the above combination of characters...............
.................................Subgenera *Hygrophorus*, p. 48

Subgenus *Pseudohygrophorus* Sm. & Hes.

Lloydia 5: 6. 1942

Neohygrophorus Singer, Lilloa 22: 149. 1951.

Spores smooth, amyloid, hyaline in KOH under the microscope. Hymenophoral trama of intricately interwoven hyphae 5–12 μ in diameter.

Type species: *H. angelesianus* Sm. & Hes.

1

Hygrophorus angelesianus Sm. & Hes.
Lloydia 5: 6. 1942

> *Neohygrophorus angelesianus* (Sm. & Hes.) Singer, Lilloa 22: 149. 1951.

Pileus 2–2.5 cm broad, convex, the disc becoming slightly and shallowly depressed, "hair brown" on the disc, "drab" on the margin (dark sordid gray to grayish brown), not fading, glabrous, viscid, appearing as if varnished when dry, margin crenate-plicate. Context dark gray, thin, firm; odor and taste not distinctive.

Lamellae short-decurrent, "dark vinaceous drab" (purplish drab), distant, moderately broad, edges even.

Stipe 4–5 cm long, 3–4.5 mm thick, concolorous with the pileus, slightly enlarged above, apex fibrillose-furfuraceous, base whitish with appressed fibrils, the remainder glabrous, stuffed.

Spores 7–9 × 4–5.5 μ, ellipsoid, smooth, amyloid (pale blue to dark blue in Melzer's reagent). Basidia 42–60 × 7–8 μ, 4-spored. Pleurocystidia and cheilocystidia none. Gill trama of distinctly interwoven (somewhat less so in dried material), vinaceous red to haematite red in KOH, hyphae 4–12 μ broad. Cutis a narrow gelatinous zone. Clamp connections present in the pileus trama and gill trama.

HABIT, HABITAT, AND DISTRIBUTION—Singly on soil, under heather, Washington, June.

MATERIAL STUDIED—WASHINGTON: Smith 14649 (type, from near Heather Park, Mt. Angeles, Olympic Mts., June 28, 1939, at 6000 feet).

OBSERVATIONS—This is a most peculiar species. It appears at first sight to be a typical member of the section *Camarophyllopsis* because of its waxy consistency, long flexuous basidia, and the distinctly interwoven gill trama. However, its amyloid spores and the very distinctive reaction of the flesh and gill trama in KOH are unique in *Hygrophorus*. The fungus bears a striking resemblance to *H. subviolaceus* both in color when fresh and in stature, but does not fade in the same manner. *H. lacmus* Fr. of Europe also has a superficial resemblance to it, but should be readily distinguished by the yellow base of its stipe and non-amyloid spores. Amyloid spores have been found in two other species, *H. translucens* (Murr.) Murr. and a specimen identified as *H. metapodius* (Fr.) Fr. from Denmark. In both, parallel to subparallel hymenophoral trama has caused us to consider them as a separate section.

Subgenus Hygrophorus

KEY TO SECTIONS

1. Hymenophoral trama of intricately interwoven to moderately interwoven hyphae; epicutis of pileus not hymeniform (but some species with a trichodermial epicutis) ...Section *Camarophyllopsis*, below
1. Not as above 2
    2. Hymenophoral trama somewhat interwoven; epicutis of pileus an hymeniform palisade of enlarged cells....................
    ....Section *Hygrotrama*, p. 96
    2. Not with above combination of characters 3
3. Hymenophoral trama of hyphae divergent from a thin to distinct central strand ....Section *Hygrophorus*, p. 248
3. Hymenophoral trama parallel to slightly interwoven 4
    4. Spores nodulose ....Section *Hygroaster*, p. 245
    4. Spores smooth 5
5. Spores non-amyloid ....Section *Hygrocybe*, p. 107
5. Spores amyloid ....Section *Amylohygrocybe*, p. 246

SECTION CAMAROPHYLLOPSIS nom. nov.

Camarophyllus (Fr.) Kummer. Führ. in Pilzk., p. 117. 1871.

Spores not amyloid; hymenophoral trama interwoven; epicutis of pileus not in the form of an hymeniform layer.

Type species: *Hygrophorus pratensis* (Fr.) Fr.

Donk (1949) has pointed out that the generic or sectional name *Camarophyllus* must be based on *Agaricus camarophyllus* as the type. As he stated, this amounts to a designation of the type of the group by the original author. Since it was found later that *Agaricus camarophyllus* is actually a "*Limacium*" (*Hygrophorus* in the sense of the type species of the genus) because of its divergent gill trama, the name is no longer available at any level for *Hygrophori* with inter-woven hymenophoral trama. Hence a new name is proposed. There are a number of *Hygrophori* almost identical in aspect but readily separated by the hyphal arrangement in the trama of the hymeno-phore. We take this, along with such basic characters as the long ba-sidia and waxy hymenophore, to indicate extremely close relationships between the two groups.

KEY TO SUBSECTIONS AND SERIES

1. Spores 6–8 μ or more long, mostly ellipsoid . . . .
. . . . .Subsection *Camarophyllopsis*, below
 1. a. Pileus white and not discoloring appreciably . . .Series *Virginei*, below
   a. Pileus soon colored . . . . .b
     b. Pileus viscid from a gelatinous epicutis . . . . . .Series *Viscidi*, p. 61
     b. Pileus moist to dry . . . . .Series *Camarophyllopsis*, p. 69
1. Spores up to 6–6.5 μ long but typically shorter and globose to subglobose
. . . . .Subsection *Microspori*, p. 82
   a. Pileus with a gelatinous pellicle . . . . .Series *Pelliculosi*, p. 93
   a. Pileus moist to dry, epicutis of appressed hyphae or in the form of a
     trichodermium . . . . .Series *Microspori*, p. 83

SUBSECTION CAMAROPHYLLOPSIS

SERIES VIRGINEI (Bataille) stat. nov.

Subsection Virginei Bataille, Flore Monogr. Hygrophores, p. 43. 1910.

Characters as given in key.

Type species: *H. virgineus* (Fr.) Fr.

According to the system used by Bataille for indicating generic categories. The taxon *Virginei* is the next step below that of section, hence we attribute it to him as a subsection.

KEY TO SPECIES

1. Spores 10–14 × 7–9 μ; pileus dry . . . . .2. *H. niveicolor*
1. Spores smaller 2
   2. Odor strong of arbor vitae; taste medicinal . . . . .3. *H. lawrencei*
   2. Odor and taste not distinctive 3
3. Pileus viscid to lubricous 4
3. Pileus moist to dry 5
   4. Pileus snow white, viscid, conspicuously translucent-striate fresh . . .
. . . . .4. *H. niveus*
   4. Pileus milk white to pale cream, moist to lubricous; margin striatulate
     moist . . . . .6. *H. borealis* f. *borealis*

5. Pileus 1–1.5 cm broad, convex-umbilicate (see *H. berkeleyi* Orton, page
   68, also) ....5. *H. buccinulus*
5. Pileus larger and convex to umbonate 6
   6. Lamellae white until maturity 7
   6. Lamellae pale yellow when young ....8. *H. cremicolor*
7. Spores 5–8 × 3–5 μ ....10. *H. angustifolius*
7. Spores larger 8
   8. Spores 8–12 × 5–7 μ; pileus entirely white ....9. *H. virgineus*
   8. Spores 7.5–10 × 4–5.5 μ; pileus watery white, flushed pinkish orange
      on one side ....7. *H. borealis* f. *salmoneus*

2
Hygrophorus niveicolor (Murr.) Sm. & Hes.
Lloydia 5: 23. 1942

> *Clitocybe niveicolor* Murr., Mycologia 3: 190. 1911.
> *Camarophyllus niveicolor* (Murr.) Singer, Lloydia 5: 99. 1942.

Pileus 3–7 mm broad, compressed-convex, snow white, smooth, glabrous, appearing subtomentose when dry because of loosely-woven context, margin slightly irregular, decurved.

Lamellae decurrent, slightly arcuate, white, rather narrow, distant.

Stipe 1–1.5 cm long, 1 mm thick above, 1.5 mm thick below, white, cylindric, slightly tapering upward, glabrous, fleshy, fistulose.

Spores 10–14 × 7–9 μ, ellipsoid, smooth, pale yellow in Melzer's reagent. Basidia 62–76 × 9–12 μ, mostly 4-spored, a few 2-spored. Pleurocystidia and cheilocystidia none. Gill trama interwoven, hyphae broad, 8–17 μ. Cuticle of appressed, undifferentiated hyphae—a cutis. No hypodermium. Pileus trama of radially disposed, interwoven, hyphae. Clamp connections present on the hyphae of the gill trama.

HABIT, HABITAT, AND DISTRIBUTION—On ground in a moist virgin forest, Mexico, January.

MATERIAL STUDIED—MEXICO: Murrill 1058 (type, from a mountain side near Motzorongo, Jan. 15, 1910).

OBSERVATIONS—The record of microscopic characters above is based on our study of the type. Singer (1942) properly concluded that this species, at first described by Murrill as *Clitocybe niveicolor*, is a *Camarophyllopsis*. It differs from *H. niveus* in its dry pileus and larger spores.

3
Hygrophorus lawrencei, sp. nov.

Pileus 1–3 cm latus, late convexus, glaber, siccus, albus; graveolens; lamellae decurrentes, latae, albidae; stipes albidus, siccus; sporae

6.5–8 × 5–6 μ. Specimen typicum in Herb. Mich. conservatum est, legit prope Applegate, Oregon, Jan. 24, 1959. Fred Lawrence 1162.

Pileus 1–3 cm broad, broadly convex to plane, when mature the margin uplifted, at first with a small conic umbo but this disappearing in age, surface smooth, dry and white. Context white, fragile, odor very strong of cedar, taste medicinal or almost like cedar.

Lamellae decurrent, broad, distant, intervenose, thick, edges even, white, drying dingy ochraceous.

Stipe 3–6 cm long, 5–8 mm thick, widest at apex and tapered to narrow base or subequal, smooth, white, dry.

Spores 6.5–8 × 5–6 μ, broadly ellipsoid to subglobose, hyaline in KOH, pale yellowish in Melzer's solution, smooth, thin-walled. Basidia 36–50 × 7–8.5 μ, 2- and 4-spored. Pleurocystidia and cheilocystidia none. Pileus epicutis of narrow hyaline hyphae not showing any appreciable gelatinosity in KOH. Clamp connections present.

HABIT, HABITAT, AND DISTRIBUTION—Under conifers, Applegate Area, Oregon, Jan. 24, 1959.

MATERIAL STUDIED—OREGON: Fred Lawrence 1162.

OBSERVATIONS—The fruiting bodies darkened to blackish in some parts in drying, but this may have been due to overheating. The aspect dried is that of *H. recurvatus*, to which it is closely related but is at once distinct by the white color throughout and pronounced odor and taste. Kühner and Romagnesi (1953) include *H. russocoriaceus* in *Camarophyllus* but ascribe spores 7–11 × 4–5.5 μ to it, which is sufficient to separate it from *H. lawrencei*. The two are obviously closely related however.

4

Hygrophorus niveus Fr.
Epicr. Myc., p. 327. 1838

> *Camarophyllus niveus* (Fr.) Wünsche, Die Pilze, p. 115. 1877.
> *Hydrocybe nivea* (Scop.) Murr., North Amer. Flora 9: 377. 1916.

Illustrations:
> Fig. 11.
> Bresadola, Icon. Myc. 7, pl. 329. 1928.
> Dufour, Atl. Champ., pl. 19, fig. 42.
> Lange, Flora Agar. Dan. 5, pl. 164F.
> Ricken, Die Blätterp., pl. 7, fig. 3.
> Wakefield and Dennis, Common British Fungi, pl. 34, fig. 2.

Pileus 1–3(6) cm broad, submembranous, obtuse to convex then plane, often becoming depressed or umbilicate, pure white to whitish, glabrous, viscid when fresh and translucent-striate to the disc. Context thin and pliant, white, unchanging; odor and taste not distinctive.

Lamellae decurrent, white, gradually yellowish in age, distant, rather narrow, thin, somewhat intervenose, edges even.

Stipe 2–7 cm long, 2–6(8) mm thick, white, equal or tapering downward, at times somewhat striate, dry, glabrous, stuffed, becoming hollow.

Spores 7–10(11) × 4–5.5(6.5) μ, ellipsoid, smooth, pale yellowish in Melzer's reagent. Basidia 38–50 × 5–7 μ, 4-spored (Lange finds 2- and 4-spored). Pleurocystidia and cheilocystidia none. Gill trama of interwoven hyphae, 4–8 μ broad, yellowish in Melzer's reagent. Cuticle an ixocutis, a thin gelatinous zone, 20–40 μ broad, hyphae colorless, repent, 1.5–3 μ in diameter. Hypodermium not differentiated. Pileus trama homogeneous, hyphae more or less radial but rather intricately interwoven. Clamp connections on the cuticular and gill trama hyphae.

Fig. 11. *H. niveus*

HABIT, HABITAT, AND DISTRIBUTION—Gregarious to scattered on humus and soil, in deciduous and coniferous woods, Massachusetts, Maryland, Michigan, Tennessee, Alabama, California, Oregon, Washington, August–January; also Europe.

MATERIAL STUDIED—ALABAMA: Burke 2057. CALIFORNIA: Smith 3693, 8724, 8738, 9427. MARYLAND: Kelly 1822. MASSACHUSETTS: Bigelow 8767. MICHIGAN: Kauffman, New Richmond, Sept. 25, 1911; Smith 20947, 21352, 33935, 62134. OREGON: Smith 7821, 7856, 7897, 8223, 19989, 28327. TENNESSEE: Hesler 23511, Hesler & Smith 11329. WASHINGTON: Smith 4677, 17931. BELGIUM: Heinemann, near Brussels, Nov. 1, 1960.

OBSERVATIONS—This species is very close to *H. borealis* and there is some question whether the two are distinct. *H. borealis* as we know it has a moist, fleshy pileus, whereas in *H. niveus* the pileus is thin, pliant, and viscid. The translucent striations of *H. niveus* are very pronounced, but *H. borealis* may also have them to some extent. In color, stature, habit, spore size, and in the interwoven gill trama they are practically identical. Sections of the pileus of *H. borealis* show a few narrow subgelatinous hyphae over the surface, whereas those of *H. niveus* show a pellicle of appreciable thickness made up of distinctly gelatinous hyphae. In our estimation the recognition of these two species hinges on the differences noted in the pellicle of the pileus. If these prove to be variable, then *H. borealis* would be a synonym of *H. niveus*. We have recognized both here because our evidence points to the existence of two rather than a single species.

H. niveus is also related to *H. virgineus*. In *H. niveus* the content of the pileus is very thin, and the surface viscid; in *H. virgineus* the flesh is thick on the disc and the pileus is not viscid.

A form of *H. niveus* with a pinkish stipe-base has been found in Massachusetts by Bigelow (B-7858), and in England by Orton (1960, p. 247, footnote). Orton says that *H. niveus, H. virgineus,* and *H. berkeleyi* are all prone to a pathological condition (not investigated—perhaps bacterial) in which the stipe and pileus surface turns pink in places; this is var. *roseipes* of older authors, and he considers this a worthless name.

5
Hygrophorus buccinulus (Speg.) Dennis
Kew Bull. 2: 256. 1953

> *Clitocybe buccinula* Speg., Bol. Acad. Nac. Cienc. Cordoba. 11: 388. 1889.
> *Marasmiellus buccinulus* (Speg.) Singer, Lilloa 22: 299. 1951.

Illustration:
Dennis, Kew Bull. 2, fig. 1 (drawings).

Pileus 1–1.5 cm broad, convex with a small umbilicus, white, dry, silky. Context white, thick; odor none.

Lamellae decurrent, white, narrow, subdistant, thick.

Stipe white, tapering downwards, undulating, dry, fibrous, solid or, in age, becoming hollow above.

Spores 7–8(10) × 6–7 μ, subglobose to broadly ellipsoid, nonamyloid. Basidia 67–75 × 10 μ, 4-spored. Gill trama interwoven. Cuticle of radiating hyphae, 4–5 μ broad.

HABIT, HABITAT, AND DISTRIBUTION—On bare soil, Trinidad and Brazil, April and September.

OBSERVATIONS—The above description is adapted from Dennis' report (1953) of his collection in Trinidad. After his study of Spegazzini's type, Dennis, with some hesitancy, concluded that his collections were identical with *Clitocybe buccinula* Speg. We have had no opportunity to study fresh material, but are inclined to follow Dennis in considering the spore size as given by Spegazzini on the type packet as correct, especially since Dennis has found specimens with such spores.

6

Hygrophorus borealis Pk. f. **borealis**
N. Y. State Mus. Ann. Rept. 26: 64. 1874

> *Camarophyllus borealis* (Pk.) Murr., North Amer. Flora 9: 385. 1916.
> *Omphalina tepeitensis* Murr., North Amer. Flora 9: 348. 1916.

Illustrations:
> Fig. 12; also 7c.
> Coker, Elisha Mitchell Sci. Soc. Jour. 64, pl. 17 (top).
> Smith, Mich. Acad. Sci., Arts and Letters 17, pl. 31.

Pileus 1–4.5 cm broad, obtuse to convex, becoming subumbonate, plane or with the disc slightly depressed, the margin remaining decurved or spreading and somewhat undulate in age, watery white when moist, dead white to nearly chalk white when faded, glabrous, moist, somewhat lubricous at times, the margin striatulate when expanded and moist, even or wrinkled slightly after losing moisture. Context thick on the disc, thin on margin, whitish, soft and fragile; odor and taste not distinctive.

Lamellae arcuate, becoming decurrent, white, subdistant to distant, intervenose, generally narrow, broadest next to the stipe, edges even.

Stipe 2–9 cm long, 2–8 mm thick, dull white, equal or tapering downward, firm, dry, glabrous or rarely innately silky, straight or flexuous, stuffed.

Spores 7–9(12) × 4.5–6.5 μ, ellipsoid, smooth, white in mass, pale yellowish in Melzer's reagent. Basidia 40–56 × 6–8 μ, 2- and 4-spored. Pleurocystidia and cheilocystidia none. Gill trama interwoven, cells 6–10(14) μ broad, yellowish in iodine. Cuticle of repent hyphae not sharply differentiated from the pileus trama. Pileus trama of radial subparallel hyphae. Hypodermium not differentiated. Clamp connections present on the cuticular hyphae.

HABIT, HABITAT, AND DISTRIBUTION—On soil, in deciduous and conifer woods, Nova Scotia to Washington, California, Oregon, Wyoming, Idaho, Michigan, Tennessee, North Carolina, Pennsylvania, New

Fig. 12. *H. borealis* f. *borealis*

York, Massachusetts, and Maine, August–December; also Canada, Mexico, and Jamaica.

MATERIAL STUDIED—CALIFORNIA: Smith 3878, 8180, 8204, 9147, 9248, 56189, 56286, 56423. IDAHO: Kauffman, Copeland, Sept. 8, 1922; Smith 16049, 53207, 53524, 53541, 53596, 53763, 54974, 55343, 60562. MAINE: H. E. Band, M. E. Bigelow 4452, 4500, 4501, 4502, 4616, 4617, 4694, 4752; Parlin 15216, 15512. MASSACHUSETTS: Bigelow 6227, 6228, 6229, 6230, 6242, 7814, 8690, 9357. MICHIGAN: Imshaug 4527, 4631; Kauffman, Marquette, Sept. 4, 1906, and Rock River, Sept. 14, 1929; Mains 32–685; Pennington 1358; Smith 1241, 7697, 18548, 20945, 23493, 32006, 32913, 34206, 38110, 42614, 42816. NEW YORK: Kauffman, Adirondack Mts., Sept. 14, 1921, and Ithaca, Sept. 19, 1913; R. Lowe, Adirondack Mts., Aug. 30, 1934; Peck (type, from Croghan and Copake, Sept.–Oct.); Singer 239. NORTH CAROLINA: Coker 13209. OREGON: Smith 8007, 19222. PENNSYLVANIA: Kauffman, Mt. Gretna, Sept. 7, 1924; Overholts 15998. TENNESSEE: Boarts 10095, 16574; Drew & Billings 9717; Hesler 1093, 12951, 22415, 22667, 22940, 23508; Mason 9667; Sharp 10947; J. Smith 14753; Wallace 4449, 4451, 4454, 4455, 4456, 4460, 4461. WASHINGTON: Smith 30311, 30883, 49128. WYOMING: Kauffman, Medicine Bow Mts., Sept. 5, 1923. CANADA: Kelly 914; Smith 882, 4577.

OBSERVATIONS—Kauffman (1918) described a variety which he named *subborealis* in which the spores measured 10–12(13) × 4–5.5 μ. Kauffman's specimens have been examined, and the basidia were found to be consistently 2-spored. Hence we regard his variety as merely a 2-spored form of the species. In a Tennessee collection (Hesler 14469), all basidia observed were 2-spored, none 4-spored. In Hesler 16574, the number of 2- and 4-spored basidia are about equal, and the spores measure 8–11 × 5–7 μ. In Hesler 10938, the 4-spored basidia predominate, and the spores measure 7.5–12 × 4.5–5.5(7) μ; but smaller and larger spores are about equal in numbers. In Hesler 10095, 2-spored basidia predominate and the spores are 7–9 × 4–5.5 μ. It appears then that not all the large spores are borne on 2-spored basidia. In Hesler 14469, however, only 2-spored basidia were observed, and the spores were 9–12 × 5–6 μ.

From Peck's collection we have studied the material marked "types." The specimen-box contains both the Croghan and Copake collections; when studied these were found to be identical. Notes on the Croghan collection: Spores 8–11(12) × 4.5–6 μ, the majority 8–9 × 4.5–5 μ, ellipsoid, smooth, yellowish in Melzer's reagent. Basidia 37–49 × 6–7(8) μ, 2- and 4-spored, the majority 2-spored. Pleurocystidia and cheilocystidia none. Gill trama interwoven. Cuticle of appressed hyphae which are only slightly gelatinous. Clamp connections present on the cuticular hyphae.

Singer (1951) and others have raised the question as to whether *H. borealis* is different from *H. niveus*. The latter species, however, is viscid from the gelatinous cuticle.

Dennis (1953) has studied the type of *Omphalina tepeitensis* Murr., and concludes that it is the same as *H. borealis*.

7
Hygrophorus borealis f. salmoneus Coker
Elisha Mitchell Sci. Soc. Jour. 64: 137. 1948

Pileus 2.5 cm broad, convex, not umbilicate, watery white, flushed with pinkish orange on one side, hygrophanous, opaque white when not soaked, glabrous, obscurely striate when wet, margin even when dry. Context white, less than 2 mm thick near disc; odor faintly of wood, taste slight.

Lamellae arcuate-decurrent, white but turning pinkish orange when cut, 3 mm broad at center, slightly venose, margins even.

Stipe 4 mm long, 3 mm thick below, 4 mm above, tapering slightly downward, white above, dull pink below, the pink extending when handled, nearly glabrous (with a few scattered fibrils).

Spores 7.5–10 × 4–5.5 μ, ellipsoid, smooth, pale yellow in Melzer's reagent. Basidia 34–42 × 5.5–8 μ, 4-spored. Pleurocystidia and cheilocystidia none. Gill trama of interwoven hyphae. Cuticle of repent hyphae. Clamp connections not observed.

HABIT, HABITAT, AND DISTRIBUTION—On soil, in mixed woods, North Carolina, November.

MATERIAL STUDIED—NORTH CAROLINA: Coker 3745 (type, from mixed woods, Chapel Hill, collected by H. R. Totten, Nov. 13, 1919).

OBSERVATIONS—The description of microscopic characters given above is based on our study of the type. The macroscopic characters are taken from the account by Coker (1948). A more detailed study of this form from fresh material is needed as the chemical reactions in addition to the color change already noted might be sufficient to establish it as a species. The color here is certainly not caused by the action of a pathogen.

8

Hygrophorus cremicolor (Murr.) Murr.
Mycologia 4: 217. 1912

> *Hydrocybe cremicolor* Murr., Mycologia 4: 209. 1912.
> *Camarophyllus cremicolor* Murr., North Amer. Flora 9: 389. 1916.

Illustration:
   Fig. 8a.

Pileus 1–3 cm broad, obtuse with an incurved cottony margin, expanding to broadly umbonate with a spreading margin, white to creamy ochraceous or with a salmon tint, unpolished and whitish faded, surface canescent, pallid but moist and hygrophanous. Context cream color to near pale pinkish buff; odor none (or faintly fragrant in Smith 54279), taste not distinctive.

Lamellae "maize yellow" or paler yellow, distant, narrow, decurrent, edges even.

Stipe 5–7 cm long, 8–12 mm thick at apex, narrowed downward or nearly equal, more or less concolorous with pileus or basal portion paler (pale yellow below in one immature carpophore), surface glabrous and naked, no pruinosity above and no veil seen.

Spores 5–7 × 3.5–4.5 μ, broadly ellipsoid to subglobose, smooth, hyaline in Melzer's solution. Basidia 40–50 × 5–6 μ, 4-spored. Pleurocystidia not seen. Gill trama of interwoven narrow hyphae, 1.5–3 μ broad. Cuticle a trichodermium, hyphae 2–5 μ broad, more or less erect to loosely tangled, some with cystidioid terminal elements, nongelatinous. Hypodermium not differentiated. Pileus trama chiefly of radial, subparallel hyphae, a few periclinally disposed. Clamp connections present.

HABIT, HABITAT, AND DISTRIBUTION—On the ground in woods and in a dried-up pool, Massachusetts, Michigan, Idaho, and Washington, July–November.

MATERIAL STUDIED—IDAHO: Smith 54279, 58239. MASSACHUSETTS: Bigelow 9130. MICHIGAN: Imshaug 4812; Smith 33115, 33151, 33159, 33163, 41726, 50254. WASHINGTON: Kauffman, Lake Quinault, Oct. 16, 1925; Murrill 568 (type, from Seattle, Oct. 20 to Nov. 1, 1911).

OBSERVATIONS—Notes on the type: Spores 5.5–7(8) × 3.5–4.5 μ, ellipsoid, smooth, pale yellow in Melzer's reagent. Basidia 34–46 × 4–6 μ, 4-spored. Pleurocystidia and cheilocystidia none. Gill trama interwoven. Cuticle of loosely tangled non-gelatinous hyphae. Clamp connections present on the cuticular hyphae. The species is very close to *H. pratensis* but differs in color.

9
Hygrophorus virgineus (Fr.) Fr.
Epicr. Myc., p. 327. 1838

> *Agaricus virgineus* Fr., Syst. Myc. 1: 100. 1821.
> *Camarophyllus virgineus* (Fr.) Kummer, Führ. in Pilzk., p. 117. 1871.

Illustrations:
> Fig. 13.
> Boudier, Icon. Myc., pl. 37.
> Bresadola, Icon. Myc., tab. 328.
> Jacquin, Misc. Austr. 2, pl. 15, fig. 1.
> Lange, Flora Agar. Dan. 5, pl. 164C.
> Peck, N. Y. State Mus. Bull. 5, pl. 58, figs. 8–12.
> Peck, N. Y. State Mus. Mem. 3, pl. 52, figs. 8–12.
> Sowerby, Engl. Fungi, pl. 32.
> Vittadini, Descr. Fungi Mang., pl. 32, fig. 2.
> Wakefield and Dennis, Common British Fungi, pl. 24, fig. 1.

Pileus 2–5 cm broad, at first convex and usually weakly umbonate, later nearly plane or finally slightly depressed, margin incurved at first, later nearly plane, white, finally tinged yellow at least over the disc, at first moist, later dry and becoming rimose, finally somewhat pruinose or fibrillose, central portion rather fleshy, margin thin, even when dry, at times striatulate when wet. Context white, soft, watery, thick on disc; odor none or slightly pleasant, taste mild.

Lamellae decurrent, white, finally tinged yellow, 3–5(7) mm broad, rather thick, subdistant to distant, venose.

Stipe 3–7 cm long, 3–8 mm thick, white, rarely pale pinkish lavender downward, smooth, glabrous, sometimes pruinose, narrowed below, often broadened above, sometimes flexuous, solid at first, later stuffed.

Spores 8–10(12) × 5–7 μ, ellipsoid, more rarely ovoid, smooth, white in mass, yellowish in Melzer's reagent. Basidia 38–60 × 5–8 μ, 4-spored, rarely 2-spored. Pleurocystidia and cheilocystidia none. Gill trama interwoven, hyphae 5–12 μ broad. Cuticle of undifferentiated,

Fig. 13. *H. virgineus*

repent, non-gelatinous hyphae, 2–3 μ broad—a cutis. Hypodermium not differentiated. Pileus trama of radially disposed hyphae. Clamp connections on the hyphae of the cuticle and gill trama.

HABIT, HABITAT, AND DISTRIBUTION—Gregarious on soil, at times among moss, in deciduous, coniferous, and mixed woods, Colorado, Michigan, Tennessee, and North Carolina, July–November; also Europe and Japan.

MATERIAL STUDIED—COLORADO: Whetstine, Grand Co., Aug. 9, 1917. MICHIGAN: Kauffman, Saline, July 18, 1923; Smith 62131. NORTH CAROLINA: Hesler 21005. TENNESSEE: Billings and Drew 9511; Hesler 14083, 17214, 19548, 22691, 23449; Sharp 17717, 22693. NETHERLANDS: Bas 1674. DENMARK: J. P. Jensen (Hesler 23960, 23961, 23962).

OBSERVATIONS—This species is related to *H. borealis* which has a more slender stipe and smaller spores; to *H. niveus* in which the pileus is viscid and the flesh thin; and to *H. pratensis* which has a colored pileus (buff, orange, or rufous).

In one North Carolina collection, Hesler 21005, the spore deposit, although white at first, became "maize yellow" on standing in the herbarium. In another collection (from Tennessee, Hesler 19548), the stipe was pale pinkish lavender downward. This condition suggests *H. virgineus* var. *roseipes* Massee. However, Orton (1960, p. 247, footnote) observes that *H. virgineus*, *H. niveus*, and *H. berkeleyi* are all prone to a pathological condition (see discussion of *H. niveus*).

10

Hygrophorus angustifolius (Murr.), comb. nov.

Camarophyllus angustifolius Murr., North Amer. Flora 9: 386. 1916.
Illustration:
  Fig. 14.

Pileus 2–5 cm broad, obtuse to plane, at times umbonate, the disc becoming more or less depressed and margin uplifted (very similar in shape to *H. pratensis*), pure white, surface dry and unpolished, appearing innately fibrillose under a lens. Context thick and firm, white; odor none, taste mild.

Lamellae decurrent, pure white, close, narrow, thickish, very brittle, some forked, edges even.

Stipe 2–4 cm long, 10–20 mm thick, pure white, subequal, solid, glabrous or with scattered fibrils.

Spores (3.5)4.5–6 × 3–4.5 μ, drop-shaped to subglobose, smooth, hyaline, not amyloid. Pleurocystidia and cheilocystidia none. Basidia 28–46 × 5–6 μ, 4-spored. Gill trama of narrow (2.5–4 μ), intricately interwoven hyphae, yellowish in iodine. Pileus trama homogeneous, yellowish in iodine. Cuticle a cutis, the surface hyphae not greatly differentiated from the pileus tramal hyphae, 2–3 μ broad, colorless,

Fig. 14. *H. angustifolius* (photograph by H. E. Bigelow)

repent to more or less erect, tangled. Hypodermium not differentiated. Pileus trama of radial, more or less parallel hyphae. Clamp connections present, scarce.

HABIT, HABITAT, AND DISTRIBUTION—On soil, in woods, including redwood, New Jersey, Massachusetts, and California, September and December.

MATERIAL STUDIED—CALIFORNIA: Smith 3879. MASSACHUSETTS: Bigelow 8986. NEW JERSEY: Earle and Murrill 1387 (type, from Fort Lee, Sept. 13, 1902).

OBSERVATIONS—The type has been studied, and notes have been recorded as follows: Spores 4.5–5.8 × 3.5–4.5 μ, ellipsoid to subglobose, apiculate, smooth, very pale yellow in Melzer's reagent. Basidia 30–46 × 4–6 μ, 4-spored. Pleurocystidia and cheilocystidia none. Gill trama interwoven. Cuticle a cutis, the surface hyphae repent, or more or less erect, not greatly differentiated from the subjacent tramal hyphae, clamp connections rare on the cuticular hyphae.

This species is a member of the *H. pratensis* series, and is distinguished from pale forms of the latter by its very small spores and close lamellae.

SERIES VISCIDI Hes. & Sm. stat. nov.

Subsection Viscidi Sm. & Hes., Lloydia 5: 17. 1942.
Characters as given in key to series, page 49.
Type species: *H. subviolaceus* Pk.

KEY TO SPECIES

1. Lamellae pallid to white ....24. *H. recurvatus*
1. Lamellae colored 2
   2. Lamellae dull violaceous to violaceous drab 3
   2. Lamellae yellowish to avellaneus 5
3. Taste bitter to subnauseous, finally somewhat acrid ....
       ....11. *H. subviolaceus*
3. Taste mild or essentially so 4
   4. Spores 5–6.5(7) × (3.5)4–5.5 μ.............12. *H. rainierensis*
   4. Spores 7–11 × 4.5–5.5 μ ....13. *H. nordmanensis*
5. Pileus walnut brown to cinnamon brown ....14. *H. colemannianus*
5. Pileus yellowish to buff 6
   6. Buttons with yellow caps, color not fading to white ....
       ....15. *H. burgdorfensis*
   6. Buttons whitish, finally dingy honey color on the disc ....
       ....16. *H. berkeleyi*

11

Hygrophorus subviolaceus Pk.

N. Y. State Mus. Ann. Rept. 53: 842. 1901

Camarophyllus subviolaceus (Pk.) Singer, Lilloa 22: 148. 1951.

Illustrations:
Fig. 15.
Peck, N. Y. State Mus. Ann. Rept. 53, pl. C, figs. 11–15.

Pileus 2.5–6 cm broad, broadly convex, expanding, at times depressed and margin upturned, "violet gray," "mouse gray," "dark Quaker drab," or "benzo brown" (dark violet to brownish violaceous), disc often pallid, viscid-lubricous to subviscid, hygrophanous, glabrous, pellicle separable, margin even when dry, pellucid-striate when wet. Context thick and firm on disc, thin on margin, concolor or paler; odor mild or earthy, taste at first mild, soon bitter to subnauseous, finally somewhat acrid, at times leaving a burning in the throat.

Lamellae decurrent, arcuate, whitish at first, soon smoky-violaceous or "vinaceous drab," subdistant to distant, medium broad, acuminate at the ends, subtriangular, intervenose, edges even.

Stipe 3–7 cm × 4–11(17) mm, white or tinted like the color of the pileus, dry, appressed-fibrillose, usually tapering below, often curved at base, solid becoming hollow.

Spores 6–7(8) × 4–5(7) μ, ellipsoid to ovoid, apiculate, smooth, white in mass, yellowish in Melzer's reagent. Basidia (31)43–62 × (4)5–8 μ, mostly 4-spored, some 2-spored. Pleurocystidia and cheilocystidia none. Gill trama intricately interwoven, hyphae 3–8 μ broad. Cuticle a colorless zone, 60–90 μ broad, of gelatinous narrow (2–3 μ) hyphae, the surface hyphae more or less erect and forming a turf—an ixotrichodermium. Hypodermium not differentiated. Pileus trama of radial hyphae. Clamp connections present on the hyphae of the cuticle and gill trama.

Habit, Habitat, and Distribution—Gregarious on soil in swamps and deep humus, in deciduous and coniferous woods, Ontario, Massachusetts, New York, Pennsylvania, Michigan, Tennessee, Idaho, Oregon, and Washington, September–November. Orton (1960) has reported it from England; also from Austria (Hesler 24128).

Material Studied—idaho: Imshaug 4911, 5050; Smith 54587. massachusetts: Bigelow 9412; Smith 1166, 21050, 21356, 32061, 33967, 36042, 38534, 38648, 38676, 38717, 38789, 43425, 44044, 51017, 51036. new york: Peck (type, from Meadowdale, Oct.). oregon: Smith 27364, 27792. pennsylvania: Overholts 23073. tennessee: Hesler 22928; Jones 4448. washington: Grant, Langley, Nov. 1923; Smith

Fig. 15. *H. subviolaceus*

17516, 17995. AUSTRIA: Moser, Oct. 6, 1948 (Hesler 24128).

OBSERVATIONS—Notes on Peck's type: spores 7–8(9) × 4.5–6 μ, ellipsoid, to ovoid, smooth, yellowish in Melzer's reagent. Basidia 42–48 × 6–8 μ, 2- and 4-spored. Pleurocystidia and cheilocystidia none. Gill trama intricately interwoven, hyphae 3–7 μ broad. Cuticle of colorless, gelatinous hyphae. Clamp connections present on the cuticular hyphae. The pileus in the dried state is "sayal brown" to "verona brown."

Although Peck (1901) and Murrill (1916) assigned *H. subviolaceus* to the section *Hygrophorus* (*Limacium*), it is clear that it is a *Camarophyllopsis*. *Hygrophorus caerulescens* Berk. & Curt., collected by Sprague in New England, is similar to *H. subviolaceus* in appearance; however, a study of the type *H. caerulescens* shows that, having a subparallel gill trama, it is a member of the section *Hygrocybe;* or possibly it is a member of section *Hygrophorus* in which, on revived sections, the hyphae of the gill trama do not regain their normal arrangement.

The pellicle of the pileus may not always be bitter. Overholts sent us specimens from Pennsylvania which apparently had no distinctive taste but otherwise seem to belong here. In the 2-spored form from Washington, the taste was very slight. Since Peck did not mention the taste in his original account, we cannot be sure the type was bitter. Ricken's *H. colemannianus* is very likely the 2-spored form of *H. subviolaceus*. He gives the spore size as 8–9 × 6–7 μ which is exactly the same as in the 2-spored form collected in Washington.

12

Hygrophorus rainierensis, sp. nov.

Illustration:
  Fig. 10a.

Pileus 1–3 cm latus, convexus demum planus, subpurpureus de-mum cinereus, viscidus, hygrophanus; odor proprius; lamellae decur-rentes, pallido-purpureo-cineraceae demum ochreae, confertae vel subdistantes, angustae; stipes 3–4 cm longus, 3–5 mm crassus, siccus, albidus; sporae 5–6.5(7) × (3.5)4–5.5 µ, ellipsoideae vel subglobosae. Specimen typicum in Herb. Univ. Mich.; lectum juxta Lower Tahoma Creek, Mt. Rainier National Park, Wash., Sept. 27, 1955, A. H. Smith 47958.

Pileus 1–3 cm broad, obtuse with a decurved margin, expanding to plane with a slightly depressed disc or merely convex, sometimes with a low obtuse umbo, dark purple drab when moist, fading to cinereous on margin and a tinge of cinnamon buff on disc, surface glabrous, viscid, hygrophanous. Context with a strong odor of freshly husked green corn, taste mild.

Lamellae decurrent, pale purplish drab young, becoming dingy buff in age or on drying, close to subdistant, narrow.

Stipe 3–4 cm long, 3–5 mm thick, equal or nearly so, surface dry, dull white over all and unchanging when bruised, when dried pale tan, solid.

Spores 5–6.5(7) × (3.5)4–5.5 µ, broadly ellipsoid to subglobose, rarely globose, thin-walled, hyaline in KOH, yellowish-hyaline in Melzer's reagent. Basidia 4-spored 38–55 × 6–8 µ (occasionally 2-spored). Pleurocystidia and cheilocystidia none. Gill trama intricately interwoven, hyphae 4–7 µ broad, hyaline to dingy in KOH, yellowish-hyaline in Melzer's reagent (no dark granules present). Cuticle a zone of gelatinous hyphae 1.5–2.5 µ broad, the zone 60–100 µ thick, originating as a trichodermium but the hyphae greatly elongating and becoming appressed, hyaline in KOH and Melzer's reagent. Pileus trama of subparallel, radially disposed hyphae, 4–10 µ broad. Clamp connections present, usually small.

HABIT, HABITAT, AND DISTRIBUTION—Scattered in mixed conifer-hardwood forests, Washington and Michigan, September to October.

MATERIAL STUDIED—WASHINGTON: Bigelow 16 (Smith 47958, type, from Lower Tahoma Creek, Mt. Rainier National Park, Sept. 27, 1955), Stuntz (Smith 31393). MICHIGAN: Smith 50850.

OBSERVATIONS—This species can be easily distinguished in the field by the odor of fresh green corn. *H. pallidus* and *H. subviolaceus*, the most closely related species, have no odor and the taste of their flesh is mild or bitter finally. The white stipe showed no yellow tints even after handling, a character of *H. lacmus* Fr. However, this is the nearest to *H. lacmus* of any North American species we have studied. ›In the dried specimens the cap has retained the purplish-fuscous tone over the marginal area, but the disc, the gills, and the stipe show varying tones of cinnamon buff to darker tan.

13
Hygrophorus nordmanensis, sp. nov.

Pileus 2 cm latus, convexo-extensus, "benzo brown," glaber, viscidus, margine striato; caro modice tenuis, odore proprio; stipes 2 cm longus, siccus, pallidus; sporae 7–11 × 4.5–5.5 μ, ellipsoideae. Specimen typicum in Herb. Univ. Mich.; lectum juxta Granite Creek, Nordman, Idaho, Oct. 9, 1956, A. H. Smith 54328.

Pileus 2 cm broad, convex-expanding, "benzo brown," glabrous, viscid, margin striate. Context medium thin; odor of green corn.

Lamellae decurrent, pale drab, becoming dingy buff in age, distant, medium broad.

Stipe 2 cm long, dry, pallid.

Spores 7–11 × 4.5–5.5 μ, ellipsoid, smooth, yellow in Melzer's reagent. Basidia 38–50 × 5–8 μ, 2- and 4-spored. Pleurocystidia and cheilocystidia none. Gill trama interwoven, hyphae 5–12 μ broad. Cuticle a narrow (20–40 μ) gelatinous zone, hyphae 1.5–3 μ broad, repent, radial, not differentiated from the hyphae of the pileus trama. Hypodermium not differentiated. Pileus trama of radially disposed, subparallel hyphae. Clamp connections not found.

HABIT, HABITAT, AND DISTRIBUTION—On soil, under hemlock, Idaho, October.

MATERIAL STUDIED—IDAHO: Smith 54328 (type, from Granite Creek, Nordman, Oct. 9, 1956).

OBSERVATIONS—This species is related to *H. rainierensis*, *H. subviolaceus*, and *H. lacmus* but has longer spores than any of them. The apparent absence of clamp connections may turn out to be an additional difference, but we hesitate to emphasize it because of the small amount of material available for study.

14
Hygrophorus colemannianus Blox. apud Berk.
Outl. Brit. Fungol., p. 200. 1860

> *Camarophyllus colemannianus* (Blox.) Ricken, Vademecum für Pilzfreunde, p. 197. 1920.

Illustrations:
Fig. 16.
Bresadola, Icon. Myc., tab. 338.
Juillard-Hartmann, Icon. Champ., pl. 49, fig. 1.
Kauffman, Agar. Mich., pl. 29.
Konrad and Maublanc, Icon. Sel. Fung., pl. 378.
Ricken, Die Blätterp., pl. 7, fig. 5.
Smith and Hesler, Lloydia 5, pl. 1a.

Pileus 1–4.5 cm broad, obtuse to turbinate, sometimes broadly convex to nearly plane in age or with the margin recurved slightly, sometimes with a low obtuse umbo, the margin decurved, color evenly "walnut brown" to "cinnamon brown," hygrophanous, fading to "fawn color" or "avellaneous" and finally "cinnamon buff" to "vinaceous buff" (dull deep rusty brown fading to avellaneous or buff), glabrous, viscid and shining, with a thin separable pellicle, the margin translucent striate when moist. Context concolorous with the surface, no color change when bruised, thick under the disc, thin toward the margin, fragile; odor and taste mild.

Lamellae arcuate and soon distinctly decurrent, "avellaneous" to "vinaceous buff" fading to "tilleul buff" (whitish) at times, close to subdistant (20–26 reach the stipe), narrow to moderately broad, many forking near their outer extremities, usually one tier of lamellulae, edges entire.

Stipe 3–6(8) cm long, 4–7 mm thick, white, equal or narrowed toward the base, solid or with a narrow tubule, glabrous, not viscid, apex merely silky and not pruinose.

Spores 6–8 × 4.5–6 μ, ellipsoid, a few subovoid, smooth, yellowish in Melzer's reagent. Basidia 37–51 × 6–8 μ, 4-spored, sterigmata 4–8 μ long. Pleurocystidia and cheilocystidia none. Gill trama intricately interwoven, hyphae 5–8 μ broad. Cuticle a gelatinous zone 40–70 μ thick, hyphae repent, colorless, 3–4 μ broad—an ixocutis. Hypodermium a conspicuous zone of brownish, radially parallel hyphae. Pileus trama of interwoven hyphae. Clamp connections present on the hyphae of the cuticle and gill trama.

HABIT, HABITAT, AND DISTRIBUTION—Gregarious on humus in oak and beech woods, Michigan, Washington, and Ontario, Canada, September–October; also Europe.

MATERIAL STUDIED—MICHIGAN: Kauffman 817; Porter & Smith 20660; Smith 6056, 7577, 11058, 21056, 21310, 31989, 43519, 43816, 43831, 51024. WASHINGTON: Brown, Lake Quinault, Oct. 31, 1925; Kauffman, same, Oct. 30, 1925; Smith 18078. CANADA: (Ontario) Smith 4570.

OBSERVATIONS—The reddish-brown pileus with its thin gelatinous

Fig. 16. *H. colemannianus*

pellicle, the white stipe, and broadly ovoid spores distinguish the species. It is closely related to *H. subviolaceus,* but very easily distinguished by the color of the gills. The greatest difficulty is encountered in distinguishing it from *H. uliginosus.* Both have the pileus conspicuously striate when moist and fresh. The latter, as we recognize it, lacks a viscid pellicle, and has a more highly colored stipe. Our data on *H. colemannianus* do not agree exactly with the European description, but at the same time the differences do not appear really significant. Hence we have referred the viscid species to *H. colemannianus* and the typically moist one to *H. uliginosus.*

15
Hygrophorus burgdorfensis, sp. nov.

Pileus 1–3.5 cm latus, viscidus, hygrophanus, pallido-luteus vel "warm buff" deinde "pinkish buff"; lamellae decurrentes, "cartridge buff" demum "pale pinkish buff," latae, distantes; stipes 5–7 cm longus, 2.5–4 mm crassus, albidus, cylindricus vel deorsum constrictus; sporae 7–9(10) × 4–5 μ, ellipsoideae. Specimen typicum in Herb. Univ. Mich.; lectum prope Burgdorf, Idaho, Aug. 12, 1958, A. H. Smith 60169.

Pileus 1–3.5 cm broad, convex with an inrolled margin, becoming plane or nearly so, viscid, hygrophanous, when young and fresh pale yellow ("warm buff"), fading to pinkish buff (never white), translucent-striate when moist and mature. Context thin but firm, unchanging when bruised or in $FeSO_4$; odor faintly medicinal (but scarcely diagnostic), taste mild.

Lamellae decurrent, "cartridge buff" to "pale pinkish buff" (not white), broad, distant, unchanging when bruised but gradually becoming more yellow in age.

Stipe 5–7 cm long, 2.5–4 mm thick at the apex, surface dull white, twisted striate in some specimens, equal to slightly narrowed downward.

Spores 7–9(10) × 4–5 μ, ellipsoid, smooth, yellow in Melzer's reagent. Basidia 38–50 × 6–8 μ, 4-spored. Pleurocystidia and cheilocystidia none. Gill trama intricately interwoven, hyphae 5–10 μ broad. Pileus cuticle a medium to narrow gelatinous zone, 30–60(100) μ thick. Clamp connections on the cuticular hyphae.

HABIT, HABITAT, AND DISTRIBUTION—Gregarious at edge of bog under lodgepole pine, Idaho, August.

MATERIAL STUDIED—IDAHO: Smith 60169 (type, from Burgdorf, Aug. 12, 1958).

OBSERVATIONS—This species obviously is related to *H. niveus* but is distinctly colored. The spores of the two species are similar. It is also related to *H. berkeleyi* Orton (1960) which has a whitish (ivory) pileus when young and is only slightly viscid.

16

Hygrophorus berkeleyi Orton
Trans. Brit. Mycol. Soc. 433: 259. 1960

Pileus 3–6 cm broad, plane to slightly depressed with a decurved margin, in age shallowly infundibuliform, surface glabrous, lubricous to slightly viscid, dull white to cream color, pale dingy honey color on the disc finally, the margin dull white and conspicuously striate, drying out to whitish on disc and yellowish at margin. Context whitish, thin, pliant, odor and taste not distinctive.

Lamellae distant, decurrent, narrow to moderately broad, milk white to pale cream color, edges even, drying whitish with dingy ochraceous edges.

Stipe 3–6 cm long, 4–6 mm thick, equal or enlarged either way, naked over-all, dingy watery pallid to dull white, discoloring only slightly in drying, base with appressed white mycelium.

Spores 8–10 × 5.5 μ, subovate with a prominent oblique sterigmal appendage as seen in profile, thin-walled, non-amyloid (yellowish hyaline in Melzer's). Basidia 4-spored; pleurocystidia and cheilocystidia none. Gill trama of interwoven hyaline hyphae, merely yellowish in Melzer's reagent. Epicutis of pileus a thin (6–15 μ) layer of narrow (1.5–3 μ) hyaline appressed gelatinous hyphae. Clamp connections present.

HABIT, HABITAT, AND DISTRIBUTION—Under spruce and balsam, Reese's Bog, University of Michigan Biological Station, Douglas Lake, Mich., Sept. 14, 1960.

MATERIAL STUDIED—MICHIGAN: Smith 63285.

OBSERVATIONS—This fungus has puzzled us for some years, but in the light of Orton's description it seems to have a natural position between *H. niveus* and *H. borealis*, but differs from both in the tendency to become yellow. From *H. borealis* it differs in its thinner pileus which expands to shallowly funnel-shaped, and in the thin gelatinous epicutis of very narrow hyphae. *H. borealis* is intermediate in color between *H. niveus* and *H. berkeleyi*. The latter as far as color is concerned differs distinctly from *H. niveus* but in other respects is exceedingly close to it. *H. burgdorfensis* is not white at first. Orton described the gills as subcrowded, and the habitat as in pastures, hence there is the possibility that the Smith collection cited here is a distinct form or variety. However, we cannot help but recall the fact that in North America *H. pratensis* typically grows in the woods in spite of its name. Here again, we have a series of taxa distinguished on progressive differences in pigmentation, a situation occurring throughout the genus as a whole and one which, it is hoped, can some day be studied from the standpoint of the chemistry involved.

SERIES CAMAROPHYLLOPSIS

KEY TO SPECIES

17

Hygrophorus cinereus Fr.

Sv. Aetl. Svamp., t. 30, 1863

Camarophyllus cinereus (Fr.) Karst., Bidr. Finl. Nat. Folk, p. 226. 1879.
Illustration:
Lange, Flora Agar. Dan., pl. 163B.

Pileus 8–25(30) mm broad, obtuse, expanding to broadly convex or nearly plane, glabrous, "benzo brown" (purple drab), fading to pale vinaceous drab when dried avellaneous to dingy pinkish buff. Context thin, whitish; taste mild, odor none.

Lamellae distant decurrent, moderately broad, "Quaker drab," (lilac gray), distant, edges even.

Stipe 1–3 cm long, 2.5–5 mm at apex, narrowed downward, pallid, naked, dry, no veil.

Spores 7–8(10) × 4.5–5.5 μ, ellipsoid, smooth, pale yellow in Melzer's reagent. Basidia 41–55 × (5)6–8 μ, 2- and 4-spored. Pleurocystidia and cheilocystidia none or the latter present as a few hairs 18–30 × 2–3 μ. Gill trama interwoven, hyphae 6–9 μ broad. Cuticle of repent hyphae, a few hyphae appearing slightly gelatinous. Clamp connections present on the cuticular hyphae.

HABIT, HABITAT, AND DISTRIBUTION—On soil, on a stream bank, Washington, Mt. Rainier National Park, September; also Europe.

MATERIAL STUDIED—WASHINGTON: Smith 48072.

OBSERVATIONS—It differs from *H. subviolaceus* and *H. pallidus* in its larger spores and mild taste; from *H. lacmus* in its lack of a yellow stipe-base; from *H. uliginosus* in its pileus color and lack of a striate pileus.

18
Hygrophorus uliginosus, sp. nov.

Pileus 2.5–3 cm latus, convexus, glaber, udus, cinnamomeo-brunneus; ad marginem substriatus; lamellae decurrentes, distantes, angustae, pallide vinaceo-brunneae; stipes 3–5 cm longus, 3–4 mm crassus, cavus, fragilis, glaber, pileo subconcolor; sporae 8–10 × 4–5.5 µ. Specimen typicum in Herb. Univ. Mich. conservatum, legit prope Rose City, Mich., Smith 31925.

Pileus 2.5–3 cm broad, convex, glabrous, moist and hygrophanous, dark dull rusty to vinaceous brown, not viscid, "warm sepia" to "russet" or "Rood's brown" throughout when moist, fading more or less to "wood brown" (dark rusty brown fading to pale dull vinaceous brown), at times the margin striate in age. Context concolorous to pallid (faded), thin, fragile; odor and taste mild.

Lamellae decurrent, distant, narrow, "fawn color" (pale vinaceous brown) to "wood brown," edges even.

Stipe 3–5 cm long, 3–4 mm thick, concolorous with the gills above, "cinnamon drab" (gray tinged with cinnamon) below, equal, hollow, fragile, glabrous.

Spores 8–10 × 4–5.5 µ, ellipsoid, smooth, thin-walled, hyaline in KOH and yellowish in Melzer's reagent. Basidia 38–50 × 7–9 µ, 4-spored, hyaline in KOH, yellowish in Melzer's reagent. Pleurocystidia and cheilocystidia none. Gill trama of intricately interwoven hyphae, 6–9 µ broad, orange-yellowish in Melzer's reagent (subhymenium same color). Pileus trama homogeneous, or showing a rudimentary, non-gelatinous cuticle of radial, repent, brownish hyphae, all tissues yellowish in Melzer's reagent. Clamp connections present.

HABIT, HABITAT, AND DISTRIBUTION—Scattered to gregarious on muck in cedar swamps and in *Sphagnum* bogs, autumn, Michigan, Trinidad, and Europe.

MATERIAL STUDIED—MICHIGAN: Smith 1160, 31925, 31952 (type, from Rose City, Oct. 16, 1948).

OBSERVATIONS—We earlier (1942) referred this species to *H. subradiatus*, but this is not tenable in view of the whitish gills as described and illustrated for the European species. Actually, *H. subradiatus* is more like *H. recurvatus* (see discussion of that species). *H. uliginosus* differs from *H. colemannianus* by its non-viscid pileus, slightly larger spores, different habitat, and colored stipe. However, it appears to be most closely related to *H. colemannianus*, especially in pigmentation.

19

Hygrophorus graveolens Sm. & Hes.
Sydowia 8: 316. 1954

Illustrations:
    Fig. 17; also 7f.

Pileus 3–6.5 cm broad, obtuse when young, expanding to plane with a low obtuse umbo or in some the margin strongly uplifted and split radially, surface moist and "pinkish cinnamon" beneath a "pale pinkish cinnamon" canescent coating, in age remaining "pinkish cinnamon" on disc but becoming "pinkish buff" toward the "pale pinkish buff" margin (generally pale cinnamon to pale alutaceous), some with watery spots around the disc. Context nearly concolorous with the pileus-surface, not staining when bruised; odor sickening (sweetish), taste slight and hardly distinctive.

Lamellae short-decurrent to broadly adnate, light "pinkish cinnamon" young, "pinkish buff" in age, distant, strongly intervenose, edges even.

Stipe 4–7 cm long, 5–14 mm thick, about "pinkish buff" within, about concolorous with the gills, narrowed downward, silky-striate

Fig. 17. *H. graveolens*

somewhat canescent at first from a silky coating but no veil seen, solid.

Spores 7–9 × 4.5–5.5 μ, ellipsoid or nearly so, smooth, yellowish in Melzer's reagent. Basidia 48–60 × 8–10 μ, 4-spored. Pleurocystidia and cheilocystidia not seen. Gill trama intricately interwoven, hyphae 2.5–5 μ broad, hyaline in KOH. Surface hyphae repent, non-gelatinous, forming an undifferentiated cutis. Hypodermium not differentiated. Pileus trama loosely but intricately interwoven, the hyphae chiefly disposed radially. Clamp connections abundant.

HABIT, HABITAT, AND DISTRIBUTION—Caespitose-gregarious in a swampy area under cedar and alder, Oregon, October.

MATERIAL STUDIED—OREGON: Smith 27411 (type, from East Fork, Salmon River, Mt. Hood, Oct. 8, 1947), 27448.

OBSERVATIONS—The interwoven gill trama clearly places this species in *Camarophyllopsis* where it is distinguished by the pinkish cinnamon color and sweetish sickening odor. It has much the stature of *H. pratensis* but differs in color and in having a peculiar odor. Because of the odor one might regard this species as close to *H. russocoriaceus*, a European species, but it cannot be considered identical without making major alternations in the concept of the latter.

20
Hygrophorus pratensis (Fr.) Fr. var. pratensis
Epicr. Myc., p. 326. 1838

> *Agaricus pratensis* Fr., Syst. Myc. 1: 99. 1821.
> *Camarophyllus pratensis* (Fr.) Kummer, Führ. in Pilzk., p. 117. 1871.
> *Hydrocybe pratensis* (Fr.) Murr., Mycologia 6: 2. 1914.
> *Camarophyllus fulvosus* Murr., North Amer. Flora 9: 387. 1916.

Illustrations:
> Figs. 18 and 19; also 4, 7e.
> Böhme, Norsk Soppbok, pl. 2, fig. 16.
> Bresadola, Fung. Mang., pl. 69.
> Bresadola, Icon. Myc., tab. 327.
> Bulliard, Herb. Fr., pl. 587, fig. 1.
> Dufour, Atl. Champ., pl. 43.
> Fries, Sv. Aetl. Svamp., pl. 30.
> Gillet, Champ. Fr., pl. 131 (345).
> Güssow and Odell, Mushrooms and Toadstools, pl. 47.
> Juillard-Hartmann, Icon. Champ., pl. 47, fig. 9.
> Lange, Flora Agar. Dan. 5, pl. 165 F & F [1] (as *Camarophyllus*).
> Murrill, Mycologia 2, pl. 27, fig. 1 (as *Hydrocybe*).
> Murrill, Mycologia 6, pl. 113, fig. 3 (as *Hydrocybe*).
> Peck, N. Y. State Mus. Ann. Rept. 48. pl. 28, figs. 11–17.
> Pomerleau, Mushrooms of Eastern Canada and the U. S., fig. 16B.
> Ricken, Die Blätterp., pl. 7, fig. 2.
> Sowerby, Engl. Fungi, pl. 141 (as *Agaricus miniatus*).
> Wakefield and Dennis, Common British Fungi, pl. 33, fig. 3.

Fig. 18. *H. pratensis* var. *pratensis*

Pileus 2–7 cm broad, obtuse to convex, then more or less expanded, broadly convex, umbonate, or turbinate in age, "rufous" to "zinc orange" when young and moist and becoming "cinnamon rufous," fading slowly to "light ochraceous buff" or remaining some shade of pale tawny, glabrous to minutely fibrillose under a lens, moist then dry, unpolished, often areolate or irregularly cracked around the disc. Context thick, brittle, whitish or pale fulvous; odor and taste mild.

Lamellae decurrent, more or less concolorous with the pileus, or paler, at times "apricot buff" or "ochraceous buff" then "salmon buff," finally pallid, subdistant to distant, thick, narrow to moderately broad, usually intervenose.

Stipe 3–8 cm × 5–20 mm, whitish or tinged like the pileus, usually tapering downward to nearly equal, dry and unpolished, glabrous, even, stuffed.

Spores 5.5–8 × 3.5–5 μ, ellipsoid, subovoid, or subglobose, smooth, white in deposits, yellowish in Melzer's reagent. Basidia 40–54 × 5–7 μ, 4-spored. Pleurocystidia and cheilocystidia none. Gill trama intricately interwoven, hyphae 3–7 μ broad. Cuticle of the cutis type, the cuticular hyphae are undifferentiated at the surface. Pileus trama interwoven, hyphae more or less radially disposed. Hypodermium not differentiated. Clamp connections present on the hyphae of the pileus trama and gill trama.

HABIT, HABITAT, AND DISTRIBUTION—Solitary, gregarious, or caespitose, in open places, on grassy areas, in thickets or dense forests, common throughout the United States and Canada, May–December; also Europe, Greenland, Iceland, Japan, and South America.

MATERIAL STUDIED—CALIFORNIA: Smith 3694, 3829, 3867, 9150, 9175, 9289, 9359, 9418. IDAHO: Slipp 1301; Smith 54579. INDIANA: Cottingham 13. MAINE: Bigelow 3525, 3587. MARYLAND: Kauffman, Tacoma Park, Aug. 24, 1919; Kelly 218, 1548, 1677, 1731. MASSACHUSETTS: Bigelow 7230, 7396, 7670, 7789, 7815, 8360, 8801, 8831. MICHIGAN: Brooks 1252; Koch 3130; Pennington (C.H.K.) 759; Potter 4167; Smith 5047, 6483, 6568, 7677, 7716, 15408, 15492, 18713, 20548, 21684, 21844, 21858, 32576, 32752, 33405, 43860, 62133, 62137; Thiers 790, 1099, 3161, 3347, 3457, 3511, 3542, 3570, 3590, 3623, 4016, 4177, 4298. NORTH CAROLINA: Hesler 4336, 12256, 16353; King 9395; Sharp

Fig. 19. *H. pratensis* var. *pratensis*

9316. TENNESSEE: Hesler 4464, 9533, 9558, 10387, 10864, 10908, 14432, 12880, 21379, 21388, 22577, 22937, 24325; Kauffman, Elkmont, Sept. 13, 1916; Smith 10300, 10899. WASHINGTON: Flett, Zenith, Nov. 1, 1941; Smith 18079, 39902. CANADA: (Ontario) Smith 4660, 26422; Smith & Cain 4724; (Quebec) Conners 16324; (Nova Scotia) Smith 668, 778. BELGIUM: Heinemann, Oct. 1960 and Nov. 1, 1960. DENMARK: J. P. Jensen (Hesler 23963, 23964, 23965). NETHERLANDS: Bas 1656.

OBSERVATIONS—Kauffman (1918) listed a var. *pallidus* and a var. *cinereus*. We have not seen the latter, but the former is occasionally encountered throughout the range of the type variety in North America. Since the fruiting bodies of the species are common and do not decay very rapidly, one frequently encounters old faded specimens which are in good condition and which might lead one to think he had one of the typically pale forms.

It has been reported from Japan by Hongo (1958a), from Argentina by Singer (1950), from Greenland (Lange, 1955), Iceland (Larsen, 1931–32), and the Faeröes (Möller, 1945).

21

Hygrophorus pratensis var. robustus, var. nov.

Illustration:
> Fig. 20.

Pileus 4–10 cm latus, obtusus, obscurus, "pinkish cinnamon" demum "light pinkish cinnamon," margo flavescens demum brunneus contusus; odore et gustu mitis; lamellae decurrentes, "pale pinkish cinnamon," distantes, latae; stipes 4–11 cm longus, 10–25 mm crassus, angustior ad basim, albidus demum striatus colore rubicundo-coriaceo; sporae 7–8 × 5–5.5 μ, ellipsoideae. Specimen typicum in Herb. Univ. Mich.; lectum in Sharon Hollow, Washtenaw County, Mich., Oct. 6, 1961, Smith 64616.

Pileus 4–10 cm broad, obtuse to convex, often with an obtuse umbo when expanded, but mostly becoming broadly convex, margin spreading or remaining decurved and finally crenate to lobed, surface dull and unpolished from button stages until maturity, often uneven, color "pinkish cinnamon" to "light pinkish cinnamon" and in age merely "pinkish buff" (slight reddish tone disappears), margin never translucent striate, staining yellowish along the margin and finally brownish when injured. Context thick, firm, brittle, pale pinkish buff to pinkish buff with a slight tendency to stain yellowish when cut; no reaction with KOH and FeSO₄; odor and taste mild.

Lamellae decurrent (often unequally so), "pale pinkish cinnamon" or in age slightly paler and nearly concolorous with pileus, distant, intervenose, thick, broad, edges even.

Stipe 4–11 cm long, 10–25 mm at apex, narrowed to the base, pale pinkish buff within, surface whitish and unpolished at first, in age more or less streaked pinkish buff on a pallid ground color, not discoloring in age or on drying, solid, firm, hard, rather deeply rooting.

Spores 7–8 × 5–5.5 μ, ellipsoid, non-amyloid. Basidia 4-spored, 42–55 × 7–8 μ. Pleurocystidia and cheilocystidia none. Gill trama compactly interwoven, of hyaline hyphae. Pileus trama homogeneous, no epicutis differentiated; clamp connections present.

Fig. 20. *H. pratensis* var. *robustus*

HABIT, HABITAT, AND DISTRIBUTION—Scattered under hardwoods, Sharon Hollow, Washtenaw County, Michigan, Oct. 6, 1961.

MATERIAL STUDIED—MICHIGAN: type, Smith 64616.

OBSERVATIONS—This material answers the descriptions of European authors better than does our common form which is actually rather thin-fleshed, and when perfectly fresh practically hygrophanous. The two were compared fresh the same day from the same woods. Specimens of *H. pratensis* sensu Smith & Hesler (1942) were moist and hygrophanous, thin-fleshed, and very fragile, and the stipes were not deeply rooting. Since these characters deal with those of fresh fruiting bodies, one has to rely mainly on descriptions for comparisons.

The colors of var. *robustus* are apparently paler than in var. *pratensis*, the stipe is much harder and more deeply rooting, and there is a color change to yellow on injury which may also be significant. The photograph (Fig. 20) shows young specimens.

22

Hygrophorus cremeus (Murr.) Dennis
Kew Bull. 2: 257. 1953

   Omphalina cremea Murr., North Amer. Flora 9: 350. 1916.

Pileus up to 4 cm broad, convex, then expanded, flat or slightly umbilicate, warm buff to light buff, smooth, dry. Context white, thin.

Lamellae decurrent, light ochraceous buff, broad, subdistant, thick, lamellulae present, veined at base.

Stipe white, dry, equal or slightly enlarged upwards, smooth, solid.

Spores 8–9 × 4.5–6 μ, broadly ellipsoid, with a large oil drop. Basidia 35–40 × 7 μ, 4-spored. Pleurocystidia and cheilocystidia none. Gill trama of interwoven hyphae, 5–7 μ broad.

HABIT, HABITAT, AND DISTRIBUTION—On soil and decayed stump, Trinidad and Jamaica, September to December.

MATERIAL STUDIED—Trinidad: Dennis 73.

OBSERVATIONS—Dennis (1953) has studied the type of *Omphalina cremea* Murr., and, because of its thick gills and long basidia, concludes that it is an *Hygrophorus*. He suggests that it might be treated as a variety of *H. pratensis* with yellower gills and paler stipe than the type. We have studied Dennis collection 73, and our observations are as follows: Spores 7.5–9 × 4.5–6 μ, ellipsoid, smooth, yellowish in Melzer's reagent. Basidia 37–46 × 5–6.5 μ, 2- and 4-spored. Pleurocystidia and cheilocystidia none. Gill trama interwoven, hyphae 3–5 μ broad. Cuticle not differentiated, surface hyphae repent, 3–5 μ broad, with clamp connections. Pileus trama of radial hyphae. The dry pileus and paler color distinguish it from *H. pratensis*.

23

Hygrophorus fulvosiformis (Murr.) Murr.
Lloydia 5: 156. 1942

   Camarophyllus fulvosiformis Murr., Lloydia 5: 136. 1942.

Pileus 3–4 cm broad, convex to expanded, turbinate, pallid to avellaneous-isabelline, glabrous, dry, margin even. Context thin, white; odor fragrant, taste mild.

Lamellae long-decurrent, white, rather narrow, distant to subdistant, inserted, intervenose, edges even.

Stipe 4–6 cm long, 4–7 mm thick, white, shining, glabrous, equal or slightly enlarged upward, becoming somewhat hollow.

Spores (5)6–7(9) × 4.5–5.5 μ, ellipsoid to ovoid, smooth, non-amyloid. Basidia 36–54 × 6–8.5 μ, 2- and 4-spored. Pleurocystidia and cheilocystidia none. Gill trama of interwoven hyphae. Cuticle of non-gelatinous, repent hyphae which are radially arranged, 2–3 μ broad, brownish, with more or less erect free ends forming a type of trichodermium. No hypodermium differentiated. Pileus trama of radial hyphae, with scattered lactifers. Clamp connections present on the cuticular hyphae.

HABIT, HABITAT, AND DISTRIBUTION—In leaf mold in a climax hammock, Florida, January.

MATERIAL STUDIED—FLORIDA: Murrill & Watson F20129 (type, southwest of Gainesville, Jan. 21, 1940).

OBSERVATIONS—In the dried condition the carpophores somewhat resemble *H. virgineus*. Murrill says that when fresh it suggests *H. fulvosus* (*H. pratensis*) but has a more slender stipe. It also has a fragrant odor.

The description of microscopic characters given above is based on our study of Murrill's type.

24

Hygrophorus recurvatus Pk.

N. Y. State Mus. Bull. 157: 28. 1912.

> *Camarophyllus recurvatus* (Pk.) Murr., North Amer. Flora 9: 388. 1916.
> *Clitocybe praticola* Murr., Lloydia 5: 136. 1942.
> *Omphalina australis* Murr., Florida Acad. Sci. Proc. 7: 111. 1945.

Illustrations:
> Fig. 21.
> Smith, Torrey Bot. Club Bull. 64, pl. 11c.

Pileus 1–2.5(3) cm broad, obtuse to convex at first, in age plane, sometimes with a recurved margin, sometimes with a depressed disc, with or without a papilla, "clove brown," "olive brown," or "buffy brown" (dark or pale olive brown), margin paler in age, lubricous to subviscid when wet, disc rugulose or smooth, at times the margin faintly translucent-striate, margin wavy or subplicate, cuticle often cracking circumferentially in age and at times lacerate. Context thin, dark olive brown, fragile; odor and taste not distinctive.

Lamellae decurrent, grayish white, distant to subsistant, broad.

Fig. 21. *H. recurvatus*

Stipe 2–4 cm long, 3–6 mm thick, whitish or concolorous with the pileus, grayish within, tapering slightly downward, moist, occasionally faintly longitudinally striate.

Spores 7–9(10) × 4–5(6) μ, ellipsoid, smooth, yellowish in Melzer's reagent. Basidia 42–55 × 6–8 μ, 4-spored, occasionally 2-spored. Pleurocystidia and cheilocystidia none. Gill trama intricately interwoven, hyphae 3–7 μ broad. Cuticle a clearly defined narrow zone, the innermost layer brownish, the outer colorless, gelatinous, hyphae 2–3.5 μ broad. Hypodermium a distinct layer of brownish hyphae. Pileus trama of periclinal hyphae. Clamp connections present on the cuticular and gill trama hyphae.

HABIT, HABITAT, AND DISTRIBUTION—Gregarious under conifers and in pastures, New York, Michigan, Idaho, Washington, Oregon, California, and Florida, October–January.

MATERIAL STUDIED—CALIFORNIA: Smith 3883, 3923, 3944, 8525, 8526, 8897, 9447. FLORIDA: Murrill F19334 (type of *Omphalina australis* Murr., Gainesville, Jan. 8, 1940). IDAHO: Smith 54976, 55132. MICHIGAN: Smith 62129. NEW YORK: E. C. Webster (type of *H. recurvatus*

Pk., from Canandaigua, Oct. 1911). OREGON: Smith 7997, 18028, 28324.

OBSERVATIONS—Notes on Peck's type of *H. recurvatus:* Spores 7.5–9(10) × 4.5–5.5(6) μ, ellipsoid, smooth, yellowish in Melzer's reagent. Basidia 44–55 × 6–8 μ, 4-spored. Pleurocystidia and cheilocystidia none. Gill trama interwoven, hyphae 4–7 μ broad. Cuticle well-defined, composed of parallel hyphae with an inner brown zone and an outer, clear, subgelatinous zone. Clamp connections present.

Singer (1951) suggests that both *Omphalina australis* Murr. and *Clitocybe praticola* Murr. are synonyms. Our studies of the types of each of these species confirm his suggestion.

The species is very common in the pastures and grassy areas of northern California. In collections from shady habitats the stipes are white; those from open fields had darker pilei and darker colored stipes. The gelatinous pellicle is so thin that it can be easily overlooked or lost in sectioning either fresh or dried specimens. It does not appear to be sufficiently well developed to cause fresh wet specimens to be truly viscid. On the basis of descriptions this species is very close to *H. subradiatus,* if not actually identical. A critical study of these two should be made.

25
Hygrophorus bakeri Dennis
Kew Bull. 2: 258. 1953

Illustration:
Dennis, Kew Bull. 2, fig. 3.

Pileus 2.5 cm broad, convex, umbilicate, avellaneous, glabrous, slightly striate. Context white, very thin.

Lamellae decurrent, white, narrow.

Stipe about 3–5 cm long, slender, white, base attenuated, glabrous, solid.

Spores 6–8 × 5–5.5 μ, subglobose, apiculate, non-amyloid. Basidia 35–40 × 5–6 μ, 4-spored, cylindric-clavate. Pleurocystidia and cheilocystidia none. Gill trama subparallel in the center of the gill, irregularly woven toward its sides. Cuticle of undifferentiated, radiating hyphae, 5.5–7 μ broad, non-gelatinous, with clamp connections.

HABIT, HABITAT, AND DISTRIBUTION—On soil under bamboo, Trinidad.

MATERIAL STUDIED—TRINIDAD: Dennis IIA (type, from St. Joseph).

OBSERVATIONS—Dennis (1953) suggests that this agaric might be sought in *Omphalina,* but the long basidia indicate an *Hygrophorus.* He adds that *H. albipes* Pk. and *H. sphaerosporus* Pk. differ from it in their obtuse, viscid pilei. Dennis properly places it under *Camarophyllus* (*Camarophyllopsis*).

26
Hygrophorus fumosellus Sm. & Hes.
Sydowia 8: 316. 1954

Pileus 2.5–5 cm broad, convex, expanding to concave as margin becomes elevated, hygrophanous but not viscid, "sayal brown" when moist, "pinkish cinnamon" faded, margin faintly striatulate when moist, innately silky faded (under a lens). Context dingy white, thick on disc, thin on margin; odor and taste mild.

Lamellae arcuate-decurrent, near "pale pinkish buff" but with a smoky tint, moderately broad and close, intervenose, somewhat forked, edges even.

Stipe 3–5 cm long, 5–10 mm thick, dingy white, tapered downward, glabrous, dry, rigid, solid.

Spores 9–11 × 5–6 μ, ellipsoid, smooth, yellowish in Melzer's reagent, hyaline in KOH. Basidia 50–62 × 6–7 μ, 4-spored. Pleurocystidia and cheilocystidia none. Gill trama compactly and intricately interwoven, hyphae 4–10 μ broad. Cuticle a cutis, hyphae chiefly repent, radially disposed, 3–4 μ broad. No hypodermium differentiated. Pileus trama of radially disposed, more or less parallel hyphae. Clamp connections present on the cuticular hyphae and at the base of the basidia.

Habit, Habitat, and Distribution—Gregarious on soil in deciduous woods, Tennessee, December.

Material Studied—tennessee: Hesler 14105 (type, from New Hopewell, Knox County, Dec. 17, 1941).

Observations—The sayal brown, striatulate pileus, peculiar smoky tint of the gills, and the interwoven gill trama, along with the appearance of the dried specimens, relate this species to *H. pratensis* and, at the same time, distinguish it from the latter. The long, narrow basidia distinguish it from species of *Clitocybe* if one is inclined to disregard the character of waxiness.

SUBSECTION MICROSPORI (Sm. & Hes.) stat. nov.

Section Microspori Sm. & Hes., Lloydia 5: 7. 1942.

Key to Series

1. Pileus dry to moist .... Series *Microspori*
1. Pileus viscid .... Series *Pelliculosi*

SERIES MICROSPORI

KEY TO SPECIES

1. Odor distinctive, fragrant to offensive 2
1. Odor not distinctive 3
  2. Lamellae broad; pileus smoky brown to blackish ....
  ....27. *H. peckianus*
  2. Lamellae narrow; pileus yellowish becoming gray,
    fading to whitish ....28. *H. paupertinus*
3. Lamellae pale drab to deep bluish gray at first 4
3. Lamellae white to pallid at first 6
  4. Clamps absent from hyphae of fruiting body; spores 5–6 × 4–5 μ....
  ....29. *H. fallax*
  4. Clamps present; spores slightly narrower than in above 5
5. Stipe white; gills drab; pileus gray-brown ....30. *H. basidiosus*
5. Stipe violaceous gray; gills bluish gray; pileus violaceous gray to violaceous brown, canescent ....31. *H. canescens*
  6. Spores (3)4–4.5 × 2.5–3 μ ....32. *H. microsporus*
  6. Spores larger 7
7. Lamellae narrow; stipe white, unchanging 8
7. Not as above 9
  8. Pileus grayish brown ....33. *H. albipes*
  8. Pileus vinaceous buff, fading to a chalky white .....34. *H. silvaticus*
9. Basidia 46–62 × 5–7 μ; spores globose ....35. *H. umbrinus*
9. Basidia 32–47 × 5–6 μ; spores 4–5.5 × 3–6 μ, short ellipsoid ....
....36. *H. obconicus*

27

Hygrophorus peckianus Howe
Torrey Bot. Club Bull. 5: 43. 1874

  Camarophyllus peckianus (Howe) Murr., North Amer. Flora 9: 389.
    1916.

Illustrations:
  Fig. 8c.
  Coker, Elisha Mitchell Sci. Soc. Jour. 64, pl. 16 (inset).

Pileus 1–3 cm broad, convex, mouse gray when dry, smoky brown to blackish when wet, appearing smooth but minutely fibrillose under a lens, margin even or wavy. Context whitish to grayish, fragile; odor strong, offensive, taste slight.

Lamellae adnate to arcuate-decurrent, pallid to white at first, soon pale gray, subdistant, broad, thick.

Stipe 1–3 cm long, 1.5–2 mm thick, white-pruinose above, elsewhere glabrous, dark below, tapering downward, hollow.

Spores 4–5 × 3.5–4.5 μ, subglobose to globose, more rarely short-ellipsoid, smooth, yellowish in Melzer's reagent. Basidia 28–38 × 4–6 μ, 4-spored. Gill trama interwoven, hyphae 3–8 μ broad. Pileus trama homogeneous, composed of subparallel hyphae, the surface hyphae fuscous, the end-cells inflated (globose, ovoid, pyriform, clavate), more or less erect (forming a trichodermium) or appressed against the surface. Clamp connections none.

HABIT, HABITAT, AND DISTRIBUTION—On soil, in deciduous and mixed woods, swamps, on lawns, and under bracken fern, Michigan, Massachusetts, Tennessee, and North Carolina, July–October.

MATERIAL STUDIED—MICHIGAN: Mains 32622; Smith, Oakland County, Oct. 1939. MASSACHUSETTS: Davis, from Stow, Aug. 30, 1906. NORTH CAROLINA: Coker 2620, 2798; Couch 5334. TENNESSEE: Hesler 19241; Smith & Hesler 7397.

OBSERVATIONS—The whitish gills which become gray furnish a good character to separate this species from *H. hymenocephalus.* An interesting feature of our collections is the manner in which the ends of the hyphae forming the surface of the pileus are frequently differentiated. The end cell is somewhat oval to club-shaped, and slightly thicker than the main filament. All that is necessary here for the production of an hymeniform surface layer is for all these hyphae to produce the same type of end cell, and for these cells to become oriented perpendicularly to the surface and more enlarged. The hymenium and gill trama of *H. peckianus* become very dark rusty brown in iodine and the pileus trama yellowish to sordid yellowish brown.

28
Hygrophorus paupertinus Sm. & Hes.
Lloydia 5: 13. 1942

Armillariella paupertina (Sm. & Hes.) Singer, Lilloa 22: 216. 1951.
Illustration:
Fig. 22.

Pileus (5)10–20 mm broad, convex to nearly flat, the thin margin usually becoming wavy or somewhat elevated, sordid Isabella color when young but soon changing to sordid drab or dark brownish gray, sometimes fading to whitish or pallid sordid gray, surface appearing dry and under a lens minutely appressed fibrillose, sometimes fibrillosefurfuraceous near the margin. Context thin, very fragile, grayish; odor exceedingly strong, penetrating, disagreeable, taste mild; no color change noted on bruised portions.

Lamellae distant to subdistant, pallid or pale drab, very narrow (almost fold-like in some), decurrent.

Stipe 1–2(3) cm long, 3–6 mm thick at the apex, concolorous with

Fig. 22. *H. paupertinus*

the pileus or paler, usually enlarged upward, solid, becoming hollow near the apex at least, fragile, moist, glabrous, faintly longitudinally striate from fine cracks in the cuticle.

Spores 5–6 × 4–5.5 μ, subglobose to short-ellipsoid, rarely globose, smooth, yellowish in Melzer's reagent. Basidia 30–46 × 4–7 μ, 4-spored. Pleurocystidia and cheilocystidia none. Gill trama interwoven, hyphae 2–3 μ broad. Cuticle a limited trichodermium, hyphae at times more or less scattered, 2–5 μ broad, the terminal elements at times cystidioid. No hypodermium differentiated. Pileus trama of radial hyphae. Clamp connections none.

HABIT, HABITAT, AND DISTRIBUTION—Gregarious on humus and soil under redwoods, California, December.

MATERIAL STUDIED—CALIFORNIA: Smith 3680, 3793 (type, Orick, Dec. 5, 1935), 3941, 9367, 9463.

OBSERVATIONS—This species resembles *H. hymenocephalus* in its color change from Isabella color to dark brownish gray or drab, but differs in having a strong odor, and in the nature of the cuticle of the pileus. It is very close to the little known *H. peckianus*, but differs from that species as we know it in having very narrow instead of broad gills and different colors when fresh. *H. foetens* is a somewhat similar species, but the pileus is dark brown, becoming squamulose, and the stipe is squamulose. Bresadola (1928) illustrates *H. foetens* as having a glabrous stipe but a somewhat scaly pileus. Aside from the presence or absence of scales, *H. foetens* differs from *H. paupertinus* in having much broader gills, and in the structure of the cuticle.

29

Hygrophorus fallax Sm. & Hes.

Sydowia 8: 315. 1954

Pileus 10–18 mm broad, convex, dark smoky gray to fuscous black when moist, opaque at all stages, fading to a dull dingy gray, moist, somewhat hygrophanous, glabrous, not becoming squamulose when faded. Context fragile; no distinctive odor or taste.

Lamellae adnexed, dingy drab gray, edges usually paler, subdistant, broad, ventricose, fragile, and the edges very readily fracturing.

Stipe 2–3.5 cm long, 2–2.5 mm thick, concolorous with pileus or darker, equal or enlarged at both ends or at either end, glabrous, apex faintly pruinose, moist to dry.

Spores 5–6 × 4–5 μ, broadly ellipsoid to globose, smooth, hyaline in KOH and yellowish in Melzer's solution. Basidia 20–25 × 5–6 μ, 4-spored. Pleurocystidia and cheilocystidia none. Gill trama interwoven, hyphae 4–8 μ broad, dingy in KOH, in Melzer's reagent with yellowish, granular content variously distributed. Cuticle of repent hyphae 8–12 μ broad, at times more or less erect, the terminal elements inflated and usually repent. Pileus trama of radially disposed, compactly interwoven hyphae. Clamp connections none.

HABIT, HABITAT, AND DISTRIBUTION—On moss, Tennessee, August.

MATERIAL STUDIED—TENNESSEE: Hesler (type, Univ. Mich., No. 10661, Indian Camp Creek, Sevier County, Great Smoky Mts. National Park, Aug. 30, 1938).

OBSERVATIONS—This species differs from *H. microsporus* in its larger spores and in its non-squamulose pileus. The dark granules in the hyphae as seen in Melzer's reagent are common to both.

30

Hygrophorus basidiosus (Pk.) Pk.

N. Y. State Mus. Bull. 116: 57. 1907

Clitocybe basidiosa Pk., N. Y. State Mus. Bull. 1: 215. 1887.
Camarophyllus basidiosus (Pk.) Murr., North Amer. Flora 9: 389. 1916.

Illustration:
Fig. 23.

Pileus 1–4 cm broad, convex to plane, subumbonate at times, grayish brown when moist, fading to pale gray, near "pale gull gray" (no comparable colors in Ridgway), glabrous or appearing glaucous, hygrophanous, pale ashy buff when dry, radiate-streaked in fading. Context whitish; odor and taste not distinctive.

Lamellae adnate to short decurrent, pale gray to "drab gray," broad, subdistant, arched, thick, edges even.

Stipe 2.5–5 cm long, 3–10 mm thick at the apex, white, tapering downward to a slender base, solid becoming hollow, surface glabrous or appearing innately fibrillose under lens.

Spores 4–5.5(–6) × 3–4.5 μ, subglobose, smooth, pale yellowish in Melzer's reagent. Basidia 38–50 × 5–6.5 μ, 2- and 4-spored, sterigmata 5–9 μ long, curved. Pleurocystidia and cheilocystidia none. Gill trama interwoven, hyphae cylindrical, 2–4.5 μ broad. Cuticle not gelatinous, cuticular hyphae cylindrical, 1–3 μ in diameter, repent or free ends more or less erect; pileus tramal hyphae of the pileus mostly cylindrical, 1–4 μ in diameter, radially disposed and interwoven. No hypodermium differentiated. Clamp connections present.

HABIT, HABITAT, AND DISTRIBUTION—Gregarious in woods, swamps, and *Sphagnum* bogs, New York, Massachusetts, and Maine, July–September.

MATERIAL STUDIED—MAINE: Bigelow 4494, 4669. MASSACHUSETTS: Bigelow 7503, 8301, 8347. NEW YORK: Peck (type, from Sandlake, August).

OBSERVATIONS—Notes on the type follow: Spores 4–5.7(6) × 3–4.5 μ subglobose, ovoid, or short-ellipsoid, smooth, pale yellow in

Fig. 23. *H. basidiosus* (photograph by H. E. Bigelow)

Melzer's reagent. Basidia 37–44 × 4.5–6 μ, 4-spored, sterigmata up to 8 μ long. Pleurocystidia and cheilocystidia none. Gill trama intricately interwoven, hyphae 2–4.5 μ broad. Cuticle repent-fibrillose, some hyphae more or less erect. Clamp connections present on the cuticular hyphae. The pileus cuticle is non-gelatinous in KOH. The lamellae apparently vary in color from whitish to pale gray, or they may be whitish with a violaceous tint.

This species is distinguished from *H. albipes* in its paler color when dried, its larger stature, its broader, grayish to violaceous lamellae, and its lack of a gelatinous or even a subgelatinous cuticle. The types of these two species do not resemble each other.

31
Hygrophorus canescens Sm. & Hes.
Lloydia 5: 10. 1942

Camarophyllus canescens (Sm. & Hes.) Singer, Lilloa 22: 148. 1951.

Pileus 2–4.5 cm broad, obtuse, becoming convex, the margin incurved and lobed or somewhat irregular, "benzo brown" to "drab gray," fading to pallid sordid gray in age, surface at first canescent from a thin coating of appressed fibrils, glabrescent, dry or moist, not viscid, opaque at all stages. Context grayish, unchanging, thin, fragile; odor and taste mild.

Lamellae broadly arcuate-adnate to subdecurrent, "Quaker drab," becoming "light mouse gray" (deep bluish gray), fading when dried and then concolorous with the pileus, subdistant to distant, narrow, broadest near point of attachment, narrowed outward, edges even.

Stipe 4–6 cm long × 6–8 mm thick, white at the base, elsewhere near "pallid purplish gray," enlarged above, glabrous and somewhat longitudinally streaked, hollow.

Spores 4–5.5(6) × 4–4.5 μ, at times globose, more often subovoid, smooth, pale yellowish in Melzer's reagent. Basidia 34–51 × 4.5–6 μ, 2- and 4-spored, mostly 4-spored; sterigmata 5–8 μ long. Pleurocystidia and cheilocystidia none. Gill trama compactly and intricately interwoven, hyphae 2.5–5 μ broad. Cuticle of interwoven hyphae with numerous more or less erect, slender (1–3 μ) hyphae, non-gelatinous, a trichodermium. Pileus trama more or less radial, interwoven. Clamp connections present on the cuticular and gill trama hyphae.

HABIT, HABITAT, AND DISTRIBUTION—Singly on soil, under hemlock, Massachusetts, North Carolina, and Michigan, August–September.

MATERIAL STUDIED—MASSACHUSETTS: Bigelow 9125. MICHIGAN: Smith 38537, 39515, 41824, 61288. NORTH CAROLINA: Smith 10031 (type, from Newfound Gap, Great Smoky Mts. National Park, Aug. 11, 1938).

OBSERVATIONS—This is a very beautiful species and apparently very similar to *H. pallidus* and *H. subviolaceus*. It differs in its canescent pileus when young, dark-colored stipe (the specimens were growing in deep shade), and smaller spores. In the dried condition it resembles *H. basidiosus* in appearance, but since most members of the *H. pratensis* series look much alike when dried, a great deal of emphasis cannot justifiably be placed on that character. When fresh *H. basidiosus* and *H. canescens* should be readily distinguishable by the difference in the colors of the pileus and stipe and the lack of striations on the pileus of *H. canescens*.

32
Hygrophorus microsporus Sm. & Hes.
Lloydia 5: 11. 1942

> *Hygrotrama microsporum* (Sm. & Hes.) Singer, Sydowia 12: 223. 1958 (1959).
> *Armillariella microspora* (Sm. & Hes.) Singer, Lilloa 22: 216. 1951.

Illustration:
> Fig. 8h.

Pileus 1–2 cm broad, broadly convex becoming plane, the margin regularly recurved in age, "fuscous" (very dark gray with a tinge of brown) over all, opaque when moist, fading to "drab" or paler (medium to pale gray), surface moist, glabrous at least in age, somewhat hygrophanous, somewhat atomate after losing moisture. Context thin, fragile, waxy, dark grayish becoming pallid; taste perfectly mild, odor none.

Lamellae long-decurrent, whitish to pallid, becoming sordid gray in age but drying much lighter than the pileus (yellowish in spots on one old individual), close, narrow, intervenose, edges even.

Stipe 2.5–3.5 cm long, 2–3 mm thick at the apex, surface evenly colored and concolorous with the pileus, narrowed toward the base, flexuous, stuffed, becoming hollow, perfectly glabrous.

Spores (3)4–4.5 × 2.5–3 μ, ellipsoid to subglobose, smooth, pale yellowish in Melzer's reagent. Basidia 23–32 × 4–6 μ, 4-spored. Pleurocystidia and cheilocystidia none. Gill trama of slightly interwoven hyphae to subparallel in dried material (definitely interwoven in fresh material—see Smith and Hesler, 1942, p. 11), 2.5–5(8) μ broad. Cuticle of more or less erect (but finally repent), septate, fuscous, constricted non-gelatinous hyphae, the terminal elements cystidioid—a trichodermium (not a palisade), accompanied by a few slender hyphae with clamp connections. No hypodermium differentiated. Pileus-trama hyphae more or less radial. Pileus and gill trama, and especially the hymenium, a very dull sordid yellowish brown in Melzer's reagent.

HABIT, HABITAT, AND DISTRIBUTION—Gregarious on sandy soil, under aspen, Michigan, September.

MATERIAL STUDIED—MICHIGAN: Smith 15455 (type, from Oakland County, Sept. 24, 1940).

OBSERVATIONS—The usual iodine reaction for *Hygrophori* is a bright yellow for the gill trama, hymenium, and flesh of the pileus. The reaction for this species is strikingly different and very characteristic. The species has the stature of *H. recurvatus,* but is at once distinguished by its minute spores. It differs from *H. peckianus* in lacking a distinctive odor and in having ellipsoid spores. The short basidia are very narrow and flexuose, so that the impression one gets is that they are typical *Hygrophorus* basidia even though small. The rather tangled turf-like covering of the pileus is quite similar to that found in the *H. cantharellus* series, but the pileus was not observed to become scaly and the iodine reactions of the flesh and hymenium indicate a closer relationship to *H. peckianus.*

If one were to judge *H. schulzeri* by Bresadola's (1928) illustration, the above species might be considered a 4-spored form of it. However, if one refers to Bresadola's description, certain significant differences are apparent. He described his species as "luride cinnamomeus vel brunneo cinnamomeus." These colors at once exclude our specimens and indicate that the colors as reproduced on the plate of *H. schulzeri* are not accurate. In addition, the gills of *H. microsporus* are close instead of distant, and the stipe is glabrous.

33
Hygrophorus albipes Pk.
Torrey Bot. Club Bull. 25: 323. 1898

Camarophyllus albipes (Pk.) Murr., North Amer. Flora 9: 388. 1916.

Pileus about 1.2 cm broad, convex, grayish brown, glabrous, margin strongly decurved.

Lamellae arcuate and commonly very decurrent, whitish, becoming darker with age, narrow, subdistant.

Stipe 2.5–3.5 cm long, 3–5 mm thick, white without and within, glabrous, attenuated at the base, solid.

Spores 5.5–7(8) × 4.5–5.5(6) μ, subglobose or broadly ellipsoid to ovoid, smooth, pale yellowish in Melzer's reagent. Basidia 37–58 × 5–7 μ, 4-spored. Pleurocystidia and cheilocystidia none. Gill trama intricately interwoven, hyphae narrow, 1.7–2.3 μ broad. Cuticle fibrillose, hyphae repent to more or less erect, appearing slightly subgelatinous. Clamp connections present on the cuticular hyphae.

HABIT, HABITAT, AND DISTRIBUTION—On soil, in Maine, Massachusetts, and Alabama, September and October.

MATERIAL STUDIED—ALABAMA: Burke 85. MASSACHUSETTS: Peck (type, collected by Dr. G. E. Francis, Sept.).

OBSERVATIONS—In the above description the macroscopic characters are taken from Peck's account. The description of microscopic characters is based on our study of the type.

This species is related to *H. sphaerosporus* which has broader hyphae in its gill trama, more spherical spores, and broader lamellae.

34
Hygrophorus silvaticus, sp. nov.

Pileus 3–6 cm latus, convexus, se amplificans ferme planum, hygrophanus, "vinaceous buff," madidus demum albidus; odore et gustu mitis; lamellae decurrentes, albae, angustae, distantes; stipes 4–6 cm longus, 4–9 mm crassus, albus, siccus, apice nudus, basi obscurus; sporae 6–7 × 4 μ, ellipsoideae. Specimen typicum in Herb. Univ. of Mich.; lectum in Washtenaw County, Mich., Sept. 22, 1961, Smith 64392.

Pileus 3–6 cm broad, broadly convex with an incurved margin, expanding to nearly plane, margin lobed and irregular in age at times, surface glabrous, moist, hygrophanous, "vinaceous buff," moist, fading to a chalky white and retaining this color when dried. Context thin but waxy, white; odor and taste not distinctive.

Lamellae decurrent, narrow, distant, strongly intervenose, waxy, white and merely pallid as dried, edges even.

Stipe 4–6 cm long, 4–9 mm thick at apex solid, white within and unchanging, surface glabrous, dull white and dry, naked at apex, surface at the base dingy yellowish, whitish when dried except for the dingy base.

Spores 6–7 × 4 μ, ellipsoid, smooth, non-amyloid. Basidia 4-spored. Pleurocystidia and cheilocystidia none. Gill trama of intricately interwoven hyaline hyphae. Epicutis of pileus of repent narrow (2.5–4 μ), hyaline, non-gelatinous hyphae. Clamp connections present.

HABIT, HABITAT, AND DISTRIBUTION—Gregarious on low wet ground under hardwoods (*Quercus, Acer, Ulmus* and *Fraxinus*), Sharon Hollow, Washtenaw County, Mich., Sept. 22, 1961, Smith 64392, type.

OBSERVATIONS—The narrow gills along with the pale color of the pileus serve to separate the species from both *H. pratensis* and *H. al-*

bipes. The spores are typically smaller, also, but the various measurements for *H. pratensis* indicate enough variation in size to invalidate the character as a difference between these two species.

35
Hygrophorus umbrinus Dennis
Kew Bull. 2: 257. 1953

Illustration:
> Dennis, Kew Bull. 2, fig. 2.

Pileus 5 cm broad, expanded, umbonate to depressed, grayish brown to avellaneous, dry, innately-fibrillose. Context white, firm.

Lamellae decurrent, white then pallid brown ("bubalinae"), broad, margins obtuse.

Stipe white then avellaneous, fibrillose, base attentuated, solid.

Spores 4.5–5.5 μ in diameter, globose, smooth, pale yellow in Melzer's reagent. Basidia 46–62 × 5–7 μ, 2- and 4-spored. Pleurocystidia and cheilocystidia none. Gill trama: (1) a mediostrate of somewhat parallel hyphae, 3–4 μ broad; (2) elsewhere the hyphae are more or less interwoven 4–6 μ broad. Cuticle undifferentiated, surface hyphae non-gelatinous, fuscous to brown, repent or erect, with clamp connections. Pileus trama distinctly radial.

HABIT, HABITAT, AND DISTRIBUTION—On soil, under bamboo, Trinidad.

MATERIAL STUDIED—TRINIDAD: Dennis 177 (type, from St. Joseph).

OBSERVATIONS—We have studied the type and have recorded our observations in the account of microscopic characters above. Our observations agree with those of Dennis. Singer (1955) has also studied the type at Kew. He found the basidia 42– × 6–7.3 μ (the 4-spored ones), and 4.3 μ broad (the 2-spored ones); the gill trama is interwoven.

36
Hygrophorus obconicus Pk.
N. Y. State Mus. Bull. 131: 36. 1909

> *Camarophyllus obconicus* (Pk.) Murr., North Amer. Flora 9: 386. 1916.

Pileus 1–2.5 cm broad, convex, moist or hygrophanous, soon dry, "light buff" to "avellaneous," fading to whitish, pruinose to innately fibrillose or canescent, margin even, often lobed. Context thick on the disc, thin on the margin, white, waxy, fragile; odor none, taste slightly sour or none.

Lamellae adnate or subdecurrent, white, slightly arcuate, broad, subdistant to close, venose, edges even.

Stipe 2–5 cm long, 2–7 mm thick, concolorous with the pileus, equal, compressed, glabrous, dry, hollow.

Spores 4–5.5 × 3–5 μ, subglobose to short-ellipsoid, smooth, non-amyloid. Basidia 32–47 × 5–6 μ, 2- and 4-spored. Pleurocystidia and cheilocystidia none. Gill trama interwoven, hyphae 3.5–5 μ broad, yellowish in iodine. Cuticle at times a cutis, again almost a trichodermium (with scattered, more or less erect, septate hyphae, the terminal elements cystidioid, similar to *H. microsporus*). No hypodermium differentiated. Pileus trama homogeneous, hyphae radial, yellowish in iodine. Clamp connections rare on the cuticular hyphae.

Habit, Habitat, and Distribution—On soil, in mixed woods, Massachusetts, Pennsylvania, and Tennessee, July–September.

Material Studied—massachusetts: Davis (type, from Stow, Sept. 16, 1907). pennsylvania: Sumstine, Pittsburgh, Oct. 1942. tennessee: Sharp 12172; Smith, Great Smoky Mts. National Park, Aug. 30, 1938.

Observations—The description above was drawn from No. 12172 which agrees well with the type. Notes on the type: Spores 4–6 × 3.5–4.5 μ, subglobose to short-ellipsoid, smooth non-amyloid (Davis, in his notes accompanying the type, says spores are white). Basidia 38–51 × 5–6 μ, 2- and 4-spored. Pleurocystidia and cheilocystidia none. Gill trama interwoven, hyphae 2.5–4 μ broad. Cuticle of non-gelatinous hyphae. Clamp connections rare on the cuticular hyphae.

This species is related to *H. albipes*, but its lamellae are narrow and white, the spores are larger, and the pileus is not hygrophanous. *H. cremicolor* has yellow lamellae.

SERIES PELLICULOSI (Sm. & Hes.) stat. nov.

Subsection Pelliculosi Sm. & Hes., Lloydia 5: 15. 1942.
Pileus viscid; spores typically less than 6.5 μ long.
Type species: *H. pallidus* Pk.

Key to Species

1. Lamellae pale yellow .... 37. *H. pseudopallidus*
1. Lamellae smoky violaceous at first (see *H. rainierensis,* page 64, also) ..
.... 38. *H. pallidus*

37

Hygrophorus pseudopallidus, sp. nov.

Pileus 2–4 cm latus, "pale ecru-drab," demum cineraceus, subviscidus; lamellae decurrentes, luteae, latae; stipes 3–4.5 cm longus, 4–6 mm crassus, albus, basi subflavus; sporae 5–7 × 4–5 μ, subglobosae vel subovoidae. Specimen typicum in Herb. Univ. Tenn.; lectum in Cades Cove, Great Smoky Mts. National Park, Tenn., June 8, 1957, Hesler 14439.

Pileus 2–4 cm broad, convex, expanding-convex, subviscid, "pale ecru-drab" when young, paler (grayish, not matched) at maturity, innately appressed-silky, faintly ridged radiately. Context thin, rather brittle-fragile, whitish or pallid; odor mild, taste slightly astringent.

Lamellae arcuate-decurrent, "ivory yellow," venose at cap, broad, tapering at both ends, subdistant or nearly distant, thin, edges even.

Stipe 3–4.5 cm × 4–6 mm, glabrous, striate, white-shining, basal third tinged yellow, spongy, fragile.

Spores 5–7 × 4–5 μ, subglobose to subovoid, rarely ellipsoid, smooth, apiculate, white in mass, yellowish in Melzer's reagent. Basidia 40–60 × 6–9 μ, 4-spored. Pleurocystidia and cheilocystidia none. Gill trama interwoven, hyphae 3–7 μ broad. Cuticle a thin gelatinous zone 25–50(100) μ, hyphae more or less erect to repent, 2–4 μ broad. No hypodermium differentiated. Pileus trama of radial, subparallel to slightly interwoven hyphae. Clamp connections on hyphae of cuticle, subhymenium and gill trama.

HABIT, HABITAT, AND DISTRIBUTION—On soil, in pine woods, Tennessee, June.

MATERIAL STUDIED—TENNESSEE: Hesler 14439 (type, in pine woods, Cades Cove, Great Smoky Mts. National Park, June 8, 1957), 23760 (same station, June 28, 1960).

OBSERVATIONS—This species belongs in the *pratensis-cinereus-lacmus* complex. Except for its ivory yellow gills, it closely resembles *H. lacmus* as illustrated by Lange (1935–40) pl. 165, fig. B. Similarly it appears to be related to *cinereus,* and to *H. pallidus,* but these two entities, like *H. lacmus,* have grayish gills.

38

Hygrophorus pallidus Pk.
Torrey Bot. Club Bull. 29: 69. 1902

Camarophyllus pallidus (Pk.) Murr., North Amer. Flora 9: 386. 1916.
Illustration:
Kauffman, Agar. Mich., pl. 29 (above).

Pileus 2–6 cm broad, convex, becoming convex-campanulate or subumbonate, sometimes plane or slightly depressed, margin recurved at times, smoky violaceous or smoky lilac when fresh and moist, fading to near "violet-gray," nearly whitish at times in age, viscid or subviscid, soon dry and shining, and then minutely fibrillose-floccose under a lens, hygrophanous, pellicle thin, separable, margin often striate. Context white to grayish or smoky violaceous near the margin, thick and firm on the disc; odor mild, taste mild at first but becoming bitterish.

Lamellae arcuate-adnate to decurrent, then decurrent, concolorous with the pileus when moist, becoming whitish or grayish white, narrow to moderately broad, distant to subdistant, intervenose, edges even.

Stipe 3–6 cm long, 3–8(11) mm thick, white or silvery gray, equal or narrowed downwards slightly, fibrillose or glabrous, naked at the apex, stuffed but becoming hollow.

Spores 5–6 × 4–5 μ, globose to subglobose, smooth, pale yellow in Melzer's reagent. Basidia (31)38–44 × 5–6 μ, 4-spored. Pleurocystidia and cheilocystidia not differentiated. Gill trama yellowish brown in iodine, of intricately interwoven, narrow hyphae (3.5–6 μ broad). Cuticle of slightly gelatinous hyphae which are colorless, more or less erect, 1–2 μ broad, and forming an ixotrichodermium. No hypodermium differentiated. Pileus trama of radial hyphae which are subparallel to slightly interwoven. Clamp connections on the cuticular hyphae.

HABIT, HABITAT, AND DISTRIBUTION—On moist soil or in swampy areas, Massachusetts, Michigan, California, and Canada, late summer and fall.

MATERIAL STUDIED—CALIFORNIA: Smith 3880. MASSACHUSETTS: Davis (Peck's type, Sept. 11, 1901). MICHIGAN: Kauffman 537 (1356), Rock River, Sept. 11, 1927; Smith 1110, 1166, 21333, 38801, 50810, 50496, 62130. CANADA: (Ontario) Smith 4828.

OBSERVATIONS—The smoky lilac colors of the pileus and gills, small globose to subglobose spores, gelatinous pellicle of the pileus and whitish stipe are distinctive. The small spores best distinguish it from *H. subviolaceus.* Both have somewhat the same shades of color and fade in a similar manner. *H. lacmus* of Europe apparently has about the same colors but the base of the stipe is tinted bright yellow. A critical comparative study of *H. lacmus* and *H. pallidus* should be made.

We have studied a collection from the Peck Herbarium which is labeled *H. pallidus*—type. But, the specimens are confusing. They are buff-colored and give the appearance of never having been smoky-violaceous. Moreover, the pilei do not appear to have been hygrophanous nor striatulate. One feels that the specimens in the box are not those originally sent to Peck by Simon Davis.

SECTION HYGROTRAMA (Singer) stat. nov.

Hygrotrama Singer, Sydowia 12: 221. 1958.

Hymenophoral trama of interwoven to somewhat interwoven hyphae; epicutis of pileus an hymeniform layer of clavate to pedicellate cells; clamp connections present or absent; hymenophore waxy; basidia hygrophoroid.

Type species: *Hygrotrama dennisianum* Singer.

The species grouped here have been the cause of more discussion than any other group in the family or genus, and the end is not yet in sight. Smith and Hesler (1954) objected to classifying members of this group in *Armillariella*. Singer (1958) erected *Hygrotrama* as a genus of the *Hygrophoraceae* to contain them, and we think this is certainly a step in the right direction. We prefer, however, to go two steps farther and recognize the group at the level of a section under subgenus *Hygrophorus*. The latter, classically, as a genus or subgenus, has been subdivided into groups on single-character differences involving hyphal arrangement in the hymenophore. However, careful study showed, and we (1942) pointed out, that the difference between *Camarophyllus* (now *Camarophyllopsis*) and *Hygrocybe* was not very sharp. This was our chief reason for refusing to recognize these two groups at the generic level. Now a third group, *Hygrotrama*, also characterized by a single feature, the hymeniform epicutis of the pileus in which the hyphae of the hymenophoral trama are mostly intermediate in arrangement between the parallel type and the interwoven type, has been introduced into the discussion. In view of the intermediate position of *Hygrotrama* and the fact that it is very clear, at least to us, as to how this type of epicutis originated in the genus, the recognition of genera at this level still is, to us, unjustified. The problem is just what is meant by hymeniform. We do not consider that a trichodermium of hyphae, in which the end cells are somewhat cystidioid, represents an hymeniform layer. Singer includes this species in *Hygrotrama*, but we exclude it. If one looks to other genera for a comparable situation as regards the epicutis of the pileus, *Pluteus* is the best example. In this genus there are many degrees of epicuticular types from appressed narrow gelatinous hyphae to the true hymeniform type. A large intermediate group, the *Hispidodermi* is more or less trichoder-mial, depending on which of the numerous species one examines.

KEY TO SPECIES

1. Odor strong, pungent or disagreeable 2
1. Odor not distinctive 3
  2. Pileus cinnamon brown to bistre ....39. *H. foetens*
  2. Pileus Isabella color (dingy ochraceous) becoming olive-buff and then gray ....41. *H. subfuscescens* var. *odora*
3. Pileus pale to dark dingy yellow, cinerescent ....
  ....40. *H. subfuscescens* var. *subfuscescens*
3. Pileus color and changes not as above 4
  4. Stipe with black punctate squamules over upper surface ....
  ....42. *H. atropunctus*
  4. Stipe not as above 5
5. Pileus buffy brown, then olive-buff, hygrophanous and fading to whitish, rugulose ....43. *H. rugulosus*
5. Not as above 6
  6. Spores 5–7 × 3.5–5 μ ....44. *H. dennisianus*
  6. Spores globose to subglobose 7
7. Pileus pinkish cinnamon to clay color, becoming gray to blackish; stipe blackish in age ....45. *H. hymenocephalus*
7. Pileus and stipe not as above 8
  8. Pileus yellowish cinnamon becoming chocolate gray; stipe not darken-ing ....46. *H. schulzeri*
  8. Pileus dark olive brown fading to cinereous .....47. *H. rugulosoides*

39
Hygrophorus foetens Phillips apud Berk. & Br.
Grevillea 7: 74. 1878–79

> *Camarophyllus foetens* (Phillips) J. Lange, Dansk Bot. Ark. 4: 18. 1923.
> *Hodophilus foetens* (Phillips) Heim, Les Champ. d'Eur. p. 219. 1957.

Illustrations:
  Fig. 10c.
  Lange, Flora Agar. Dan., pl. 166H.
  Phillips, Grevillea 7, t. 121, f. 13.
  Bresadola, Icon. Myc., tab. 321. (1).
  Favre and Poluzzi, Vita Helvetica, Taf. VII B.

Pileus 1–4 cm broad, plane to broadly convex, becoming turbinate or the margin uplifted, moist, hygrophanous, "cinnamon brown" to "bister" on disc and over striae, paler between the striae, fading to near avellaneous and then atomate, surface glabrous, in age at times somewhat diffracted scaly. Context concolorous with surface, brittle-waxy; taste mild, odor pungent (reminding one of chloride of lime).

Lamellae decurrent, "wood brown" or darker, thick, distant, me-dium broad, waxy, brittle, edges even.

Stipe 2–4 cm long, 2–3 mm thick at apex, concolorous with pileus or over the lower portion darker, narrowed downward, glabrous, surface scabrous-dotted at first but naked in age.

Spores 4.5–6 × 4.5–5 μ, subglobose to broadly elliptic, smooth, yellowish in Melzer's reagent. Basidia 34–42 × 5–7 μ, 4-spored, elongate-clavate, lower part often flexuous. Pleurocystidia and cheilocystidia none. Gill trama interwoven, brownish in water when fresh, dull cinnamon revived in KOH. Pileus trama colored like the gill trama (pigment thinly incrusted on the hyphae), interwoven. Cuticle a dense palisade layer of more or less upright enlarged pseudoparenchymatous elements varying from 20 × 12 μ and subglobose (the cross wall just beneath the enlargement) to elongated pyriform to ventricose capitate elements 10–60 × 5–20 μ. Pileus trama of compactly and slightly interwoven hyphae, disposed more or less radially. Clamp connections absent.

HABIT, HABITAT, AND DISTRIBUTION—Caespitose in an open young stand of hardwoods, on naked soil, Michigan and Idaho, August; also Europe.

MATERIAL STUDIED—IDAHO: Smith 60437. MICHIGAN: Smith 39673. NETHERLANDS: Bas, Oct. 8, 1957.

OBSERVATIONS—This is a most distinctive species by reason of the hymeniform cuticle, pungent disagreeable odor, cinnamon brown color, small spores, wood-brown gills, and incrusted pigment on the hyphae. Our collections appear to be identical with *H. foetens*, and we place them there in spite of slight difference in the odor, foetid as against pungent. Moreover, our material agrees well, in macroscopic and microscopic characters, with specimens kindly communicated to us by Bas, at Leiden, Netherlands.

In our estimation Nüesch's (1922) account of *H. foetens*, in which the stipe is described as olive-yellow, applies to some other species. Information on the type of *H. foetens*, if it exists, is needed to establish the presence (or absence) of clamp connections and whether or not the cuticle is hymeniform.

40

Hygrophorus subfuscescens Sm. & Hes. var. **subfuscescens**
Sydowia 8: 317. 1954

Illustration:
    Fig. 24.

Pileus 6–15(25) mm broad, convex when young but margin straight to connivent, in age broadly convex or the margin flaring, "baryta yellow" to "old gold" to "Isabella color" moist, fading to "pale pinkish buff" but then gradually changing to "wood brown" or "olive brown" in age, or a grayish cast developing before fading takes place, atomate when faded, glabrous, moist, hygrophanous, in some the margin becoming crenate. Context brittle; odor none, taste slight and sub-nauseous.

Lamellae decurrent, "Isabella color" to yellowish becoming pallid, and soon darkening to "wood brown" or "benzo brown," (violaceous brown) distant, moderately broad, edges even.

Stipe 2–4 cm long, 1.5–3 mm thick at apex, "colonial buff" (pale yellow), becoming paler in age but not entirely losing the yellow tint and not cinerescent like the pileus, narrowed downward, often flexuous, naked and polished.

Spores 5–6 × 4–5 μ, subglobose to broadly ellipsoid, hyaline smooth, yellowish in Melzer's reagent. Basidia 30–42 × 7–8 μ, 4-spored. Cheilocystidia and pleurocystidia none. Gill trama intricately interwoven, hyphae 7–10 μ broad, hyaline in KOH. Cuticle an hymeniform layer of pear-shaped to vesiculose, hyaline cells, 10–30 μ broad and 20–50 μ long, the layer of cells staggered somewhat in arrangement of the elements but very compact as a layer. Pileus trama of compactly interwoven hyphae radially disposed. Cells of carpophore lacking dark colored content (as particles or granules) when mounted in Melzer's reagent. Clamp connections absent.

HABIT, HABITAT, AND DISTRIBUTION—Densely caespitose under maple, birch, and basswood, along with poison ivy, also under conifers (*Thuja*), Michigan and Maine, August.

Fig. 24. *H. subfuscescens* var. *subfuscescens*

MATERIAL STUDIED—MAINE: Bigelow 4424. MICHIGAN: Smith 22072, 22107, 22149, 22306, 26244, 32894 (type, from Mackinaw City Hardwoods, Aug. 6, 1949), 37356, 39377, 50193.

OBSERVATIONS—This is a striking species by virtue of the changing colors of the pileus, the distant, decurrent, waxy lamellae, the well-developed hymeniform cuticle of the pileus, the persistently yellowish, naked stipe, and the small, globose to subglobose spores. The caespitose habit and growth on bare soil under hardwoods is characteristic at the type locality where the fungus has been found regularly every season since its discovery. However, several collections from other locations appear to belong here and were all from black muck under arbor vitae. In these collections the fruiting bodies were scattered, the gills were "Isabella color" (concolorous with pileus) at first, and often changed to "tawny olive" before becoming "benzo brown." The persistently yellow, naked stipe, however, was characteristic. In view of the changing colors not much emphasis can be placed on a particular tint or shade at any one stage in the development of the fruiting body. The constant features appear to be the persistently yellow stipe, the cap being atomate when faded as well as the initial yellow to olive tint, and the dark violaceous brown end-point of the color change.

41
Hygrophorus subfuscescens var. **odora** Sm. & Hes.
Sydowia 8: 318. 1954

Pileus 6–10 mm broad, convex, becoming broadly convex, margin decurved but not inrolled in young caps, "Isabella color" and in age fading to "pale olive buff," finally ashy gray with scarcely any olive or yellow tint showing, no color changes when bruised, glabrous, moist, hygrophanous, atomate when faded. Context "Isabella color" fading through yellow to pallid, waxy; odor very distinctly disagreeable when flesh is bruised, taste mild to slightly farinaceous.

Lamellae arcuate becoming decurrent, "pale olive buff" becoming somewhat grayer at maturity, soon subdistant or nearly so, moderately broad.

Stipe short, 1–2 cm long, 1–2.5 mm thick, "deep colonial buff" (or grayer) at apex, no color change when bruised, slightly enlarged above, glabrous, moist.

Spores 5–6 × 3.5–4 μ, broadly ellipsoid, smooth, yellowish in Melzer's reagent. Basidia 35–42 × 6–7.5 μ, 4-spored. Pleurocystidia and cheilocystidia none. Gill trama interwoven, hyphae 2.5 μ broad. Cuticle an hymeniform palisade composed of vesiculose-pedicellate to vesiculose-sessile or pear-shaped cells 10–35 × 20–50 μ. No hypodermium differentiated. Pileus trama of nearly parallel, radially disposed hyphae which are without dark staining content in Melzer's reagent. Clamp connections not present.

HABIT, HABITAT, AND DISTRIBUTION—Gregarious on sand bank under bracken ferns, Michigan, July.

MATERIAL STUDIED—MICHIGAN: Smith 35670 (type, from Middle Bridge, Maple River, Cheboygan, July 13, 1947).

OBSERVATIONS—This is exceedingly close to *subfuscescens* to which we attach it as a variety, but it differs in the strong disagreeable odor of fresh specimens when their flesh is crushed and in the more ellipsoid spores. It is similar in lacking the curious granules in Melzer's solution, lack of clamp connections, in the color change to gray of cap and gills (but the color not changing when bruised), and hymeniform cuticle of pileus. Also the stipe retains its yellow tone. *H. paupertinus* Sm. & Hes. differs in not having a cellular pileus cuticle, in narrower gills, and less yellow in its coloration.

42
Hygrophorus atropunctus J. E. Lange
Dansk Bot. Ark. 9: 96. 1938

> *Omphalia atropuncta* sensu Bresadola, pl. 271, vol. 6. 1928.
> *Hodophilus atropunctus* (Lange) Heim, Les Champ. d'Eur., p. 219. 1957.

Pileus 1–1.5 cm broad, convex, margin incurved, hygrophanous, bister, darker in the center, paler toward the margin, surface slightly velutinous-pruinate, paler and atomate when faded, rather fleshy, odor and taste none.

Lamellae distant (16–20 reach the stipe), lamellulae about equal in number to lamellae, plano-arcuate and adnate-decurrent, thick, pale brownish, somewhat powdery, at last dark grayish brown and white pruinose from spores.

Stipe 2–3.5 cm long, about 2 mm thick, concolorous with pileus, paler above, undulating, upper half with scattered minute blackish punctae or squamules. Veil none.

Spores about 5×4 μ, smooth, ovate-spheric. Basidia about 5 μ broad, narrowly clavate. Hymenophoral trama of interwoven hyphae 3–5 μ broad. Epicutis of pileus an hymeniform layer of inflated cells 18–30 μ broad. Squamules on stipe of flexuous septate hyphae with subfuscous contents.

HABIT, HABITAT, AND DISTRIBUTION—Gregarious on the ground under *Fraxinus* in beech woods. Europe (Denmark, by Morten Lange).

OBSERVATIONS—We include this as an extralimital species very likely to be found here. The minute blackish punctae over the upper part of the stipe should be a good field character.

43

Hygrophorus rugulosus Sm. & Hes.
Sydowia 8: 330. 1954

Pileus 8–12 mm broad, convex when young, broadly convex in age, surface glabrous and rugulose, "buffy brown" to dark avellaneous in buttons, becoming olive-buff and finally fading to whitish as if subhygrophanous. Context unchanging when bruised, firm but very brittle; odor and taste none.

Lamellae arcuate-decurrent, pinkish buff when young, becoming avellaneous, concolorous with the pileus in age, thickish, subdistant, medium broad, edges even.

Stipe 1–2 cm long, 1.5–2 mm thick, equal or narrowed downward, olive brown or grayer at apex, paler (pallid) below, in age more or less concolorous with the gills (no yellow anywhere at any time), naked, translucent.

Spores 4–5 μ, globose or nearly so, smooth, hyaline, yellowish in Melzer's reagent. Basidia 28–40 × 6–7 μ, 4-spored. Pleurocystidia and cheilocystidia none. Gill trama somewhat interwoven, hyaline in KOH. Cuticle a trichodermium but terminating in an hymeniform layer of vesiculose to pedicellate-inflated cells (end cells of more or less upright hyphae), thin-walled and readily collapsing. No hypodermium differentiated. Pileus trama radial, more or less parallel to interwoven. Cell content of carpophore hyphae not distinctively colored in Melzer's reagent. Clamp connections absent.

HABIT, HABITAT, AND DISTRIBUTION—Gregarious on humus, Michigan, August.

MATERIAL STUDIED—MICHIGAN: Smith 37565 (type, from Pellston, Michigan, Aug. 10, 1951).

OBSERVATIONS—The cuticle of the pileus does not become broken into squamules as in *H. cantharellus* series, and the gill trama is more interwoven than in the other species of that section.

44

Hygrophorus dennisianus (Singer), comb. nov.

Hygrotrama dennisianum Singer, Sydowia 12: 221. 1958.

Pileus 4–4.4 mm broad, convex, thin with a convex to merely declivous marginal portion and flattened to depressed disc, glabrous to minutely pruinate, often rivulose-cracking, neither viscid nor hygroph-

anous, color pearly gray to drab, at times the center and one side of
the pileus fuscous. Context almost concolorous with the surfaces,
fleshy, odor none, taste agreeably farinaceous.

Lamellae horizontal or descendant, broad, subdistant to distant,
light pearl gray, more or less reticulate-intervenose.

Stipe 3–5 cm long, 9–10 mm at apex, narrowed to 3–4 mm at base,
solid, dry, innately longitudinally fibrillose-striate, at times slightly superficially fibrillose.

Spores 5–7 × 3.5–5.2 μ, oblong to ellipsoid, less often subglobose,
smooth, thin-walled, hyaline, inamyloid.

Basidia 23–33 × 5.5–7 μ, 4-spored. Cystidia none on faces or edges
of gills. Subhymenium of small subcellular hyaline elements. Hymenophoral trama more interwoven near junction with pileus trama, almost subparallel in places farther down, cells at times reaching 35 μ
broad, some hyphae remaining narrowly filamentous. Pileus epicutis
an hymeniform to subhymeniform layer of hyaline to pale fuscous inflated elements lacking brownish pigment in lower portion or pedicel.
Context hyphae beneath the hypodermium of more numerous broad
elements as the lamellae are approached. Clamp connections present.

HABIT, HABITAT, AND DISTRIBUTION—In open places, pastures,
meadows, sometimes under bamboo, or near plantations solitary or in
groups fruiting in the rainy season, Mexico and Trinidad.

MATERIAL STUDIED—None. The descriptive data used above have
been adapted from Singer's original description.

OBSERVATIONS—On the basis of Singer's description this appears to
be a well-defined species, close to *H. hymenocephalus* but differing in
color of the young basidiocarp and the more ellipsoid spores.

45

Hygrophorus hymenocephalus Sm. & Hes.
Elisha Mitchell Sci. Soc. Jour. 56: 311. 1940

> *Armillariella hymenocephala* (Sm. & Hes.) Singer, Lilloa 22: 217.
> 1951.
> *Camarophyllus hymenocephalus* (Sm. & Hes.) M. Lange, Friesia 4:
> 1–2. 1950.
> *Hygrotrama hymenocephalum* (Sm. & Hes.) Singer, Sydowia 12:
> 222. 1959.

Illustrations:
> Fig. 25; also 10b.
> Smith and Hesler, Elisha Mitchell Sci. Soc. Jour. 56, pl. 9 (above).
> Smith and Hesler, Lloydia 5, pl. 2b.

Pileus 5–20(30) mm broad, convex to hemispheric, margin incurved, often becoming nearly plane, glabrous, hygrophanous, when

wet "snuff brown," "light pinkish cinnamon," or "tawny olive," fading to "clay color" or "pinkish buff," slowly darker and grayer, sometimes faded specimens "drab" or "olive brown" and atomate, finally becoming "mummy brown," often the margin crenate or lobed. Context thick on the disc, thin elsewhere, waxy, pallid or concolorous with the surface; odor and taste none.

Lamellae broadly adnate, becoming decurrent, concolorous with the pileus when young, nearly so in age or "hair brown," subdistant to distant, broad, edges pallid and even.

Stipe 2–8 cm long, 2–7 mm thick, concolorous with the pileus, darkening in age, finally becoming "mummy brown," equal or tapering

Fig. 25.
H. hymenocephalus

downward, fragile, terete or compressed, the apex canescent at first, elsewhere glabrous, solid becoming hollow.

Spores 4–6 × 4–5 μ, globose to subglobose, at times short-ellipsoid, often more or less flat-sided, smooth, pale yellowish in Melzer's reagent. Basidia 34–50(64) × 5–8 μ, 2- and 4-spored. Pleurocystidia and cheilocystidia not differentiated. Gill trama of interwoven hyphae 4–10(16) μ broad, the hymenium appearing as a blackish line in sections of old material. Pileus with an epicutis of an irregular palisade of inflated cells (30)40–85 × (10)14–22(30) μ—an epithelium. Pileus trama of subparallel hyphae, radially disposed. No clamp connections.

Habit, Habitat, and Distribution—Gregarious to scattered on

soil and decaying logs (chestnut and possible others), in mixed and coniferous woods, and under rhododendron, North Carolina, Tennessee, and Michigan; also England and Denmark, August–October.

MATERIAL STUDIED—MICHIGAN: Smith 22064. NORTH CAROLINA: Smith 7397, 10383 (type, Highlands, Aug. 14, 1938), 10146; Hesler 9237, 12744, 13949, 14422, 15885, 23350. TENNESSEE: Smith 10090.

OBSERVATIONS—This species and *H. schulzeri* are exceedingly similar to each other, but we believe they are distinct. We have a critical account of *H. schulzeri* from England (Orton, 1960, p. 264) which agrees that *H. schulzeri* does not have a stipe that becomes blackish nor gills which become brownish drab ("hair brown"). There also appears to be a distinct difference in the hymenophoral trama, the hyphae being more parallel in *H. schulzeri* and more interwoven in *H. hymenocephalus*. According to our studies both lack clamp connections. For the Trinidad collection having clamped hyphae and described by Dennis (1953), see *H. dennisianus*. *H. schulzeri* sensu Josserand we consider to be the same as *H. deceptivus*.

46
Hygrophorus schulzeri Bres.
Fungi Trident. 1: 57. 1884

> *Camarophyllus schulzeri* (Bres.) Ricken, 1920 Vademecum für Pilzfreunde, p. 198. 1920.
> *Hygrocybe schulzeri* (Bres.) Joss., Bull. Soc. Mycol. France 53: 206. 1937.

Illustrations:
Bresadola, Fungi Trident. 1, pl. 67, fig. 3. 1884.
Bresadola, Icon. Myc., p. 332. 1928.

Pileus 10–25 mm broad, convex to somewhat hemispheric then expanded, sometimes depressed or with wavy-lobed margin when old, yellowish cinnamon to brownish cinnamon or chocolate gray, dry, minutely adpressedly silky-tomentose or velvet under a lens when dry, cuticle sometimes cracking in places when old. Context whitish to concolorous; odor and taste none.

Lamellae decurrent, whitish then tinged grayish or brownish, edges even but sometimes rather thick and blunt.

Stipe 1.5–3 cm long, 3–6 mm thick, up to 10 mm when compressed, equal or attenuated downward, concolorous with pileus or paler, apex furfuraceous, elsewhere minutely pruinose at first but soon smooth and shiny, stuffed then hollow.

Spores 4–5(6) × 4–4.5(5) μ, globose, subglobose, or ovoid, smooth or at times appearing faintly rough, pale yellow in Melzer's reagent.

Basidia 22–33 × 4–6 μ, 4-spored. Pleurocystidia and cheilocystidia none. Gill trama somewhat parallel, composed of large more or less rectangular cells, at times appearing somewhat interwoven, the cells 17–55 × 6–15 μ. Cuticle a surface zone of inflated cells, 12–33 × 15–23 μ, irregularly dispersed, often scattered but at times hymeniform. Clamp connections none.

HABIT, HABITAT, AND DISTRIBUTION—On soil, Michigan, August; also in Europe. It has recently been reported and redescribed from England by Orton (1960).

MATERIAL STUDIED—MICHIGAN: Smith 50294, from Tahquamenon Falls State Park, Upper Peninsula, Mich.

OBSERVATIONS—The spores of Smith's Michigan collection are slightly larger than is given for British and other European specimens. Orton (1960) says that in Britain, it appears to be a grassland species, and points out that Bresadola gives the habitat as larch woods (perhaps in grass). It resembles *H. nitratus* in color and habit but is smaller and more tough. For a comparison with *H. hymenocephalus* see that species.

47
Hygrophorus rugulosoides, sp. nov.
Illustration:
  Fig. 26.

Pileus 10–15 mm latus, convexus deinde convexo-depressus, glaber, hygrophanus, planus vel paulo rugulosus, atro-olivaceo-brunneus demum cinereus; odore et gustu mitis; lamellae arcuatae demum decurrentes, "wood brown" demum olivaceo-brunneae, latae, subdistantes; stipes 2–3 cm longus, 2-3 mm crassus, aquoso-cinereo-brunneus; sporae 4.6–5 × 4–4.5 μ, subglobosae. Specimen typicum in Herb. Univ. Mich.; lectum in Colonial Point, Burt Lake, Mich., Aug. 4, 1961, Smith 63826.

Pileus 10–15 mm broad, convex, becoming convex depressed, surface glabrous, moist, hygrophanous, even to slightly rugulose, opaque when moist, dark olive brown fading to cinereous, margin crenate to uneven. Context thin, fragile, in KOH dull olive (but not olive as revived in KOH); odor and taste mild.

Lamellae arcuate to decurrent, broad, subdistant, "wood brown" to olive brown when mature, edges even.

Stipe 2–3 cm long, 2–3 mm thick, equal, undulating, watery gray-brown, paler than the gills, translucent, naked or only with very obscure minute appressed squamules over apex as seen under a hand lens, base paler than or concolor with apex.

Spores 4.6–5 × 4–4.5 μ, subglobose, smooth, non-amyloid. Basidia 4-spored. Pleurocystidia none; cheilocystidia as sterile basidia. Gill trama with a broad central strand of subparallel hyphae, the subhymenium a narrow layer of narrower hyphae on the outside slightly divergent toward the hymenium. Epicutis of pileus composed of a palisade of much-inflated cells, 50–75 × 15–40 μ, walls dingy olive-grayish revived in KOH. Clamp connections absent.

HABIT, HABITAT, AND DISTRIBUTION—Gregarious under hardwoods (*Quercus* and *Fraxinus*) on a hummock, in low ground, Colonial Point, Burt Lake, Mich., Aug. 4, 1961.

MATERIAL STUDIED—MICHIGAN: Smith 63826 (type).

OBSERVATIONS—This species is distinct from *H. rugulosus*, the most closely related *Hygrophorus* by the hymeniform epicutis of the pileus (not as the end cells of a trichodermium), by the more parallel gill trama and in particular by the colors of the dried fruiting bodies. In *H. rugulosus* the pileus and gills are dull tan, whereas in *H. rugulosoides* they are drab. The dull olive color change in KOH of *H. rugulosoides* is very likely an additional character, but fresh material of *H. rugulosus* needs to be tested before a comparison can be made.

Fig. 26.
H. rugulosoides

SECTION HYGROCYBE Fr.

Spores smooth, hyaline, typically white in deposit; hymenophoral trama parallel to slightly interwoven; epicutis of pileus never an hymeniform palisade of clavate to vesiculose cells; clamp connections present or absent.

Type species: *Hygrophorus miniatus* (Fr.) Fr.

SUBSECTION HYGROCYBE

SERIES CONICI (Fayod) comb. & stat. nov.

Hygrocybe section *Conici* Fayod. Ann. Sci. Nat. Bot. VII (9): 309. 1889.

KEY TO SPECIES

1. Fruiting body blackening in some part when bruised 2
1. Fruiting body not blackening 3
  2. Pileus yellow, orange, or red; spores 9–12(14) μ long ....
....48. *H. conicus*
  2. Pileus pale smoky gray to yellow, streaked with black fibrils; spores 6–10 × 5–7 μ ....49. *H. erinaceus*
  2. Pileus pale ocher yellow fading to pinkish buff, blackening slightly at margin ....109. *H. tahquamenonensis*
3. Pileus shell pink; pleurocystidia 50–105 × 8–25 μ, fusoid, clavate or cylindric ....50. *H. calyptraeformis*
3. Not with above combination of characters 4
  4. Fruiting body practically unicolorous and yellow 5
  4. Fruiting body not entirely yellow 8
5. Odor mephitic; lamellae adnate with a triangular tooth ....
....51. *H. auratocephalus*
5. Odor and gill attachment not as above 6
  6. Spores 7–9 × 4–5 μ; color of fruiting body bright to deep chrome yellow ....52. *H. marginatus* var. *concolor*
  6. Spores 8–12 μ long or larger 7
7. Lamellae adnate and with a decurrent tooth ("hooked") ....
....53. *H. subflavidus*

48

Hygrophorus conicus (Fr.) Fr.

Epicr. Myc., p. 331. 1838

Agaricus conicus Fr., Syst. Myc. 1: 103. 1821.
Hygrocybe pseudoconica Lange, Dansk. Bot. Ark. 4: 24. 1923.
Hygrocybe conica (Fr.) Kummer, Führ. in Pilzk., p. 111. 1871.
Hydrocybe conica (Fr.) Karsten, Bidr. Finl. Nat. och Folk 32: 236. 1879.
Godfrinia conica (Fr.) Maire, Bull. Soc. Mycol. France 18 (Supplement): 117. 1902.

Illustrations:
>Figs. 27 and 28; also 5.
>Bulliard, Herb. Fr., pl. 50 (as *Agaricus croceus*).
>Gillet, Champ. Fr., pl. 133 (332).
>Gussow and Odell, Mushrooms and Toadstools, pl. 46, fig. 1.
>Juillard-Hartmann, Icon. Champ., pl. 49, fig. 3.
>Konrad and Maublanc, Icon. Sel. Fung., pl. 380.
>Lange, Flora Agar. Dan. 5, pl. 167D.
>Murrill, Mycologia 2, pl. 27, fig. 8.
>Pomerleau, Mushrooms of Eastern Canada and the U. S., fig. 16A, and
>   pl. 2, fig. 11.
>Ricken, Die Blätterp., pl. 8, fig. 4.
>Schaeff., Fung. Bavar., pl. 2.
>Smith, Mushrooms in their Natural Habitats, Reel 11, No. 77.
>Smith and Hesler, Lloydia 5, pls. 6 and 7.
>Thomas, Field Book of Common Gilled Mushrooms, pl. 10, fig. 59.
>Wakefield and Dennis, Common British Fungi, pl. 35, fig. 4.

Pileus 2–7(9) cm broad, sharply to obtusely conic, sometimes convex with a conic umbo, not expanding, usually reddish or scarlet-orange around and on the umbo, paler orange toward the margin, often with distinct olive tints or "citron green" all over, occasionally bright yellow, "ochraceous orange," "zinc orange," "xanthine orange" to "orange rufous," olive-gray to black in aging, quickly becoming black when bruised or broken, slightly viscid when moist, soon dry, glabrous or somewhat virgate in age, sometimes becoming fibrillose-subscaly from the lacerated cuticle, margin frequently incised or lobed, sometimes rimose. Context thin and very fragile, concolorous with the surface, blackening; odor and taste not distinctive.

Lamellae nearly free, nearly white at first, becoming grayish olivaceous, pale yellowish orange or olive-yellow ("orange buff," "sulphur yellow," "olive-ocher"), black when bruised or in age, close, broad, ventricose, edges undulate to serate or eroded.

Stipe (2)6–11(18) cm long, 5–10(15) mm thick, base whitish, remainder dark red, orange, yellow or sordid olive-yellow, becoming black in age or where bruised, equal, strict, moist or dry, not viscid, fragile, splitting, glabrous or with appressed fibrils, often longitudinally striate and twisted, hollow.

Spores (8)9–12(14) × (5)5.5–6.5(7.5) μ, subellipsoid to ellipsoid, often irregular in shape, smooth, white in deposits, yellow in Melzer's reagent. Basidia (28)34–49 × (6)9–11(12) μ, 1-, 2-, 3-, or 4-spored. Pleurocystidia and cheilocystidia none. Gill trama parallel, hyphae 8–18 μ broad, with large lactifers intermingled, yellowish to hyaline in iodine. Pileus trama homogeneous, cuticle formed by a thin (20–35 μ) poorly organized layer of colorless gelatinous hyphae which are repent or more or less erect, 5–7 μ broad. Pileus trama of radial and parallel hyphae, with conspicuous lactifers 3–4 μ broad. Clamp connections on the hyphae of the cuticle, subhymenium, and gill trama.

HABIT, HABITAT, AND DISTRIBUTION—Gregarious or singly, common in North America, spring, summer, fall, and winter; also in Canada, Europe, and Japan.

MATERIAL STUDIED—CALIFORNIA: Rea 381; Smith 3686, 3815, 8548, 9035, 9111, 55934, 56212. COLORADO: Baxter, Tolland, Aug. 26, 1920; Smith 51897, 52025. FLORIDA: Hesler 21601; Singer F290; West, Arnold,

Fig. 27. *H. conicus*

Fig. 28. *H. conicus*

& Murrill, Grove Park, July 15, 1938. IDAHO: Bigelow (Smith 46886); Smith 15990, 44154, 44220, 44690, 45106, 46373, 54577, 60039. MAINE: Bigelow 3985, 4020. MARYLAND: Krieger (Kelley 47). MASSACHUSETTS: Bigelow 7252, 7592, 8447, 9279. MICHIGAN: Boynton, St. Claire Co., Oct. 10, 1949; Brooks 1257; Chmielewski 64, 89; Davidson & Mains (Smith 32015); Harding 153; Imshaug 3461, 3713; Kauffman, Ann Arbor, June 1, 1909; M. Lange & Smith 26049; Mains 32–766, 32–808; Rea & Smith 742; Smith 1727, 6069, 6715, 6762, 7068, 7232, 7306, 7676, 15201, 15344, 15372, 15374, 22091, 37188, 41410, 41430, 49914, 50066; Thiers 2998, 3033, 3241, 3304, 3353, 3443, 3502, 3574, 3659, 3772, 3808, 3880, 3977, 4051, 4125, 4375. NEW JERSEY: Ellis & Everhart, Newfield, Oct. 1887. NEW MEXICO: Barrows 154. NEW YORK: House, Albany Co., Sept. 26, 1945; Kauffman, Ithaca, July 22, 1903; Snell (Hesler 8177). NORTH CAROLINA: Coker 7181, Smith & Hesler 11770; Underwood 4411. OREGON: Kauffman, Mt. Hood, Oct. 16, 1922; Kauffman & Brown, Talkilma, Nov. 30, 1925; Smith 8058, 24264, 24781, 55535. PENNSYLVA-

NIA: Kauffman, Mt. Gretna, Sept. 15, 1924. TENNESSEE: Hesler 4380, 4434, 4439, 8273, 9527, 9568, 10779, 10843, 10917, 11475, 11606, 12239, 12402, 12834, 13014, 13839, 18000, 19686, 21345, 24425, 24510; Sharp 4378, 8168, 18617; Sharp & Hesler 4377, 9152, 12739; Smith 9937, 10299. TEXAS: Thiers 1601. UTAH: McKnight F45. VIRGINIA: Kauffman, Potomac, Aug. 7, 1919. WASHINGTON: Brown, Quinault, Oct. 31, 1931; Conners & Smith 26385; Imshaug 964, 2105; Kauffman, Lake Cushman, Oct. 20, 1915; Smith 3066, 3286, 4078, 14091, 17554, 17731, 17996, 18022, 40231, 40768, 40939. CANADA: (Nova Scotia) Smith 659a; Wehmeyer 659; (Ontario) Kelley 857, 1076; (Quebec) Bigelow 5169, 5358, 5725; Ross & Grover F7457. FRANCE: Josserand, 1937. JAPAN: Hongo Herb. 549. NETHERLANDS: Geesteranus 13436. DENMARK: J. P. Jensen (Hesler 23936). BELGIUM: Heinemann 2049.

OBSERVATIONS—The viscidity of the pileus is caused by a very thin layer of gelatinous hyphae. This layer may be washed away by heavy rains by the time the specimens reach maturity, and the pilei then seem to be merely moist or slightly lubricous. In very dry weather, if there is not enough moisture to cause the hyphae of the pellicle to gelatinize appreciably, the pileus may seem lubricous or even dry. Thus in very wet weather or very dry weather, one may find it difficult to decide whether or not the pileus is viscid.

In North America we have certain forms which have 4-spored basidia regularly and their spores measure 9–12(14) × 5–7 μ. In other 4-spored forms the spores measure 7–10 × 4–6 μ. In addition we have many aberrant forms. Some of these are constantly 2-spored with spores 9–12 × 5–6 μ, and some occur with 1-, 2-, or 3-spored basidia all on the same pileus. In the latter both the size and shape of the spores are extremely variable. Spores 15 × 8 μ have been seen on some of these.

One of the commonest forms encountered is 2-spored, and has a pileus 1.5–3 cm high and a short (3–5 cm) narrow stipe. During the season of 1940 in the vicinity of Ann Arbor, the large 4-spored form was very common. The first of these is the one J. Lange (1935–40) considers typical *H. conicus*, whereas the second he has named *H. pseudoconicus*. *H. nigrescens*, which is said to be white when young, we have not collected. Since the 2-spored character has been shown to be of questionable value as a distinction at the species level, and since the color differences Lange mentioned do not hold true for American material, we classify all our collections under the older name. Métrod (1941) concludes that *H. nigrescens* and *H. conicus* cannot be separated on a basis of 2- and 4-spored basidia. Orton (1960) has recently described *H. conicoides*, a new species from England, which is near *H. conicus*, but in it the lamellae are soon flushed rose red or scarlet from the base, finally entirely carmine or cherry red, and with all parts blackening. It has distinctly narrower spores than typical *H. conicus.* Haller (1953) has described a new species, *H. conico-palustris,* which is distinguished by a small, papillate, striate pileus, and blackish pseudocystidia on the sides of the lamellae.

49
Hygrophorus erinaceus Pat. sensu Petch
Bull. Soc. Mycol. France 25: 10. 1909

> *Hygrophorus conicus* var. *peradenyca* Sacc., Syll. Fung. 5: 418. 1887.
> *Hygrocybe erinacea* (Pat.) Singer, Sydowia 12: 225. 1958.

Pileus up to 3 cm broad, conic with an acute umbo, then conic-campanulate, pale smoke gray or barium yellow, streaked with black fibrils, blackening throughout when touched. Context gray or yellow, blackening, thin, soft, hygrophanous.

Lamellae free, white, blackening, subdistant, broad, lamellulae present.

Stipe white to pale smoke gray, blackening, fibrillose, equal, hollow.

Spores 10 × 5 μ when broadly ellipsoid to 7–6 μ when subglobose on the same gill, white in deposit. Basidia 30–40 × 7–11 μ, 4-spored. Gill trama parallel, their hyphae forming a sterile edge.

HABIT, HABITAT, AND DISTRIBUTION—In bamboo plantation, Trinidad, September–October; and Mexico.

MATERIAL STUDIED—TRINIDAD: Dennis 72.

OBSERVATIONS—Dennis (1953) indicates a relationship of this fungus to *H. conicus,* as Saccardo had done; but the tendency to bear subglobose spores indicates an approach to *H. erinaceus* Pat. Singer (1958) has recently reported this species from Mexico.

Notes on Dennis collection No. 72: Spores 6–10 × 5–7 μ, ellipsoid, subglobose, globose, or broadly ellipsoid, smooth, yellowish in Melzer's reagent. Basidia 28–40 × 8–10 μ, 1-, 2-, and 4-spored. Pleurocystidia and cheilocystidia none. Gill trama parallel, hyphae 5–7 μ broad. Cuticle not sharply differentiated, surface hyphae numerous, repent, semi-repent, or somewhat erect, broad (6–18 μ), pale fuscous, with a few clamp connections. Lactifers present in the pileus trama.

50
Hygrophorus calyptraeformis Berk. & Br. apud Berk.
Outl. Brit. Fungol., p. 202. 1860

Agaricus conicus var. *amoenus* Lasch., Linnaea 3: 380. 1828.
Hygrophorus amoenus (Lasch) Quél., Champ. Jura et Vosges, p. 192. 1872.
Hygrocybe calyptraeformis (Berk.) Fayod, Am. Sci. Nat. Serie 7 (9): 309. 1889.

Illustrations:
Fig. 29; also 1a, 1b.
Coker, Elisha Mitchell Sci. Soc. Jour. 45, pl. 12.
Juillard-Hartmann, Icon. Champ., pl. 50, fig. 4.
Smith and Hesler, Lloydia 5, pl. 10 (as *H. amoenus*).
Wakefield and Dennis, Common British Fungi, pl. 32, fig. 1.

Pileus 2.5–6 cm broad, sharply conic to cuspidate, becoming expanded, "coral red," "Mikado orange," "terra cotta," or "vinaceous tawny" when moist (dull pinkish red or occasionally tinged with lavender), fading to "buff pink" or "shell pink" (very bright delicate pink), the disc sometimes whitish, surface slightly viscid when moist, soon dry, innately fibrillose, margin spreading or recurved and rimose or lobed in age, faintly striatulate when moist.

Context thin to moderately thick, pinkish; odor and taste not distinctive.

Lamellae ascending adnate and becoming adnexed, "hydrangea pink" (pale bright pink), close to subdistant, narrow but becoming somewhat ventricose, sometimes intervenose, edges undulated and at times minutely fimbriate.

Stipe (2)5.5–16 cm long, 4–8(10) mm thick, whitish-tinged flesh color, sometimes tinged with lavender when young, strict, equal, very fragile, splitting readily, surface glabrous and lubricous but not viscid, often longitudinally striate or twisted-striate, terete or occasionally compressed, hollow.

Spores 6.3–8(9) × 4.5–5(6) μ, broadly ellipsoid, smooth, yellowish in Melzer's reagent. Basidia 4-spored, rarely 2-spored, 36–54 × 6–9 μ, sterigmata up to 9 μ long. Pleurocystidia scattered, 50–105(140) × 8–25 μ, clavate, cylindric, or fusoid-ventricose, projecting about 20 μ, thin-walled, hyaline, simple or occasionally branched or constricted near the apex; cheilocystidia similar, smaller 62–78 × 11–15 μ. Gill trama parallel to subparallel, hyphae 10–20 μ broad, yellowish to very pale vinaceous in iodine. Cuticle a narrow, gelatinous zone, some hyphae slender (3–5 μ) and long-celled, others septate-constricted, 50–100 × 10–22 μ, the terminal cell cystidioid. No hypodermium. Pileus trama of broad radial hyphae. Clamp connections found only in the subhymenium.

HABIT, HABITAT, AND DISTRIBUTION—Scattered to gregarious on soil, often in deep humus, in coniferous and mixed woods, Maryland,

Fig. 29. *H. calyptraeformis*

Ohio, Tennessee, North Carolina, Michigan, and California, July–December; also Europe and Japan.

MATERIAL STUDIED—CALIFORNIA: Smith 9165, 9166, 9460. MARYLAND: Kauffman, Cabin John, Aug. 22, 1919. MICHIGAN: Kauffman, New Richmond, Sept. 23, 1911. NORTH CAROLINA: Hesler and Sharp 9317, 12770. OHIO: Watters 161. TENNESSEE: M. Boarts 17678; Hesler 12424, 12877, 17950; Smith & Hesler 7444, 10134.

OBSERVATIONS—This is one of our most beautiful and delicately colored *Hygrophori*. The stature is much like that of *Entoloma salmoneum* Pk., but of course the latter is at once distinguished by its angular spores. *H. calyptraeformis* appears to be related to *H. cuspidatus*, *H. marginatus*, *H. purus*, and *H. acutoconicus*, from which the colors and cystidia readily separate it. The large pleurocystidia and cheilocystidia are its outstanding microscopic character. These have been found in all of the material examined, and are usually abundant.

51

Hygrophorus auratocephalus (Ellis) Murr.
Mycologia 9: 40. 1917

> *Agaricus auratocephalus* Ellis, Torrey Bot. Club Bull. 6: 75. 1876.
> *Clitocybe auratocephala* (Ellis) Sacc., Syll. Fung. 5: 190. 1887.
> *Camarophyllus auratocephalus* (Ellis) Murr., North Amer. Flora 9: 387. 1916.
> *Tricholoma auratocephalum* (Ellis) Singer, Lilloa 22: 224. 1951.

Pileus 3–5 cm broad, at first obtusely conic, then campanulate and conspicuously umbonate, sometimes expanded and with a low obtuse umbo, colors bright yellow fading to pale yellow ("cadmium yellow," "deep chrome," or "yellow ocher" when moist, paler when faded), surface glabrous and slightly viscid when moist, pellicle subseparable, subhygrophanous and soon dry, young pilei appearing faintly innately silky, in age rimose or splitting radially along the elevated even margin. Context uniformly thin, fragile, yellow fading to white; odor strong (especially when drying) or slight, rather penetrating and mephitic, taste slightly disagreeable.

Lamellae broadly adnate with a triangular decurrent tooth, "capucine yellow" to "cadmium yellow" when fresh (not golden yellow), ventricose, very broad (up to 10 mm), subdistant to distant.

Stipe 7–10 cm long, 5–7 mm thick at apex, 2–3 mm thick at the base, "mustard yellow" (pale bright yellow) over all or whitish at the base, terete, strict, subfragile, hollow.

Spores 7–9 × (4)4.5–6 μ, ellipsoid to subovoid, smooth, pale yellow in Melzer's reagent. Basidia 36–50 × 5.5–8 μ, 4-spored. Pleurocystidia and cheilocystidia none. Gill trama subparallel to slightly interwoven, yellowish in iodine. Pileus trama homogeneous beneath a thin gelatinous pellicle, all parts yellowish in iodine. Clamp connections rare on the cuticular hyphae.

HABIT, HABITAT, AND DISTRIBUTION—On soil or on moss in swamps, usually under conifers, New Jersey, Pennsylvania, and Michigan, July–September.

MATERIAL STUDIED—MICHIGAN: Kauffman, Rock River, Sept. 22, 1929. NEW JERSEY: Ellis 3033 (type from swamp, Newfield, July 28, 1876; from the collection data, it is probable that this is the type), 1776, Ellis & Everhart, N. A. Fungi No. 1911.

OBSERVATIONS—Notes on Ellis' collection 3033 (type ?): Spores

7–9 × 4.5–6 μ, ellipsoid, smooth, pale yellow in Melzer's reagent. Basidia 36–50 × 5.5–8 μ, 4-spored. Pleurocystidia and cheilocystidia none. Gill trama subparallel to slightly interwoven. Cuticle composed of a thin zone of somewhat gelatinous hyphae. Clamp connections rare on the cuticular hyphae.

No. 1911 of Ellis and Everhart's North American Fungi has also been studied, and its spores agree with the description above. Occasional slightly larger spores are found which may arise from 2-spored basidia, although no 2-spored basidia were found. They are irregular in shape and measure up to 10 μ long. The species is very distinct from, but closely related to, *H. marginatus.* The difference in the color of their gills will readily distinguish them if the odor of *H. auratocephalus* happens to be very faint or lacking. *H. marginatus* var. *concolor* approaches it the closest but lacks an odor and also clamp connections.

52
Hygrophorus marginatus var. **concolor** Sm.
Papers, Mich. Acad. Sci., Arts and Letters 38: 59. 1953

Illustration:
Fig. 30.

Pileus 1–3 cm broad, conic to obtusely conic, becoming conic-campanulate, color "deep chrome" over all, or in some the disc "orange" in buttons, in age "Mars yellow" (brilliant orange yellow), fading finally to near "apricot yellow" over all; surface glabrous, moist and

Fig. 30. *H. marginatus* var. *concolor*

hygrophanous, margin finally spreading, thin and striatulate. Context thin, brittle, concolorous with surface; odor and taste not distinctive.

Lamellae broadly adnate, "capucine yellow" to "deep chrome" (not brighter than pileus), broad, subdistant.

Stipe 3–6 cm long, 4–8 mm thick, "primuline yellow" (clear bright yellow), equal or narrowed below, naked and glabrous, moist.

Spores 7–9 × 4–5 μ, ellipsoid, smooth. Basidia 36–44 × 7–9 μ, 4-spored. Pleurocystidia and cheilocystidia none. Gill trama of short-ellipsoid cells more or less parallel in central strand but flanked by interwoven tissue (subhymenium) on either side. Pileus trama with a rudimentary non-gelatinous cuticle, flesh floccose and interwoven. Clamp connections none.

HABIT, HABITAT, AND DISTRIBUTION—Scattered under hemlock, Tahquamenon Falls, Michigan, August–September.

MATERIAL STUDIED—MASSACHUSETTS: Bigelow 9238. MICHIGAN: Bigelow 684; Smith 33324 (type, Tahquamenon Falls State Park, Sept. 5, 1949), 37514, 38356.

OBSERVATIONS—This variety has been somewhat of a puzzle, but collections over a three-year period and comparisons with typical material have shown it to be constant and distinct. In var. *marginatus* the gills are "cadmium orange." This variety approaches *H. auratocephalus* more closely than does any other species.

53
Hygrophorus subflavidus (Murr.) Murr.
Mycologia 4: 332. 1912

Hydrocybe subflavida Murr., Mycologia 3: 197. 1911.

Pileus reaching 5 cm broad and 3 cm high, conic to subcampanulate, umbonate, pale flavous, dull luteous in very young stages and on the umbo, moist, smooth, becoming striate in old or wet specimens.

Lamellae adnate with a decurrent tooth, pale yellow, broad, ventricose, rather distant.

Stipe 4–5 cm long, 4–7 mm thick, pale flavous, glabrous, cylindric, equal.

Spores 8–12 × 4.5–6.5(7) μ, ellipsoid, smooth, yellowish in Melzer's reagent. Basidia 40–57 × 8–12 μ, 2- and 4-spored, sterigmata stout. Pleurocystidia and cheilocystidia none. Gill trama parallel to subparallel. Cuticle of appressed, non-gelatinous hyphae, 3–5 μ broad. No hypodermium. Pileus trama of radially disposed hyphae. Clamp connections absent.

HABIT, HABITAT, AND DISTRIBUTION—Gregarious on the ground,

under tree-ferns, Jamaica, Trinidad, and Michigan, September–January.

Material Studied—jamaica: Murrill 674 (type, from Morce's Gap, 5000 ft. elevation, Dec. 29, 30, and Jan. 2, 1908–09). michigan: Smith 58287. trinidad: Dennis 50, 160 (as *H. earlei*).

Observations—The microscopic characters given above are based on our study of the type. It should be noted that Murrill erred in his report of spore-measurements. He describes the spores as globose, 5 μ in diameter. We found them to be 8–12 × 4.5–6.5 μ. Dennis had also written on the type sheet that he observed the spores to be 9–12 × 5–7 μ.

Dennis (1953) describes this species from his Trinidad collection, J75. He reports that the pileus becomes finely fibrillose-scurfy, yellow to flame scarlet, the flesh thin, concolor; the spores 9–12 × 5–7 μ; the basidia 45 × 8–9 μ, 2- and 4-spored; clamp connections present on the cuticular hyphae. Dennis points out that *H. subflavidus* is near *H. puniceus* Fr. which differs in its viscid pileus.

54
Hygrophorus papillatus Dennis
Kew Bull. 2: 263. 1953

Illustration:
Dennis, Kew Bull. 2, fig. 8.

Pileus 2 cm broad, campanulate, acutely umbonate, luteus, umbo luteus-ochraceous, minutely fibrillose. Context yellow, thin.

Lamellae arcuate-subdecurrent, luteus, subdistant.

Stipe luteus, pallid and strigose below, elsewhere glabrous, solid.

Spores 9–12 × 6–8 μ, ellipsoid, smooth, yellowish in Melzer's reagent. Basidia 48–60 × 10–12 μ, 2- and 4-spored. Pleurocystidia and cheilocystidia none. Gill trama more or less parallel, of large cells, 30 × 75 × 9–20 μ, globose, ovoid, irregular. Cuticle of more or less erect hyphae, 5–12 μ broad. Clamp connections none.

Habit, Habitat, and Distribution—On humus, in woods, Trinidad.

Material Studied—trinidad: Dennis 49 (type, from Northern Range).

Observations—This species is related to *H. cantharellus* from which it is separated by its mammose umbo. Other differences, if any, may be found after further microscopic studies of fresh material have been made. The description of microscopic characters given above is based on our study of the type. Essentially our description is that of Dennis (1953).

55

Hygrophorus immutabilis Pk.

N. Y. State Mus. Ann. Rept. 51: 292. 1898

Hydrocybe immutabilis (Pk.) Murr., North Amer. Flora 9: 382. 1916.

Pileus 15–25 mm broad, conical or convex and umbonate, greenish brown or yellowish brown, not changing color on drying, margin often striate when dry.

Lamellae whitish or yellowish, subdistant, broad or medium broad.

Stipe 2.5–5 cm long, 3–4 mm thick, yellow, glabrous, hollow.

Spores 8–11 × 5–7 μ, ellipsoid, smooth, pale yellow in Melzer's reagent. Basidia 30–46 × 8–10 μ, 4-spored. Pleurocystidia and cheilocystidia none. Gill trama parallel, hyphae 3.5–8 μ broad. Cuticle of repent to more or less erect, non-gelatinous hyphae, 2–4 μ broad, brownish. No hypodermium. Clamp connections present but rare on the cuticular hyphae.

HABIT, HABITAT, AND DISTRIBUTION—On dry sandy or heathy soil, New York, August.

MATERIAL STUDIED—NEW YORK: Peck (type, from North Elba, August 1897).

OBSERVATIONS—The microscopic characters given above are based on our study of the type.

Peck (1898) comments on this species as follows: "This plant is manifestly closely allied to *Hygrophorus conicus*, and might easily be considered a mere variety of it. It differs, however, in being less regularly and acutely conical, in having no orange, scarlet or red hues, in its paler or whitish lamellae, and specially in its unchangeable color. Specimens of *H. conicus* collected at the same time and place and subjected to the same method of drying turned black, as usual, but these retained their colors."

56

Hygrophorus spadiceus (Fr.) Fr. var. **spadiceus** f. **spadiceus**
Hymen. Eur., p. 420. 1874

Hygrocybe spadicea (Fr.) Karst. 1879.

Illustrations:
  Fig. 31.
  Cooke, Illus. Brit. Fungi, pl. 1194 (1161).
  Bresadola, Icon. Myc., tab. 351.

Pileus 3–4 cm broad, conic, with a straight margin, expanding to broadly conic, "olive brown" at first but a lemon yellow reflection finally pervading in the marginal area causing it to appear near "citrine drab," viscid, often splitting radially along the margin. Context pale greenish yellow, not blackening when bruised; odor and taste mild.

Lamellae ascending-adnate, "chartreuse yellow" and scarcely changing, broad, ventricose, close, edges eroded.

Stipe 4–6 cm long, 6–8 mm thick, concolorous with the gills or paler and some whitish at base, overlaid with a thin layer of "olive brown" fibrils to give it a dusky appearance, usually more or less lacerate, equal.

Spores 8–10 × 5–5.5 μ, ellipsoid, smooth, hyaline to yellowish in Melzer's reagent. Basidia 32–40 × 9–12 μ, clavate, 4-spored. Pleurocystidia and cheilocystidia none. Gill trama parallel, yellow in water mounts of fresh material. Pileus with a gelatinous pellicle of hyphae having fuscous content. Clamp connections at the septa.

Fig. 31.
H. spadiceus
var. *spadiceus*
f. *spadiceus*

HABIT, HABITAT, AND DISTRIBUTION—Scattered under sumac on dry soil after heavy rains, Michigan, July; also Europe.

MATERIAL STUDIED—MICHIGAN: Smith 32387, 39219.

OBSERVATIONS—We have identified this material as *H. spadiceus* knowing that the spacing of the gills is not typical, and that the cap is not truly glutinous as described by European authors. Bresadola, under this name, illustrates an agaric with a stipe like that of our f. *odorus*, and with close gills, but in the description he adheres to the idea of a fibrillose stipe and distant gills. The important characters are the dark pileus toned beneath the cuticle with yellow, the yellow gills, unchanging flesh, and pale olive-yellow stipe. We did not get a good spore deposit and hence cannot verify that the deposit is yellowish as

Bresadola indicated. He also gives the spores as larger than we found them. Since the species appears to be very rare in North America, we hesitate to describe our material as new on differences that could so easily turn out to be inconstant variations.

57
Hygrophorus spadiceus var. **spadiceus** f. **odorus** Sm. & Hes.
Sydowia 8: 322. 1954

Pileus 1–5 cm broad, conic young, expanding to conic umbonate or with a spreading to recurved margin, surface "brownish olive" on disc to "Isabella color" on margin, the yellow flesh showing through in streaks, margin often lobed or split, viscid when wet but soon dry (not glutinous), in age finally darkening to date brown and becoming rimose. Context very soft and fragile; odor sharp and somewhat raphanoid, taste mild, not blackening when injured.

Lamellae ascending and nearly free, "pale olive-buff" becoming "deep colonial buff" at maturity, not staining, close, thickish, narrow but in age fairly broad and ventricose.

Stipe 3–6 cm long, 4–7 mm thick, "olive-buff" to "marguerite yellow" to "colonial buff," equal, very fragile and splitting longitudinally, moist but not viscid, not staining, no dark fibrils present.

Spores 8–11 × 5–6 μ, oblong in face view and side view, hyaline in KOH, yellowish in Melzer's reagent. Basidia 36–48 × 8–11 μ, 4-spored. Pleurocystidia and cheilocystidia none. Gill trama parallel, yellowish in water mounts of fresh material. Pellicle of pileus a layer of narrow (2–5 μ) gelatinous radial hyphae with pale bister content and clamp connections at the septa, the hyphae appressed and the layer thin. No hypodermium. Pileus trama of radially disposed hyphae 6–10 μ broad.

HABIT, HABITAT, AND DISTRIBUTION—Scattered to gregarious in a freshly burned area in company with *H. conicus*, Michigan, July.

MATERIAL STUDIED—MICHIGAN: Smith 41403 (type, near Reese's Bog, Cheboygan County, July 1, 1953), 41432.

OBSERVATIONS—A very light fire occurred about six weeks before the date of collection. The soil was sandy, and the agaric was abundant in the area for a few days following adequate rains, and then was not seen for the rest of the season. It differs from the type of *spadiceus* as we know the latter in the sharp odor and glabrous stipe.

58
Hygrophorus spadiceus var. *albifolius*, var. nov.

Pileus 2.5–5 cm latus, convexus, se expandens conico-convexum vel campanulatum et acute umbonatus, viscidus, "Dresden brown," discus niger, virgatus, demum rimosus. Odore et gustu mitis. Lamellae adnexae, albae, confertae vel subdistantes, latae. Stipes 3–6 cm longus, 5–10 mm crassus, albus, fragilis, siccus, cavus, aequalis vel sub-bulbosus. Sporae 8–10 × 4.5–6 μ, ellipsoideae, albae demum luteae. Pleurocystidia et cheilocystidia desunt. Specimen typicum in Herb. Univ. Tenn.; lectum prope Knoxville, Tenn., October 7, 1957, L. R. Hesler 22705.

Pileus 2.5–5 cm broad, convex, soon expanding conic-convex or campanulate and acutely umbonate, splitting and margin upturned, viscid. "Dresden brown," disc blackish, virgate, becoming rimose. Context thin, fragile, watery to pallid; odor and taste mild.

Lamellae adnexed, narrowly attached, white, unchanging, close or subdistant, broad, ventricose, edges even.

Stipe 3–6 cm × 5–10 mm, white, fragile, splitting easily, dry, somewhat fibrillose-striate, hollow, equal or sub-bulbous.

Spores 8–10 × 4.5–6 μ, broadly ellipsoid, smooth, white becoming "Naples yellow" to "mustard yellow" a few weeks after being stored in the herbarium, yellowish in Melzer's reagent. Basidia 42–56 × 8–10 μ. Pleurocystidia and cheilocystidia none. Gill trama parallel or subparallel, hyphae 6–20 μ broad.

HABIT, HABITAT, AND DISTRIBUTION—On soil, lawn, adjacent to oak woods, Tennessee, October.

MATERIAL STUDIED—TENNESSEE: Hesler 22705 (type, from near Knoxville, Oct. 7, 1957).

OBSERVATIONS—This appears to be *H. spadiceus* with white, instead of yellow, gills, flesh, and stipe. Murrill (1944) has described *Tricholoma hygrophorum* (from Florida) which resembles our var. *albifolius*, and the two should be compared in the fresh state.

59
Hygrophorus marginatus var. olivaceus Sm. & Hes.
Lloydia 5: 40. 1942

> *Tricholoma marginatum* var. *olivaceum* (Sm. & Hes.) Singer, Lilloa 22: 224. 1951.

Illustration:
  Fig. 32.

Pileus 2.5–3.5 cm broad, sharply conic, becoming sharply conic-campanulate and finally nearly plane except for a sharp conic umbo, color "olive brown" to "deep olive" over central portion or over all when real young, soon pale dull orange near the margin, in age the olive fading and the orange more widespread (never brilliant orange), surface glabrous and moist but not viscid, margin translucent striate.

Fig. 32. *H. marginatus* var. *olivaceus*

Context thin and fragile, more or less dull olive gray; odor and taste mild.

Lamellae ascending adnate, toothed, evenly "ochraceous orange" and scarcely fading, broad (5 mm more or less) close to subdistant (2 tiers of short individuals, 20–30 reach the stipe).

Stipe 3–5 cm long, 2–4 mm thick, "grape green" becoming pallid greenish yellow, equal, soon hollow, very fragile, glabrous.

Spores 6.5–8 × 4–5 μ, subellipsoid, colorless in Melzer's reagent. Basidia 38–50 × 7–9 μ, 4-spored. Pleurocystidia and cheilocystidia none. Gill trama subparallel, hyphae 7–16 μ broad. Cuticle at first of repent, non-gelatinous hyphae, a cutis; finally the hyphae loosening and at times more or less erect and then forming a trichodermium. Hypodermium none. Pileus trama radial hyphae. Clamp connections none.

HABIT, HABITAT, AND DISTRIBUTION—Singly on very rotten wood of conifers, Maine, Massachusetts, Michigan, and Washington, July–September.

MATERIAL STUDIED—MAINE: Bigelow 3811. MASSACHUSETTS: Bigelow 8419, 9113. MICHIGAN: Mukai, Douglas Lake, July 26, 1951; Smith 25870, 36924, 39331; Thiers 3638, 4101. WASHINGTON: Smith 16709, 26633 (type, from Baker Lake, Sept. 5, 1941), 30156a, 30284, 30285, 30649, 30833.

OBSERVATIONS—The prominent green color of the stipe and more pronounced olive color of the cap distinguish the variety from the species. The habitat may also be distinctive, but more information is needed.

60
Hygrophorus marginatus Pk. var. **marginatus**
N. Y. State Mus. Ann. Rept. 28: 50. 1878

> *Hydrocybe marginata* (Pk.) Murr., North Amer. Flora 9: 378. 1916.
> *Tricholoma marginatum* (Pk.) Singer, Mycologia 35: 154. 1943.
> *Humidicutis marginata* (Pk.) Singer, Sydowia 12: 225. 1958.

Illustrations:
Fig. 33; also 7h.
Kauffman, Agar. Mich., pl. 31.
Smith and Hesler, Lloydia 5, pl. 5.

Pileus 1–5 cm broad, obtusely conic, then convex or campanulate, sometimes plane or with a low obtuse umbo, in age occasionally lacerate-squamulose or rimose, "deep chrome," "cadmium yellow," "zinc orange" to "orange" or with a tinge of olive when moist, fading to pale yellowish or nearly white, at first glabrous, moist and hygrophanous, at times lubricous, margin at times faintly striatulate. Context thin, waxy, fragile, concolorous with the surface; odor and taste mild.

Lamellae arcuate-adnate, soon adnexed, sometimes emarginate, seceding in age, "Mikado orange," "deep chrome" to "orange chrome" (brilliant orange), color usually persisting at least on the edges, broad and ventricose, subdistant, intervenose, edges even.

Stipe 4–10 cm long, 3–6 mm thick, "warm buff" to "pale orange-yellow," equal or slightly ventricose, curved or flexuous, dry, terete or compressed, fragile, glabrous, moist, not viscid, soon dry, hollow.

Spores 7–10 × 4–6 μ, ellipsoid to suboblong, smooth, white in deposits, pale yellow in Melzer's reagent. Basidia 31–58 × 6–9 μ, 2- and 4-spored. Pleurocystidia and cheilocystidia none. Gill trama subparallel to slightly interwoven, cells 10–100 × 8–20 μ, yellowish in Melzer's reagent. Lactifers rare in the gill trama, slender (2–3 μ broad). Pileus trama homogeneous. Cuticle at first of repent hyphae, a cutis; finally the surface hyphae loosen, and become more or less erect and then form a type of trichodermium. No hypodermium. Pileus trama radial, with scattered lactifers. Clamp connections absent.

HABIT, HABITAT, AND DISTRIBUTION—Singly or gregarious on soil and humus, in mixed woods, Maine, Vermont, Massachusetts, New York, Pennsylvania, Maryland, Virginia, North Carolina, Tennessee, Florida, Alabama, Kentucky, Michigan, Idaho, Oregon; also Canada;

June–October. Kühner (1936) has reported it from Europe.

MATERIAL STUDIED—ALABAMA: Burke 57, 67, 82, 93. FLORIDA: Singer F471A, F608. IDAHO: Wehmeyer, Copeland, Sept. 8, 1922. KENTUCKY: Kauffman, Harlan, Sept. 6, 1916. MAINE: Bigelow 3662, 3695, 3810, 3928; Rea 641. MARYLAND: Kauffman, Takoma Park, Aug. 24, 1919. MASSACHUSETTS: Bigelow 7426, 8262, 8344, 8951; Davis, Stow, July 1919. MICHIGAN: Chmielewski 30, 46, 62, 91; Kauffman 482; Smith 1287, 6570, 7010, 18617, 21855, 25963, 25965, 25967, 26056, 32490, 32498, 32771, 32909, 33415, 33416, 36979, 36983, 37215, 37234, 37252, 37513, 37778, 38109, 38538, 39497, 39651, 42294; Thiers 910,

Fig. 33. *H. marginatus* var. *marginatus*

980, 3231, 3271, 3325, 3397, 3888. NEW YORK: Bigelow 5123, 5124; Peck (type, from Northville, Fulton Co., August); Smith 430; Snell (Univ. Tenn. Herb.) 8183, 8184, 9057. NORTH CAROLINA: Hesler 7348, 12253, 1395, 20930; Sharp 4405, 4414, 4415, 8217; Smith 7407, 10144; Smith & Hesler 7407. OREGON: Smith 40023. PENNSYLVANIA: Kauffman, Mt. Gretna, Sept. 7, 1924. TENNESSEE: Burke 64; Hesler 4383, 4385, 7931, 7941, 11511, 12222, 17696; Sharp 4382, 8174; Sharp & Hesler 12741, 12825; Smith 9985, 10657, 10729. VERMONT: Rea 480. VIRGINIA: Milliken (Univ. Tenn. Herb.) 10853, 21904. CANADA: Bigelow 5850; Kelly 1669, 1688; Krieger 1805, 1851; Smith 661, 4603; Wehmeyer 661a.

OBSERVATIONS—Notes on the type: Spores 7–9 × 4.5–6 μ, ellipsoid to subovoid, smooth, yellowish in Melzer's reagent. Basidia 37–44 × 7–8 μ, 4-spored. Pleurocystidia and cheilocystidia none. Gill trama subparallel to slightly interwoven. Cuticle fibrillose, non-gelatinous. Clamp connections none.

This is a very distinctive fungus readily characterized by the manner in which the gills hold their orange-yellow color after the other parts have faded or after the fruiting bodies have been dried. Our observations verify Kauffman's statement that the species is not viscid. The apparent viscidity occasionally noted is not caused by a gelatinous pellicle, but is rather the slight tackiness one frequently gets from contact with a moist surface. In many respects the species is related to *H. calyptraeformis*, but differs in color, stature, and in the absence of cystidia on the gills.

61
Hygrophorus foliirubens (Murr.) Murr.
Mycologia 33: 448. 1941

Hydrocybe foliirubens Murr., Mycologia 33: 440. 1941.

Pileus 1–1.5 cm broad, conic, purplish ruber, drying more or less blackish chestnut, glabrous, dry, margin even. Context very thin; odor none.

Lamellae narrowly adnate, ochroleucous becoming miniatous on drying, broad in front, narrow behind, distant, equal.

Stipe 3–4 cm long, 1–1.5 mm thick, red above, yellow below, slightly greenish at the base, glabrous, dry, equal.

Spores 8–11 × 3.5–4.5 μ, oblong, smooth, pale yellowish in Melzer's reagent. Basidia 30–42 × 6–9 μ, 4-spored. Pleurocystidia and cheilocystidia none. Gill trama subparallel. Cuticle of repent hyphae which are brownish and non-gelatinous, with some more or less erect, free ends, hyphae 3–9 μ broad. No hypodermium. Pileus trama of radial hyphae. Clamp connections none. Among the repent hyphae of the cuticle are several hyphae with reddish-brown contents.

HABIT, HABITAT, AND DISTRIBUTION—On a lawn, under oak, Florida, June.

MATERIAL STUDIED—FLORIDA: Murrill F16432 (type, from near Gainesville, June 8, 1938).

OBSERVATIONS—This species appears close to *H. conicus* but is smaller and does not blacken when bruised or in age. When dried, the pileus darkens normally, and the lamellae redden. The description of microscopic characters given above is based on our study of the type. In view of the reddish lamellae and very narrow spores there is a strong possibility that *H. conicoides* Orton is synonymous.

62
Hygrophorus arnoldae (Murr.) Murr.
Lloydia 7: 326. 1944

Hydrocybe arnoldae Murr., Lloydia 7: 304. 1944.

Pileus 3 cm broad, conic to broadly conic, pale fulvous, disc fulvous, glabrous, not viscid, margin even. Context thin, white; odor none, taste mawkish.

Lamellae adnate, aurantiacous, distant, medium broad, many short, edges even.

Stipe 5 cm long, 6 mm thick, stramineous, apex with a narrow white band, equal above the tapering base, glabrous, hollow.

Spores 5–7 × 3.5–5 μ, ellipsoid, smooth, pale yellowish in Melzer's reagent. Basidia 30–43 × 5–7 μ, 2- and 4-spored. Pleurocystidia and cheilocystidia none. Gill trama subparallel, hyphae 3–6 μ broad. Cuticle of repent, narrow (2.5–4 μ) hyphae with some free ends, more or less erect. No hypodermium. Pileus trama of radial hyphae. Clamp connections not found.

HABIT, HABITAT, AND DISTRIBUTION—On soil, under evergreen oaks, Florida, July.

MATERIAL STUDIED—FLORIDA: Arnold, West, and Murrill F17809 (type, from near Gainesville, July 11, 1938).

OBSERVATIONS—Murrill comments that this is a pretty little species with conic, fulvous pileus, orange gills, and pale yellow stipe, with a white collar at the stipe apex.

It is somewhat related to *H. marginatus*, but has a fulvous pileus and distinctly shorter spores. The microscopic characters given above are based on our study of the type.

63

Hygrophorus stowelii, sp. nov.

Pileus 1–2.5 cm latus, nonnihil conicus, glaber, hygrophanus, "Rood's brown" vel ferme "pecan brown," demum vinaceo-sub-brunneus, striatus; lamellae adnatae, vinaceo-brunneae, obscurius rufo-brunneae siccae, angustae deinde medio-latae; stipes 4–7 cm longus, 2 mm crassus, obscuro-vinaceo-cinnamomius sporae 5–6.5(7) × 3.5–4 μ, ellipsoideae, paulum inaequilaterales. Specimen typicum in Herb. Univ. Mich.; lectum in Black Lake, Mich., E. Stowell, Aug. 7, 1961, Smith 63864.

Pileus 1–2.5 cm broad, obtusely conic becoming broadly conic, surface glabrous, moist, hygrophanous, dark vinaceous brown ("Rood's brown") or paler and near "pecan brown," fading to vinaceous tan in streaks from the margin inward. Context very tender and brittle; odor and taste not distinctive.

Lamellae adnate, dull "Mikado brown" (vinaceous brown) and drying a darker red-brown, thickish, narrow to moderately broad, edges even.

Stipe 4–7 cm long, about 2 mm thick, equal, dull vinaceous cinnamon over all except for the whitish base, which is faintly mycelioid, naked from the lower third to the apex.

Spores 5–6.5(7) × 3.5–4 μ, elliptic in face view, slightly inequilaterial to subelliptic in profile, smooth, non-amyloid. Basidia 4-spored. Pleurocystidia and cheilocystidia none. Gill trama parallel. Epicutis of pileus of non-gelatinous filaments 3–4.5 μ wide, hyaline in KOH. Clamp connections present.

HABIT, HABITAT, AND DISTRIBUTION—Solitary in a *Thuja* swamp, Black Lake, Mich., collected by E. Stowell, Aug. 7, 1961.

MATERIAL STUDIED—MICHIGAN: Smith 63864 (type).

OBSERVATIONS—This species appears to be most closely related to *H. troyanus*, but the latter has violaceous gills and a southern distribution. The color of pileus and gills is about like that in *H. kauffmanii*, but the resemblance ceases at that point.

64

Hygrophorus acutoides Sm. & Hes. var. **acutoides**
Sydowia 8: 325. 1954

Illustration:
    Fig. 34.

Pileus 3–5 cm broad, obtusely conic with a straight margin, expanding to broadly conic, in age some with an uplifted margin and low

Fig. 34. *H. acutoides* var. *acutoides*

obtuse conic umbo, disc grayish brown to somewhat fuscous, in age near "Saccardo's umber," margin pallid watery, surface viscid to subviscid, soon dry, margin faintly striatulate in some. Context watery-pallid, thin, when cut or bruised gradually changing to flesh color; odor distinctly of fresh green corn, taste mild.

Lamellae adnate but becoming adnexed, whitish to pallid and slowly staining pale salmon color where bruised, subdistant, broad.

Stipe 6–8 cm long, 4–6 mm at apex, white, in age or where bruised staining pale salmon color, equal or slightly enlarged downward, solid, white within, surface dry, naked, apex naked to silky.

Spores 7–8 × 5–6 μ, broadly ellipsoid, smooth, hyaline, yellowish in Melzer's solution. Basidia 38–46(54) × 8–9(11) μ, 4-spored. Pleurocystidia and cheilocystidia not seen. Gill trama subparallel, hyaline in KOH, hyphae 5–8 μ broad. Cuticle an ixocutis, consisting of a thin, gelatinous zone (18–30 μ thick), the hyphae 3–5 μ broad, colorless, repent, radially disposed. No hypodermium. Pileus trama of radially disposed hyphae. Clamp connections present.

HABIT, HABITAT, AND DISTRIBUTION—Gregarious to scattered on humus, Michigan, August–October.

MATERIAL STUDIED—MICHIGAN: Thiers & Smith 35847 (type, from Mackinaw City, Sept. 16, 1950); Smith 7645, 15523, 20546, 32013, 34139, 36074, 36131, 37898, 42960, 42997, 43540, 43974, 50597, 51028.

OBSERVATIONS—The gray-brown to brown disc of the pileus, white to pallid gills, green-corn odor which is very distinct, and change to pinkish when bruised are the outstanding characters. In dry weather, however, we have found the odor to remain constant, but the color change of the flesh to develop slowly or to be entirely absent. It is most closely related to *H. acutus* and *H. odorus*. It differs from *H. streptopus* Fries in being viscid, and in usually turning red when bruised. The color change reminds one of *H. metapodius* and *H. ovinus*, and it is, indeed, very close to *H. metapodius*, but is of strikingly different stature, there is no blackening following the change to red, and the spores are non-amyloid.

65
Hygrophorus acutoides var. pallidus, var. nov.

Pileus 5 cm latus, conicus, plerumque albidus, disco pallido-cinereus, margine fulvus, salmoneo colore contusus, glaber, subviscidus; caro crassa, alba, perfragilis; odor suavis, gustus mitis; lamellae adnexae, colore ut flos lactis, colore pallido-salmone contusae, densae, modice latae; stipes 7.5 cm longus, 10 mm crassus, albus, constans, appresso-fibrillosus; sporae 6–8 × 4–5(6) μ, ellipsoideae demum subovoideae. Specimen typicum in Herb. Univ. Mich.; lectum Milford, Mich., Sept. 17, 1940, A. H. Smith 15421.

Pileus 5 cm broad, disc obliquely conic, dominantly whitish, disc pale cinereous, margin dingy, changing to pale salmon color where bruised, glabrous, subviscid, margin slightly recurved and tending to split. Context thick, white, not changing color readily when cut, very brittle; odor fragrant, taste mild.

Lamellae adnexed, creamy white, staining pale salmon where bruised, not blackening, close, medium broad, strongly veined.

Stipe 7.5 cm long, 10 mm thick, white, unchanging, base narrowed slightly, glabrous but with appressed fibrils.

Spores 6–8 × 4–5(6) μ, ellipsoid to subovoid, smooth, yellow in Melzer's reagent. Basidia 38–42 × 5–7 μ. Pleurocystidia and cheilocystidia none. Gill trama subparallel, hyphae 5–10 μ broad. Cuticle of appressed, non-gelatinous hyphae, or more rarely a few hyphae at surface somewhat gelatinous, at times a few hyphae more or less erect.

HABIT, HABITAT, AND DISTRIBUTION—Singly, on soil, under aspen, Michigan, September.

MATERIAL STUDIED—MICHIGAN: Smith 15421 (type, Milford, Sept. 17, 1940).

OBSERVATIONS—Var. *pallidus* differs from var. *acutoides* in its pallid pileus with less development of a gelatinous epicutis.

66

Hygrophorus acutus Sm. & Hes.
Lloydia 5: 57. 1942

Pileus 3–4.5 cm broad, with a sharp conic umbo and a somewhat flaring margin, color dull lead gray or putty color over the umbo, pallid umbrinous toward the margin, surface glabrous, subviscid to viscid, pellicle separable in shreds, short striate but not translucent. Context grayish, thick under the umbo, thin elsewhere, waxy and brittle; odor and taste mild.

Lamellae adnate to adnate-decurrent, close to subdistant, seceding at times, whitish to pale cinereous (just off-color from white to pale ash color), no color change on bruised portions, narrow (4–5 mm broad), intervenose, edges even.

Stipe 7–9 cm long, 6–8 mm thick, white over all both inside and out, solid, equal, glabrous or slightly scurvy above, unpolished, not changing color when bruised.

Spores 6–7(8) × 4–5.5 μ, ellipsoid, smooth, hyaline, yellowish in Melzer's reagent. Basidia 38–48 × 6–9 μ, 2- and 4-spored. Cheilocystidia and pleurocystidia none. Gill trama of subparallel hyphae, the central portion of short, interwoven hyphal cells 4–8 μ broad. Cuticle an ixocutis, consisting of a narrow (20–35 μ) gelatinous zone of colorless, repent, narrow (2–4 μ) hyphae. No hypodermium. Pileus trama of interwoven radial hyphae, 5–8 μ broad. Clamp connections present on the cuticular and pileus trama hyphae.

HABIT, HABITAT, AND DISTRIBUTION—Singly under fir and redwood, Oregon, California, and Michigan, September–December.

MATERIAL STUDIED—CALIFORNIA: Smith 9395. MICHIGAN: Smith 21366. OREGON: Smith 7986 (type, from the South Fork of the McKenzie River, Oct. 20, 1937), 19164.

OBSERVATIONS—The distinguishing features of this species are the stature which resembles that of *H. amoenus*, the dark gray viscid pileus, the white dry stipe, and small spores. The gill trama of *H. acutus* is more interwoven than that of most species in this series. *H. fornicatus* should differ in stature, but *H. acutus* is also much darker in color and its gills are adnate to adnate-decurrent rather than sinuate to adnexed.

67

Hygrophorus cuspidatus Pk.
Torrey Bot. Club Bull. 24: 141. 1897

Hydrocybe cuspidata (Pk.) Murr., North Amer. Flora 9: 379. 1916.

Illustrations:
> Fig. 35; also 1c, 1d.
> Coker, Elisha Mitchell Sci. Soc. Jour. 45, pl. 11.
> Smith and Hesler, Lloydia 5, pl. 8.

Pileus 2–7 cm broad, sharply conic, expanding somewhat, smooth, glutinous, pellicle separable, when dry merely viscid or shining, "scarlet red" to "spectrum red," finally fading to "orange chrome" or paler, margin often recurved, lobed or split, striatulate. Context "primuline yellow" or paler, at times whitish, red under the cuticle, unchanging, thin, fragile, waxy; odor and taste not distinctive.

Lamellae free or just reaching the stipe, close to crowded, becoming subdistant, at first narrow, becoming rather broad, "ochraceous orange," "orange," "pale orange yellow" to "primuline yellow," edges usually eroded.

Stipe 5–9(18) cm long, 5–10(12) mm thick, "pinard yellow" to

Fig. 35. *H. cuspidatus*

"primuline yellow" over the mid-portion, apex "deep chrome," base whitish, equal or slightly enlarged below, fragile, moist, not viscid, smooth but in age becoming longitudinally striate and sometimes slightly lacerated, stuffed then hollow.

Spores 8–12(14) × 4–6.5(9) μ, ellipsoid, smooth, white in mass, yellow in Melzer's reagent. Basidia 28–56 × 7–11 μ, 2- and 4-spored. Pleurocystidia at times present and variable: basidia-like but with the enlarged apex 10–15 μ broad, to fusoid or clavate then 40–86 × 7–17 μ; cheilocystidia somewhat fusoid, 52–68 × 4–5 μ. Gill trama of parallel hyphae, 9–20 μ broad. Lactifers yellowish, (9) 16–32 μ broad. Pileus trama homogeneous beneath a gelatinous pellicle which is 80–130 μ thick, of colorless hyphae, mostly repent, but some more or less erect, 10–20 μ broad. No hypodermium. Pileus trama composed of radially-disposed hyphae. Clamp connections present on the cuticular and gill trama hyphae.

HABIT, HABITAT, AND DISTRIBUTION—Gregarious on humus and soil, in deciduous, coniferous, and mixed woods, Canada, New Hampshire, Massachusetts, Michigan, Tennessee, Florida, Texas, Wyoming, California, and Washington, May–August.

MATERIAL STUDIED—CALIFORNIA: Smith 56221. FLORIDA: Singer F194A, F194B, F1127. MASSACHUSETTS: Bigelow 6983, 6984. MICHIGAN: Chmielewski 7; Harding 94, 287; M. Lange 1449; Potter 3827; Smith 9635, 15345, 15349, 15372, 15373, 15385, 15446, 18677, 37590, 39407, 42927; Thiers 3660. NEW HAMPSHIRE: Singer W30. TENNESSEE: Hesler 9028, 10244, 12878, 13798, 13840, 19378, 20554, 23028, 23035; Norris & Hesler 22019; Shanks & Hesler 17470; Smith 10232. TEXAS: Thiers 4483. WASHINGTON: Smith 17420. WYOMING: Solheim 3359. CANADA: Macoun (type, from Ottawa, Sept.); Kelly 631, 703, 1131, 1727, 1793.

OBSERVATIONS—Notes on the type: Spores 9–12.5 × 5–7 μ, ellipsoid, smooth, bright yellow in Melzer's reagent. Basidia 27–38 × 6–9 μ, 2- and 4-spored. Pleurocystidia and cheilocystidia none. Gill trama parallel, hyphae 6–15 μ broad. Cuticle a zone of parallel, appressed, gelatinous hyphae. Clamp connections none.

Specimens of this species do not blacken when bruised or dried, a character which at once distinguished it from *H. conicus*. The size of the basidia varies in different collections, but all are the broad clavate type. Both 2- and 4-spored basidia can be found on a single pileus, and thus we allow considerable variation in spore size. The bright red color at once distinguished *H. cuspidatus* from *H. acutoconicus*.

H. croceus sensu Bresadola appears to be very similar to *H. cuspidatus*, but is characterized by the less persistent reddish orange color of the pileus in contrast to the scarlet or blood red color of the American species. However, *Agaricus croceus* Bull. was originally described as blackening, and has been referred to *H. conicus* as a synonym. Hence Bresadola's concept does not appear to be justified.

Bigelow collected a form in Massachusetts (No. 6983) in which the apex of the stipe was reddish rather than the typical "deep chrome."

In regard to clamp connections, Hesler found none on the type, but they are present on other collections which seem to be identical with the type in all other respects. Before giving much weight to this difference, a critical study of the clampless type form should be made from fresh material.

68

Hygrophorus acutoconicus (Clements) Sm. var. **acutoconicus**
North Amer. Species of Mycena, p. 472. 1947

> *Mycena acutoconica* Clements, Bot. Survey Nebr. 2: 38. 1893.
> *Prunulus acutoconicus* (Clements) Murr., North Amer. Flora 9: 330. 1916.
> *Hydrocybe californica* Murr., North Amer. Flora 9: 382. 1916.
> *Hygrocybe langii* Kühner, Le Botaniste 18: 175. 1927.
> *Hygrophorus langii* Dodge, Rhodora 29: 239. 1927.
> *Hygrocybe constans* Lange, Dansk Bot. Ark. 4(4): 24. 1923. (Not *Hydrocybe constans* Murr.)
> *Hygrophorus ravenelii* sensu Coker, Elisha Mitchell Sci. Soc. Jour. 45: 164. 1929.
> *Hygrocybe subruber* Murr., Torrey Bot. Club Bull. 66: 159. 1939.
> *Hygrophorus subruber* Murr., Torrey Bot. Club Bull. 66: 160. 1939.
> *Hygrocybe acutoconica* (Clements) Singer, Lilloa 22: 153. 1951.
> *Hygrophorus rickenii* Maire. Bull. Soc. Mycol. France 46: 220. 1930.

Illustrations:
> Figs. 36 and 37.
> Coker, Elisha Mitchell Sci. Soc. Jour. 45, frontispiece (fig. 1), and pls. 10 and 23 (figs. 1–2) (as *H. ravenelii* B. & C.).
> Smith and Hesler, Lloydia 5, pl. 9 (as *H. langii* Kühner).
> Lange, Flora Agar. Dan. 5, pl. 167C (as *H. constans* Lange).

Pileus 2–10 cm broad, obtusely to sharply conic when young, soon campanulate or the margin finally spreading or upturned, "wax yellow," "cadmium yellow," "ochraceous buff," "ochraceous orange," to "rufous," scarcely fading, glabrous, splitting radially, viscid or glutinous, margin striatulate when wet, even when dry. Context soft, thin on the margin, thickish under the umbo, yellow; odor and taste mild.

Lamellae free or narrowly adnexed, yellow, ascending, ventricose and moderately broad, close, becoming subdistant, edges entire, becoming eroded at times, faces more or less rugulose.

Stipe 6–8(12) cm long, 3–6(12) mm thick, concolor to pileus in-

Fig. 36. *H. acutoconicus* var. *acutoconicus*

side and out, paler or white at the base, equal to subequal, terete or compressed, fibrillose to glabrous, striate, sometimes twisted-striate, easily splitting, equal or clavate to ventricose below, lubricous to the touch at times but lacking gelatinous hyphae, not blackening when wounded, but the base usually blackening in age.

Spores 9–15 × 5–9 μ, ellipsoid, some irregular, at times constricted, pale yellow in Melzer's reagent, white in mass. Basidia 38–60 × 7–12 μ, 1-, 2-, 3-, and 4-spored. Pleurocystidia and cheilocystidia none. Gill trama parallel, hyphae 5–20 μ broad. Cuticle an ixocutis, consisting of a narrow (30–50 μ), gelatinous zone of repent, radially-disposed, broad hyphae (6–18 μ) with a few to many free ends more or less erect, the terminal elements often ventricose. No hypodermium. Pileus trama of radial, parallel hyphae, which are quite similar to the surface hyphae. Clamp connections present.

HABIT, HABITAT, AND DISTRIBUTION—Single to scattered on soil and humus, in deciduous, coniferous, and mixed woods, Michigan, Tennessee, North Carolina, South Carolina, Florida, Nebraska, Texas,

Fig. 37. *H. acutoconicus* var. *acutoconicus*

Idaho, Montana, Wyoming, and California; also West Indies and Europe; April–January.

MATERIAL STUDIED—CALIFORNIA: L. S. Smith 413 (type of *Hydrocybe californica* Murr., from Berkeley, Jan. 20, 1914). FLORIDA: Murrill F18299 (type of *H. subruber*); Singer F2062. IDAHO: Smith 45500. MICHIGAN: Brooks 1253, 1265; Harding 141; Smith 1411, 1422, 6036, 6717, 7103, 7139, 15347, 15350, 21059, 21811, 25865, 25866, 32402, 32653, 32768, 32770, 36809, 36847, 57298, 57478; Thiers 888, 979, 3306, 3331, 3446, 3515, 4018, 4177, 4237, 4299. MONTANA: Kauffman, Flathead National Forest, July 6–8, 1928. NEBRASKA: Clements (?) (type of *Mycena acutoconica*). NORTH CAROLINA: Coker 3590, 3757, 3790 (as *H. ravenelii* B. & C.); Totten 3780 (as *H. ravenelii* B. & C.). TENNESSEE: Hesler 10798, 14174, 19318, 19821, 22211, 22217, 23339; Sharp & Hesler 12819; Smith & Hesler 10005. TEXAS: Thiers 1817. WYOMING: Thiers 59. WEST INDIES: Dennis, Isle of Rhum, 1951.

OBSERVATIONS—This was reported by Kauffman and Smith (1933) under the name *H. rickenii* Maire, and later by Smith and Hesler (1942) as *H. langii* Kühner. It has also been described under other names (see synonymy). When wet, the stipe may feel somewhat viscid, but it lacks a gelatinous pellicle. When faded, specimens of *H. cuspidatus* are indistinguishable from specimens of *H. acutoconicus*. Unless the red color of the former is preserved in drying, herbarium specimens of the two are also indistinguishable. Singer (1940) has referred *H. croceus* sensu Bres. and *H. langii* Kühner to *H. persistens* Britz. as synonyms. Since we recognize *H. persistens* as having a viscid stipe, we do not accept Singer's synonymy.

69
Hygrophorus acutoconicus var. *microsporus*, var. nov.

Pileus 2.5–5 cm latus, conicus, nonnihil cuspidatus, flavus vel ochraceo-aurantius, viscidus; lamellae adnatae, subflavae, nonnihil latae, confertae; stipes 5–8 longus, 3–5 mm crassus, subflavus, siccus; sporae 7–9($.10) \times 5–6 \mu$, ellipsoideae. Specimen typicum in Herb. Univ. Tenn.; lectum prope Knoxville, Tenn., Aug. 11, 1937, L. R. Hesler 10798.

Pileus 2.5–5 cm broad, conic, more or less cuspidate, "cadmium yellow" to "ochraceous orange," viscid, glabrous, innately streaked, subrimose, margin even. Context pallid or yellowish; odor and taste mild.

Lamellae narrowly attached, pale clear yellow, ventricose, moderately broad (3–4 mm), close, edges eroded.

Stipe 5–8 cm long, 3–5 mm thick, yellowish, base whitish, dry, equal, striate, fragile, easily splitting, hollow.

Spores 7–9(10) × 5–6 μ, ellipsoid, smooth, yellowish in Melzer's reagent. Basidia 28–45 × 7–10 μ, 4-spored; rarely 1-, 2-, and 3-spored. Pleurocystidia and cheilocystidia none. Gill trama of parallel hyphae, 10–20 μ broad.

HABIT, HABITAT, AND DISTRIBUTION—On soil in deciduous woods, Tennessee, August.

MATERIAL STUDIED—TENNESSEE: Hesler 10798 (type, from Knoxville, Aug. 11, 1937).

OBSERVATIONS—The yellow color excludes it from *H. ravenelii*. It lacks a distinctive odor and therefore is not *H. auratocephalus*. It differs from var. *acutoconicus* in its smaller spores.

SERIES HYGROCYBE

KEY TO SPECIES

1. Lamellae purplish, dark red, or lavender 2
1. Lamellae not colored as above 3
   2. Lamellae dark red; pileus dark purplish red; basidia dimorphous
   . . . . .77. *H. firmus* var. *purpureus*
   2. Lamellae purplish drab to lavender; pileus dark reddish orange, becoming more orange-like; basidia monomorphous . . . .
   . . . . .70. *H. purpureofolius*
3. Pileus scarlet when young, in some species fading to orange or yellow (tips of squamules becoming fuscous in *H. turundus* var. *turundus*) . .5
3. Pileus not scarlet 4
   4. Pileus yellow; basidia dimorphous . . .76. *H. firmus* var. *occidentalis*
   4. Pileus not yellow, or only a dingy yellow to buff; basidia monomorphous 14
5. Spores 9–14 μ or more long 6
5. Spores smaller 10
   6. Squamule tips over disc of pileus dark brown to fuscous at maturity
   . . . . .71. *H. turundus* var. *turundus*
   6. Squamule tips and fibrils orange-yellowish, darkening only slightly or not at all 7
7. Pileus deep pinkish red, fading slowly; gills adnate to short-decurrent; growing on *Sphagnum* . . . . .72. *H. turundus* var. *sphagnophilus*
7. Not on *Sphagnum* 8
   8. Pleurocystidia and cheilocystidia clavate to spathulate . . . .
   . . . . .73. *H. appalachianensis*
   8. Pleurocystidia and cheilocystidia none 9
9. Basidia dimorphous, the large ones with spores 14–18 × 7–8 μ, the smaller ones with spores 6 × 3 μ . . . . .74. *H. firmus* var. *firmus*
9. Basidia monomorphous; spores 7–12 × 4–8 μ . . . . .79. *H. cantharellus*
   10. Growing on *Sphagnum*, solitary to gregarious; stipe 3–8 cm × 2–4 mm; pileus thin, and striate when moist . . . .
   . . . . .81. *H. miniatus* f. *longipes*
   10. Not with the above combination of characters 11

11. Pileus 3–16 mm broad; lamellae coral red and not fading ....
    ....78. *H. firmus* var. *trinitensis*
11. Pileus 10–50 mm broad; lamellae orange-yellow, or, if red, soon fading
    to orange or yellow 12
    12. Filamentose cheilocystidia present; context of pileus thick and firm
        ....82. *H. squamulosus*
    12. Cheilocystidia absent 13
13. Pileus red, fading to orange or pale yellow and then fibrillose-scurfy;
    basidia monomorphous ....80. *H. miniatus* var. *miniatus*
13. Pileus red, not fading, silky; basidia dimorphous ....
    ....75. *H. firmus* var. *militaris*
    14. Spores weakly amyloid ....147. *H. metapodius*
    14. Spores non-amyloid 15
15. Spores 5–6(7) μ, subglobose; pleurocystidia and cheilocystidia present
    ....83. *H. subovinus*
15. Not as above 16
    16. Spores 5–6 × 3.5–4.5 μ; pileus blackish on disc, gills drab gray
        with pallid margins ....84. *H. atro-olivaceus*
    16. Not as above 17
17. Lamellae tending to stain olivaceous where bruised; pileus chamois
    colored; odor sharp and fragrant ....85. *H. olivascens*
17. Not with above combination of characters 18
    18. Pileus dingy honey color or yellower; squamules often blackish at
        tips; lamellae white becoming yellowish; spores 6–8 × 5–6 μ ....
        ....86. *H. caespitosus*
    18. Not with above combination of characters 19
19. Context, lamellae, and/or stipe becoming pinkish to brownish where
    bruised 20
19. No part of fruiting body unchanging when bruised 21
    20. Odor distinctly nitrous ....106. *H. nitiosus*
    20. Odor merely pungent ....110. *H. ovinus*
21. Odor nitrous (see *H. tahquamenonensis*, page 193) ....87. *H. nitratus*
21. Odor not nitrous 22
    22. Spores 8–11 × 6–7 μ; lamellae white, taste mild ..88. *H. erinensis*
    22. Spores 6–9 × 3.5–5; lamellae brown; taste bitter-astringent .....
        ....89. *H. cokeri*

70

Hygrophorus purpureofolius Bigelow
Rhodora 62: 190. 1960

Illustrations:
    Fig. 38.
    Bigelow, Rhodora 62, pl. 1253.

Pileus (0.7–)1–5 cm broad, conic or campanulate at first, umbo
obtuse and rather broad, margin incurved and slightly inrolled, not
striate, becoming convex to broadly convex, finally plane, margin
often somewhat undulate, surface opaque and dull watery-appearing,

Fig. 38. *H. purpureofolius*

glabrous, moist and hygrophanous, not viscid, dark reddish orange when young ("vinaceous rufous," "Hay's russet," "Kaiser brown," "Mars orange"), becoming paler and more orange-like when expanded ("burnt sienna," dull "Mars orange," "orange rufous"), usually fading from the disc outward, fading slowly and appearing radiate-streaked or squamulose, becoming a rather bright yellowish orange ("deep chrome"). Context thin, brittle, concolorous with pileus when moist, fading to whitish or a pale yellowish, odor and taste not distinctive.

Lamellae broadly adnate to short decurrent, close to subdistant, broad (2–6 mm) waxy-appearing, rather brittle, dull lavender to purple ("pale purple drab," "pale vinaceous drab," at times nearly "deep dull lavender"), yellowish in age, edges even.

Stipe 2.5–7 cm long, 4–9 mm thick at apex, equal or either end enlarged, sometimes ventricose, often compressed with a vertical groove, usually curved or flexuous, hollow (yellowish in interior of cortex), fibrous-brittle and splitting longitudinally, surface glabrous, concolorous with moist pileus and not fading appreciably, base with slight whitish tomentum or more rarely the tomentum lilac-colored.

Spores 7–11 × 4–5.5 μ, elliptic to elliptic-oblong, at times obovate, apicular end often curved in side view, smooth, not amyloid, spore print not obtained. Basidia 42–55 × 6–8 μ, 4- and 2-spored. Pleuro-cystidia and cheilocystidia none. Gill trama regular to subparallel. Clamp connections present.

HABIT, HABITAT, AND DISTRIBUTION—Gregarious to subcaespitose, on humus, under birch and maple or in mixed woods (with hemlock), Massachusetts, August.

MATERIAL STUDIED—MASSACHUSETTS: Bigelow 8361, 8362, 8363 (type, from Savoy Mt. State Forest, Florida, Mass., Aug. 17, 1959), 8364, 8365, 8421, 8422, 9086.

OBSERVATIONS—As Bigelow and Barr state (1960), the purplish gills are unusual for species in *Hygrocybe*. Here we may recall gill-color in *H. troyanus* and *H. mephiticus*. In *H. troyanus* the gills are violaceous, according to Murrill (salmon orange according to Dennis), but the hemispheric to convex, ferruginous pileus, and shorter spores will separate it from *H. purpureofolius*. In *H. mephiticus* the gills are grayish-violaceous to grayish purple, but the gills are sinuate, the pileus is yellowish brown, and the fruiting bodies have a mephitic odor.

Notes on the type: Cuticle of repent hyphae, 3–5 μ broad, non-gelatinous, hyphae undifferentiated from those of the pileus trama. No hypodermium. Pileus trama of radial and subparallel hyphae; septa relatively numerous and close together.

71
Hygrophorus turundus (Fr.) Fr. var. **turundus**
Epicr. Myc., p. 330. 1838

>*Agaricus turundus* Fr., Syst. Myc. 1: 106. 1821.
>*Hygrocybe turunda* (Fr.) Karst., Bidr. Finls. Nat. Folk 1: 235. 1879.

Illustrations:
Fig. 39; also 1e.

Pileus 1–3 cm broad, convex to flattened or the disc shallowly depressed, margin curved in slightly, expanding to more depressed in the disc and the margin arched, the ground color variable, scarlet to orange to yellow, brightest when young and dingy in age, buttons which have not developed fast may be dingy yellow, in age some-times grayish over all from appressed fibrils, surface dry and fibrillose-squamulose, the squamules fuscous to earth brown. Context thin, waxy firm, orange, odor and taste mild.

Lamellae decurrent, "cream buff" or more pallid (pale dingy yellow to pallid), distant to subdistant, broad.

Stipe 3–6 cm long, 2–3.5 mm thick, orange in midportion, pale above and below, equal or slightly enlarged at base, naked, glabrous, translucent.

Spores 9–14 × 5–8 μ, variable in size, ellipsoid to somewhat bean-shaped (in side view), smooth, hyaline in KOH and Melzer's reagent. Basidia 2- or 4-spored, 38–52 × 9–11 μ, sterigmata 6–8 μ long. Pleurocystidia and cheilocystidia similar, sporadic in appearance and often

Fig. 39.
H. turundus var. *turundus*

difficult to locate, 40–60 × 12–20 μ, clavate to broadly clavate-subcapitate, hyaline, thin-walled, buried in the hymenium. Gill trama subparallel to somewhat interwoven, hyaline in KOH. Cuticle a trichodermium of enlarged hyphal cells with cystidioid to elliptic endcells often having secondary septa. Hypodermium none. Pileus trama of radial hyphae. Clamp connections present at primary septa.

HABIT, HABITAT, AND DISTRIBUTION—Scattered to gregarious on moist soil and wet moss, often on *Sphagnum* at high elevations, Massachusetts, Michigan, Idaho, Montana, Oregon, and Washington, summer and fall; also in Greenland, Iceland, Faeröes, Europe, and Japan.

MATERIAL STUDIED—IDAHO: Smith 46281, 54329. MASSACHUSETTS: Bigelow 8252. MICHIGAN: Kauffman, Ann Arbor, July 8, 1924; Smith 1101, 7581, 42571, 43362, 50893, 57493, 58028. MONTANA: Mains 6045. OREGON: Smith 24052, 26962. WASHINGTON: Imshaug 1790; Simmons 1583; Smith 29365, 29528, 29560, 29585, 29586, 29865, 29902, 29943, 29953, 29959, 30558, 40152, 40342, 40852, 42481, 43923.

OBSERVATIONS—This species fruits during both the summer and fall. Smith and Hesler reported (1942) it from North America on the basis of a Kauffman collection. It now appears that this collection is a variety of *H. cantharellus*. The squamules of the true *H. turundus* are fuscous to brown. The Mt. Rainier collections showed conclusively that this color was not a discoloration. Möller's (1945) account covers the Mt. Rainier collections very well, even including the inflated cells which we regard as cystidia. At Mt. Rainier both a 2-spored and a 4-spored form occur, and there is a corresponding difference in spore size. Clamp connections are present at the base of the basidia in both forms, but are often difficult to demonstrate on the hyphae of the carpophore. Here they appear to be fairly regular at the primary septa, but absent at the secondary septa.

Kühner and Romagnesi (1953) described *H. turundus* as having fibrils which become dark colored. Smith has a collection from among cranberries and other heath plants on wet sand between two sand dunes at Whitefish Point on Lake Superior (Smith 42481), which appears to agree exactly with their account. It was growing in great quantity. The pileus was entirely deep scarlet when young but became squamulose, and in age the squamules were more or less fuscous. *H. sphagnophilus* Pk., in the light of this study, should be attached to *H. turundus*. Singer (1940) thought they were identical, but we have found Peck's fungus to be constant as a variety which differs chiefly from the type form in the squamules not darkening.

J. E. Lange (1935–1940) gives a beautiful illustration of brilliantly colored specimens. His treatment of *Hygrocybe* had not come to our hands at the time we first published our account of the species.

Hongo (1958a) reports *H. turundus* from Japan (July and Sept.), and says that the gill trama hyphae are interwoven, 9–30 μ broad, and that clamp connections are present. Morten Lange (1955) reports it from Greenland.

72
Hygrophorus turundus var. *sphagnophilus* (Pk.), stat. nov.
Sydowia 8: 324. 1954

> *Hygrophorus miniatus* var. *sphagnophilus* Pk., N. Y. State Mus. Rept. 53 (for 1899): 856. 1901.
> *Hygrophorus miniatus* f. *sphagnophilus* (Pk.), Hongo, Jour. Jap. Bot. 27: 160. 1952.
> *Hygrophorus turundus* f. *sphagnophilus* (Pk.) Sm. & Hes., Sydowia 8: 324. 1954.

Illustrations:
Fig. 40; also 1f, 1g.

Pileus 1–3.5 cm broad, at first broadly convex or flattened, soon broadly and often deeply depressed, at first "nopal red" to scarlet, fading to yellow or brownish orange, the tips of the scales often darkening somewhat, margin decurved and frequently becoming scalloped or wavy, in age the margin sometimes spreading, dry, minutely and densely floccose at least on the disc or in the depression, usually becoming somewhat scaly. Context thin or fairly thick, soft, concolorous with the pileus; odor and taste mild.

Lamellae at first adnate, remaining so or becoming deeply decurrent, sometimes red or orange, or sometimes pallid or faintly yellow, distant, broad or medium broad, at times forked near the margin, edges even.

Stipe 4–12 cm × 1–3 mm, vermilion-red or yellowish, whitish where buried in the moss, equal, usually flexuous, fragile, glabrous, or silky, not viscid, stuffed solid or becoming tubular.

Spores (9)10–14 × 5–9(10) μ, subellipsoid to subreniform, smooth, pale yellow in Melzer's reagent. Basidia 41–68 × 7–12 μ, 2- and 4-spored, sterigmata long, prominent. Pleurocystidia and cheilocystidia buried, scattered (see notes on type, below). Gill trama subparallel to slightly interwoven, hyphae 12–32 × 7–18 μ, yellowish in Melzer's reagent, in water mounts of fresh specimens the cells of the flesh and gill trama are filled with a bright orange fluid. Clamp connections present on the hyphae of the pileus trama.

HABIT, HABITAT, AND DISTRIBUTION—Gregarious to scattered in *Sphagnum* bogs throughout northern and eastern United States and in Ontario and Quebec, in Canada, June–October. Singer has collected it in Europe. Hongo (1958a) reports it from Japan.

MATERIAL STUDIED—MASSACHUSETTS: Bigelow 6206. MICHIGAN: Smith 1101, 25602, 25801, 32233. NEW YORK: Peck (type of *H. miniatus* var. *sphagnophilus* Pk., from Kasoog Swamp, July). NORTH CAROLINA: Hesler 4409, 10448, 12163. WEST VIRGINIA: Sharp 12562. CANADA: (Quebec) Smith 61528; (Ontario) Smith 4548; (Newfoundland) Saville & Vaillancourt 28523.

OBSERVATIONS—This form was originally described as *H. miniatus* var. *sphagnophilus* Pk. Kühner and Romagnesi (1953) describe *H. turundus* as having fibrils on the pileus which become dark colored. Since the fibrils in var. *sphagnophilus* tend to darken somewhat and because of its spore size, it seems to us that the variety is more closely related to *H. turundus* than to *H. miniatus;* therefore we have attached it to *H. turundus*. It has also been attached to *H. miniatus* as f. *sphagnophilus* by Hongo (1952a).

Notes on the type of *H. miniatus* var. *sphagnophilus* Pk.: Spores 9–12(14) × 5.5–7(8.5) μ, ellipsoid, subovoid, or broadly cuneate, smooth, yellowish in Melzer's reagent. Basidia 46–60 × 8–11 μ, 2- and 4-spored. Pleurocystidia 44–57 × 6–12 μ, buried, scattered, versiform

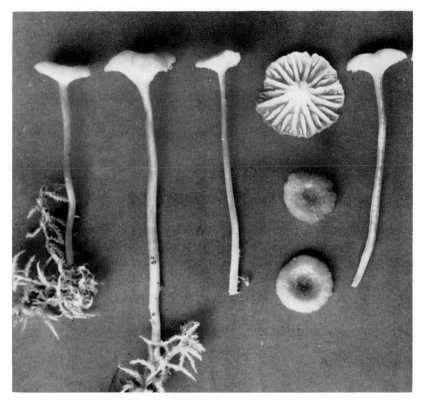

Fig. 40. *H. turundus* var. *sphagnophilus*

(clavate, fusiform, irregular); cheilocystidia 37–48 × 5–12 μ, few, versiform. Gill trama subparallel, rarely slightly interwoven, hyphae
5–12 μ broad. Cuticle bearing a mat of semi-erect to more or less repent, septate, constricted, fuscous hyphae, the terminal elements
clavate. Clamp connections present on the cuticular hyphae.

Orton (1960) has recently described *H. coccineo-crenatus* from
England, which is very close to, if not the same as, this variety.

73
Hygrophorus appalachianensis, sp. nov.
Illustrations:
  Fig. 41; also 1h, 1i.

*Pileus (1)2–7 cm latus, convexus, ruber, marcescens, discus
aurantio-luteus, fibrillosus vel squamulosus, nonviscidus; lamellae
decurrentes, albae demum pallido-aureae, distantes vel subdistantes,
sub-latae; stipes 3–7 cm longus, 4–12 mm crassus, ruber; sporae*

11–17.5 × 7–10 μ, *ellipsoideae; pleurocystidia 32–57 × 8–14 μ, cheilocystidia 34–50 × 7–11 μ. Specimen typicum in Herb. Univ. Tenn.; lectum July 28, 1958, in Cades Cove, Great Smoky Mts. National Park, Tenn., L. R. Hesler 22967.*

Pileus (1)2–7 cm broad, convex, depressed, margin finally upturned and then deeply depressed, "Nopal red," to "Pompeian red," fading, disc densely orange-yellowish fibrillose to fibrillose-squamulose, elsewhere glabrous, not viscid, at times rimose, margin even, at times subplicate. Context yellowish, tinged orange, reddish next to cuticle, medium thick on disc, thin on margin; odor and taste mild.

Lamellae at first adnate-decurrent, becoming decurrent, whitish then "pale orange yellow," distant to subdistant, medium-broad, edges even and at times sulfur yellow.

Stipe 3–7 cm long, 4–12 mm thick, "Nopal red" above, paler below,

Fig. 41. *H. appalachianensis*

fading only slightly or none, moist, not viscid, silky or squamulose, equal or tapering below, at times compressed, hollow.

Spores 11–17.5 × 7–10 μ, ellipsoid, smooth, white in deposit, yellowish in Melzer's reagent. Basidia 38–57 × 6–12 μ, 1-, 2-, and 4-spored. Pleurocystidia 32–57 × 8–14 μ, clavate, often more or less spathulate, usually with a short stalk, buried; cheilocystidia similar, 34–50 × 7–11 μ. Gill trama parallel to subparallel, hyphae 8–30 μ broad. Cuticle a trichodermial turf of septate hyphae, the apical cells of which are undifferentiated. No hypodermium. Pileus trama of radially disposed hyphae. Lactifers present in the trama of the pileus and lamellae. Clamp connections present on the hyphae of the cuticle, pileus trama, gill trama, and the subhymenium.

HABIT, HABITAT, AND DISTRIBUTION—On soil, in mixed deciduous-coniferous woods, Tennessee, June and July.

MATERIAL STUDIED—TENNESSEE: Hesler 13966, 17671, 22967 (type, from Cades Cove, Great Smoky Mts. National Park, July 28, 1958).

OBSERVATIONS—When first observed in the field, this agaric, because of its color and stature, was erroneously assumed to be either a form of *H. coccineus* or an abnormally large *H. miniatus*. More detailed microscopic study, however, revealed its conspicuous pleurocystidia and cheilocystidia. Its fibrillose-squamulose pileus and large spores indicate a relationship to *H. turundus*.

74
Hygrophorus firmus Berk. & Br. var. **firmus**
Jour. Linn. Soc. Bot. 11: 563. 1871

> *Hygrophorus firmus* Berk. & Br. var. *typicus* Corner, Trans. Brit.
> Mycol. Soc. 20(2): 176. 1936.
> *Hygrocybe firma* (Corner) Singer var. *firma*, Sydowia 11: 355. 1957.

Pileus 1.5 cm broad, convex, becoming flattened or depressed, scarlet red, innately fibrillose-squamulose with erect fibrils in the umbilicus. Context concolorous, hygrophanous, thin.

Lamellae flame-scarlet with yellowish edges, subdistant, with lamellulae.

Stipe concolorous with the pileus above, shading to yellow below, equal or slightly enlarged at the base, hollow.

Spores 14–18 × 7–8 μ, on larger basidia 40 × 15 μ; 6 × 3 μ on smaller basidia 30 × 5–6 μ. Cuticle of thin-walled ellipsoid cells 14–30 μ wide.

HABIT, HABITAT, AND DISTRIBUTION—On humus, in forest, Trinidad, September.

MATERIAL STUDIED—TRINIDAD: Dennis 48.

OBSERVATIONS—Dennis (1953) states that a possible synonym is *H. siparius* Berk., from Brazil, but he could find no spores on the type (Spruce 130, at Kew). The obvious dimorphous basidia are a striking feature of this variety.

Notes on Dennis collection No. 48: Basidia dimorphous, larger ones 42–57 × 10–14 μ, 4-spored, spores 13–18 × 7–9 μ; smaller ones 28–35 × 5–6 μ, 2- and 4-spored, spores 5–6 × 3–3.5 μ; all spores ellipsoid, smooth, yellowish in Melzer's reagent. Pleurocystidia and cheilocystidia none. Gill trama parallel, hyphae 6–17 μ broad. Lactifers present in pileus trama. Cuticle not differentiated, surface hyphae repent to erect, 15–32 μ broad. Clamp connections not found.

75
Hygrophorus firmus var. **militaris** Corner
Trans. Brit. Mycol. Soc. 20: 177. 1936

Pileus up to 4 cm broad, convex then flattened or depressed with a downcurved margin, scarlet red with a yellow line at the margin, silky, dry. Context red.

Lamellae broadly adnate, light orange-yellow becoming apricot-orange with yellow edges, rather crowded, of two lengths, intervenose in age.

Stipe white with a hint of yellow at the base, becoming orange-buff from the base upwards with age, dry, smooth, equal, hollow.

Basidia dimorphous, the larger mostly 4-spored, a few apparently 2-spored, 40 × 7–10 μ, the spores 8–11 × 5–6 μ; the smaller 30 × 5 μ, 4-spored, the spores 6–7 × 3–4 μ. Pleurocystidia and cheilocystidia none. Gill trama parallel. Cuticular hyphae parallel, the cells 270–400 × 15–30 μ.

HABIT, HABITAT, AND DISTRIBUTION—Gregarious in forest litter, Trinidad, November.

MATERIAL STUDIED—TRINIDAD: Dennis 382.

OBSERVATIONS—Apparently this variety differs from var. *firmus* by its lack of squamules on the pileus, its larger size, its crowded, orange gills, its stipe color, its smaller spores.

Dennis points out that *H. subcaespitosus* (Murr.) Murr. from Jamaica has a similar habit, but the gills of the latter are white to stramineous and the stipe yellow.

Notes on Dennis collection No. 382: Basidia dimorphous, the larger 46–57 × 8–12 μ, 2- and 4-spored, the spores 9–11 × 5.5–7 μ; smaller, 32–42 × 5–6 μ, 1-, 2-, and 4-spored, the spores 5.5–7 × 3–4 μ, all spores ellipsoid, smooth, yellowish in Melzer's reagent. Pleurocystidia and cheilocystidia none. Gill trama parallel, hyphae 6–18 μ broad.

Lactifers in both gill trama, 2–3 μ broad, and pileus trama, 3–7 μ broad. Cuticle undifferentiated, surface hyphae repent to erect, conspicuous, the terminal elements fusoid to subclavate, 12–30 μ broad. Clamp connections found only on lactifers in gill trama.

76
Hygrophorus firmus var. **occidentalis** Dennis
Kew Bull. 2: 267. 1953

Pileus up to 6 cm broad, convex, then depressed and often perforated at the center, pale lemon yellow to apricot yellow, smooth, translucent striate. Context concolorous, hygrophanous, thin.

Lamellae adnate, sulphur yellow, subdistant, of two lengths.

Stipe lemon yellow, smooth, slightly attenuated upwards, hollow.

Basidia dimorphous, the larger 35 × 9–10 μ, 2- or 4-spored, the spores 11–14 × 6–8 μ, broadly ellipsoid; the smaller more numerous, 30 × 4–5 μ, the spores 5–6.5 × 3–4 μ, ellipsoid-cylindric. Pleurocystidia and cheilocystidia none.

HABIT, HABITAT, AND DISTRIBUTION—On soil in woods, Trinidad.

MATERIAL STUDIED—TRINIDAD: Dennis 50A (type).

OBSERVATIONS—Although Corner has described seventeen varieties of *H. firmus* from Malaya, Dennis concludes that var. *occidentalis* does not fit any of the Malayan varieties. It differs from var. *firmus* in its yellow pileus.

Notes on the type: Basidia dimorphous, the larger 50–62 × 9–12 μ, mostly 2-spored, bearing spores 9–11(14) × 6–7(8) μ, ellipsoid, smooth, yellowish in Melzer's reagent; the smaller 40–46 × 5–8 μ, mostly 2-spored, bearing spores 5.5–7 × 3.5–4.5 μ, ellipsoid, smooth, yellowish in Melzer's reagent. Pleurocystidia and cheilocystidia none. Gill trama parallel, hyphae broad (12–38 μ). Cuticle undifferentiated, with repent to erect hyphae, the terminal element subfusoid to clavate (cystidioid), 95–140 × 12–18 μ, the tip usually tapering somewhat. Clamp connections not found.

77
Hygrophorus firmus var. **purpureus** Dennis
Kew Bull. 2: 267. 1953

Illustration:
    Dennis, Kew Bull. 2, fig. 12.

Pileus 1.5 cm broad, convex, becoming umbilicate, "burnt lake," silky shining, dry. Context concolorous with the pileus, with a dark purple juice which stains paper, hygrophanous, thin.

Lamellae adnate-decurrent, "Indian red," subdistant, medium broad (2 mm).

Stipe shading from pinkish-vinaceous at the apex through "Naples yellow" to an ochraceous-buff base, equal, smooth, hollow.

Basidia dimorphous, 4-spored, the larger 40–11 μ, the spores 12–14 × 8 μ; the smaller 30 × 5–6 μ, the spores 5–9 × 3–5 μ. Pleurocystidia and cheilocystidia none. Gill trama parallel. Cuticle of thin-walled hyphae, the cells 230–270 × 20 μ, filled with dark-purple sap.

HABIT, HABITAT, AND DISTRIBUTION—On soil in woods, Trinidad, October.

MATERIAL STUDIED—TRINIDAD: Dennis 111 (type).

OBSERVATIONS—This variety differs from var. *firmus* in its purple pileus, and from var. *amethystinus* Corner in its smaller spores.

Notes on the type: Basidia dimorphous, larger ones 38–46 × 7–9 μ, 4-spored, bearing spores 11–14 × 7–8 μ, smaller ones 30–33 × 5–6 μ, 4-spored, bearing spores 5–8 × 3.5–5 μ, smaller spores more numerous (4:1), all spores ellipsoid, smooth, yellowish in Melzer's reagent. Pleurocystidia and cheilocystidia none. Gill trama parallel, hyphae 6–20 μ broad. Lactifers prevalent in gill trama, 2.5–4 μ broad. Cuticle undifferentiated, surface hyphae numerous, erect or repent. Clamp connections not found.

78
Hygrophorus firmus var. **trinitensis** Dennis
Kew Bull. 2: 266. 1953

Illustration:
Dennis, Kew Bull. 2, fig. 11.

Pileus 3–10 mm broad, convex, with a shallow umbilicus, scarlet with a narrow yellow line around the margin, dry, silky, slightly scurfy in the umbilicus in large specimens. Context concolorous, thin.

Lamellae decurrent with a tooth, coral red, subdistant, broad, equal.

Stipe concolorous with the pileus except at the yellowish base, long, slender, equal, dry, smooth, solid.

Spores 6–11(13) × 3.5–6 μ, ellipsoid. Basidia 40 × 8 μ, 4-spored. Pleurocystidia and cheilocystidia none. Gill trama of parallel hyphae.

HABIT, HABITAT, AND DISTRIBUTION—On soil in woods, Trinidad, August–October.

MATERIAL STUDIED—TRINIDAD: Dennis 124 (type, from Trinidad, Oct. 5, 1949).

OBSERVATIONS—The type was collected in Arena Forest, Trinidad,

Oct. 5, 1949. Other collections of it were made there on Aug. 2, 1947, and on Oct. 30, 1949. Dennis says it seems quite constant but is too close to *H. firmus* to be regarded as a distinct species. Further, he states that in spite of great range in spore size the spores do not fall obviously into two size groups as in typical *H. firmus,* and the basidia are not obviously dimorphous.

Notes on type: Spores 7–13.5 × 4.5–7.5 μ, ellipsoid, smooth, yellowish in Melzer's reagent. Basidia 38–52 × 9–12 μ, 4-spored. Pleurocystidia and cheilocystidia none. Gill trama parallel, hyphae 7–18 μ broad. Cuticle not differentiated, surface hyphae repent to erect, broad (7–25 μ). Clamp connections none.

General comments on *H. firmus:* Not having seen fresh material we are at a disadvantage in evaluating the varieties of this species, but we cannot escape the conclusion that a critical study of the whole complex will show that it should be divided into numerous species. Var. *purpureus* Dennis is an example of such a possibility. Cytological studies including chromosome counts should be included in such a critical investigation.

79
Hygrophorus cantharellus (Schw.) Fr.
Epicr. Myc., p. 329. 1838

> *Agaricus cantharellus* Schw., Schr. Nat. Ges. Leipzig 1: 88. 1822.
> *Hydrocybe cantharellus* (Schw.) Murr., Mycologia 3: 196. 1911.
> *Camarophyllus cantharellus* (Schw.) Murr., North Amer. Flora 9: 388. 1916.

Illustrations:
> Fig. 42.
> Farlow, Icones Farlow., pl. 27.
> Krieger, Mushroom Handbook, fig. 92.
> Lange, Flora Agar. Dan. 5, fig. 167B (as *Hygrocybe*).
> Peck, N. Y. State Mus. Ann. Rept. 54, pl. 76, figs. 8–20.

Pileus 1–3.5 cm broad, convex to flattened on the disc when young, becoming broadly convex-umbilicate at maturity or sometimes the disc not depressed, sometimes the margin spreading or recurved and the cap then appearing broadly infundibuliform, color variable, "flame scarlet," "ochraceous orange," or "ochraceous buff," brighter when young, paler in age, dry, silky at first, then finely scurfy or lacerate-squamulose especially around the disc, margin even, scalloped or wavy. Context thin on the disc, thinner at the margin, reddish orange or yellow; odor and taste mild.

Lamellae decurrent, orange to yellow (usually paler than the pileus), subdistant to distant, broad but acuminate on the stipe, often triangular, edges even.

Stipe (2)4–9(12) cm long, 1.5–4(5) mm thick, concolorous with the pileus or paler, base whitish or pallid yellowish, equal or slightly enlarged above, terete to subcompressed, fragile, glabrous, dry, stuffed to hollow.

Spores 7–12 × 4–6 μ, or 8–13 × 5–8 μ in 2-spored forms (smaller on 4-spored basidia), ellipsoid to subovoid, smooth, pale yellow in Melzer's reagent. Basidia (35)45–60 × 6.5–10 μ, 2- and 4-spored.

Fig. 42. *H. cantharellus*

Pleurocystidia and cheilocystidia not differentiated. Gill trama of subparallel to slightly interwoven hyphae, the cells 57–159 × 7–36 μ, and usually filled with yellowish contents. Pileus trama homogeneous beneath a turf-like covering of hyphae with their free ends projecting, their terminal elements 66–122 × 8–22 μ, apices rounded, all parts yellowish in iodine. Clamp connections present but rare at times.

HABIT, HABITAT, AND DISTRIBUTION—Gregarious to subcaespitose on rich humus, soil, decaying logs, moss-covered logs, in bogs, eastern North America, July–October; also Jamaica (Dennis, 1953), Venezuela (Dennis, 1961), and Trinidad; Dennis suggests that the form reported from Trinidad by Baker and Dale (1951) would apparently be called *H. turundus* by Smith and Hesler (1942). In the sense of Lange it appears to be what Smith and Hesler called *H. miniatus* var. *sphagnophilus* Pk. (herein called *H. turundus* var. *sphagnophilus*).

MATERIAL STUDIED—ALABAMA: Burke 70. FLORIDA: Singer 2261. MAINE: Rea & Woodbury 551, 637, 638; Bigelow 3186, 3234, 3297, 3540. MASSACHUSETTS: Bigelow 7256, 7472, 8124, 8430, 8860, 8890. MICHIGAN: Chmielewski 67; Harding 196; Iltis, Burt Lake, Aug. 7, 1947; Kauffman 876, Bay View, July 19, 1905; Mains & Smith 33598; Pennington, Houghton, July 20, 1906; Smith 62, 1206, 1288, 1566, 6361, 6465, 6748, 6859, 15572, 18421, 21370, 21611, 21689, 21712, 21900, 33594, 33623, 39332; Thiers 3036, 3305, 3549, 3645. NEW JERSEY: Ellis & Everhart, Newfield, Oct. 1887. NEW YORK: Kauffman, Ithaca, July 28, 1903; Kauffman & Mains, Adirondack Mts., Sept. 3, 1914; Smith 126. NORTH CAROLINA: Caton 4418; Hesler & Sharp 9313, 12788; Hesler 4410, 4419. PENNSYLVANIA: Kauffman, Mt. Gretna, Sept. 1, 1926. TENNESSEE: Bain 7903, 7912; Cotner, Elkmont, Sept. 16, 1916; Hesler 4368, 4386, 4387, 4390, 4433, 7986, 7987, 10107, 10439, 10861, 11436, 12165, 12185, 17480, 24326, 24383, 24436, 24500, 24509; Sharp 4388; Sharp & Hesler 7969, 12740; Smith 9737, 10652. WASHINGTON: Imshaug 1288; Smith 16475, 29430, 29890, 29899. CANADA: (Ontario) Krieger 1850; (Quebec) Bigelow 5024, 5513, 5666, 5994. TRINIDAD: Baker 1496 (Kew). VENEZUELA: Dennis 1091, 1091A.

OBSERVATIONS—This species differs from *H. miniatus* in its taller, more slender stature, arcuate-decurrent lamellae, paler colors, and drier pileus. Kauffman in an unpublished manuscript had arranged *H. cantharellus* in section *Camarophyllus* and *H. miniatus* in *Hygrocybe*. The two species are too closely related to allow for their arrangement in different sections. *H. cantharellus* is separated from *H. turundus* by its smaller spores and by the lack of fuscous colors in the tips of squamules and fibrils over the disc of the pileus.

80

Hygrophorus miniatus (Fr.) Fr. var. **miniatus**
Epicr. Myc. p. 330. 1838

> *Agaricus miniatus* Fr., Syst. Myc. 1: 105. 1821.
> *Hygrophorus congelatus* Pk., N. Y. State Cab. Ann. Rept. 23: 114. 1872.
> *Hygrocybe miniata* (Fr.) Kummer, Führ. in Pilzk., p. 112. 1871.
> *Hygrophorus flammeus* Schroeter, Die Pilze Schlesiens 31: 528. 1889.
> *Hygrophorus miniatus* var. *congelatus* Pk., N. Y. State Mus. Bull. 116: 61. 1907.
> *Hydrocybe constans* Murr., Mycologia 4: 208. 1912.
> *Hygrophorus constans* Murr., Mycologia 4: 217. 1912.
> *Hydrocybe flammea* (Scop.) Murr., North Amer. Flora 9: 381. 1916.
> *Hygrophorus miniatus* Fr. var. *typicus* Sm. & Hes., Lloydia 5: 28. 1942.

Illustrations:
> Fig. 43; also 8e.
> Bresadola, Icon. Myc., tab. 337, fig. 2.
> Juillard-Hartmann, Icon. Champ., pl. 48, fig. 14.
> Lange, Flora Agar. Dan. 5, pl. 166F (as *Hygrocybe*).
> Murrill, Mycologia 2, pl. 27, fig. 9.
> Peck, N. Y. State Mus. Ann. Rept. 48, pl. 28, figs. 1–10.
> Pomerleau, Mushrooms of Eastern Canada and the U. S., pl. 2, fig. 15.
> Ricken, Die Blätterp., pl. 8, fig. 9.
> Smith, Mushrooms in their Natural Habitats, Reel 12, No. 78.
> Thomas, Field Book of Common Gilled Mushrooms, pl. 10, fig. 60.
> Wakefield and Dennis, Common British Fungi, pl. 36, fig. 1.

Pileus (1)2–4 cm broad, broadly convex margin incurved when young, in age convex or plane, the disc often depressed or slightly umbilicate, brilliant scarlet when moist and then appearing glabrous, subhygrophanous, fading to orange or pale yellow and then minutely fibrillose-scurfy, at times translucent striate when moist, occasionally slightly rimose in age or when dried. Context thin, brittle, waxy, concolorous with or paler than the surface, varying from scarlet to orange or pale yellow, unchanging; odor not distinctive, taste mild or slightly earthy.

Lamellae bluntly adnate but becoming broadly adnexed, at times subdecurrent, almost concolorous with the pileus, fading to orange or yellow, close to subdistant, broad, becoming ventricose, the edges eroded.

Stipe 3–5 cm long (up to 7 cm long when in deep humus), 3–4 mm thick, concolorous with the pileus and fading slowly, hence usually more reddish than the faded pilei, the cortex orange, glabrous or in faded specimens faintly fibrillose, stuffed with a yellow pith, equal.

Spores 6–8(10) × 4–5(6) μ, ellipsoid (a few apparently abnormal spores shaped more or less like corn kernels are sometimes found),

Fig. 43. *H. miniatus* var. *miniatus*

smooth, yellow in Melzer's reagent. Basidia 34–48 × 5–8 μ, 1-, 2-, and 4-spored. Pleurocystidia and cheilocystidia not differentiated. Gill trama subparallel, the hyphae with long cylindric cells, 7–19 μ broad, often with an opaque mediostrate. Pileus trama homogeneous. Cuticle composed of erect to repent hyphae which are septate, more or less constricted, the terminal elements somewhat clavate. There is no hypodermium. The pileus trama interwoven, and the hyphae radially disposed. Clamp connections present on the cuticular hyphae.

HABIT, HABITAT, AND DISTRIBUTION—Gregarious on soil, at times among moss, or on rotting logs and humus, in deciduous and mixed woods, general throughout the United States, and the world, July–November.

MATERIAL STUDIED—ALABAMA: Hesler 21969. CALIFORNIA: Smith 3939, 9169. COLORADO: Mains 5206. FLORIDA: Singer F422. IDAHO: Slipp 1300; Smith 53527. MAINE: Bigelow 4448; Rea 624. MASSACHUSETTS: Bigelow 6939, 7231, 7232, 8483, 8605, 8680, 9214. MICHIGAN: Brooks 1254; Chmielewski 111; Imshaug 3714, 3920, 3928; Johnson 1833; Lowe F1143; Mains 32393; Povah 157; Smith 6667, 7041, 7277, 15449, 18514, 18761, 18882, 25877, 25961, 33016, 33586, 37113, 41719, 42467,

42490, 50458, 53765, 57204, 57308, 57625, 61245, 61348; Thiers 2742, 2757, 2870, 2960, 2992, 3117, 3206, 3440, 3922. MONTANA: Mains 6028. NEW JERSEY: Ellis 303. NEW YORK: Smith 662, 804. NORTH CAROLINA: Hesler 4408, 8067, 14338; King 9455; Sharp 4416; Sharp & Hesler 12746; Smith 10827; Smith & Hesler 11775. OREGON: Gruber 691; Smith 7911, 19029. TENNESSEE: Hesler 4431, 4437, 7975, 8201, 9154, 9565, 10934, 11605, 12201, 12833; King 9397; Smith 7475, 9738, 9870, 9895, 10098, 10744. WASHINGTON: Imshaug 1097; Slipp 1003; Smith 16474, 17176, 17546, 18035, 18074, 30880, 30989, 31035, 39512, 48306, 49131, 49132, 49247. CANADA: (Ontario) Groves 11229; Jackson 3748; Kelly 765; Smith 26313, 26314, 26287; (Nova Scotia) Smith 651a; (Quebec) Bigelow 6171. WEST INDIES: Dennis, Isle of Rhum, July 18, 1951. DENMARK: J. P. Jensen (Hesler 23941, 23942); BELGIUM: Heinemann (Hesler 23993).

OBSERVATIONS—Hesler has taken the following color notes on specimens from Tennessee: Pileus "dragon's blood red," "scarlet red," "flame scarlet," "rufous," "ochraceous orange," "orange," "pinkish buff," or "salmon buff," fading to "light orange-yellow" or paler. Lamellae "ochraceous buff" to "apricot orange." Thus it may be said that the colors are variable. It is not always possible to determine whether one has truly fresh material or specimens that have been remoistened.

The attachment of the gills also varies considerably. One would naturally assume that a mushroom with adnexed, ventricose gills was distinct from one in which the gills were truly decurrent. However, after studying many collections we are inclined to doubt the validity of maintaining such a distinction. The gills of the species are typically bluntly adnate. From this condition they may become ventricose and adnexed if the pileus does not expand completely, or subdecurrent if it does.

Hygrophorus constans Murr. was said by its author to retain its red color on drying and thereby be distinct from *H. miniatus*. In Oregon, Smith has collected specimens answering to Murrill's description but was unable to distinguish them from *H. miniatus*. The type of *H. constans* has been studied and no distinctive characters found. The pileus trama and the hyphae forming the surface-covering of the cap are similar to those of *H. miniatus*. As a result of the above observations we consider *H. constans* to be synonymous with *H. miniatus*.

Hongo (1958a) reports it from Japan. He found 2- and 4-spored basidia, and thus he accounts from variability in spore-size which he gives as 8–10.5(11) × 4.5–5.5 μ, basidia 35–54 × 6–7 μ. He says it occurs in Japan, India, Europe, North America, and Australia.

81

Hygrophorus miniatus f. longipes Sm. & Hes.

Sydowia 8: 321. 1954

Illustration:
Fig. 44.

Pileus 1–3 cm broad, convex becoming plane or slightly depressed, often remaining convex, color "English red" to "flame scarlet" gradually fading out to pale-yellow margin, surface glabrous and moist, only in age slightly squamulose, surface shining but not viscid, when faded becoming unpolished to faintly furfuraceous, distinctly translucent striate when moist (often conspicuously so). Context orange to yellowish; odor and taste none.

Fig. 44.
    H. miniatus f. *longipes*

Lamellae broadly adnate, orange-yellow to pale yellow, close, broad, edges even and pallid.

Stipe 3–8 cm long, 2–4 mm thick, concolorous with pileus and changing color with it, usually paler below, equal, hollow, fragile, transversely undulating.

Spores 7–8 × 4.5–5 μ, ellipsoid, smooth, hyaline, yellowish in Melzer's solution. Basidia 48–60 × 7–8 μ, 4-spored. Pleurocystidia and cheilocystidia none. Gill trama parallel. Pileus trama floccose-interwoven, cuticle a trichoderm of elongate hyphae which become appressed to the pileus, clamp connections mostly absent at the cross walls, end-cells cylindric to ellipsoid. Clamp connections present quite regularly at the base of the stipe.

HABIT, HABITAT, AND DISTRIBUTION—Gregarious in a *Sphagnum* bog, Michigan, September.

MATERIAL STUDIED—MICHIGAN: Smith 42560 (type, from Pike Lake, Luce County, Sept. 11, 1953), 42561, 42562, 42563, 42564, 42565, 61247, 61249.

OBSERVATIONS—This agaric might, at first sight, appear to be a growth form with a long slender stipe, a variation caused by the habitat. However, the rather conspicuously striate pileus which becomes squamulose only in age is not a combination of characters likely to be influenced by habitat. In addition, clamp connections are relatively rare on the septa of the cuticular hyphae—a character which may indicate a trend toward the clampless species, most of which appear to have been derived from the *miniatus* group.

82
Hygrophorus squamulosus Ellis & Ev.
Phil. Acad. Sci. Proc. 1893: 440. 1894

> *Hygrophorus miniatus* var. *firmus* Sm. & Hes. Lloydia 5: 27. 1942.
> *Camarophyllus squamulosus* (Ellis & Ev.) Murr., North Amer. Flora
>   9: 388. 1916.

Illustrations:
> Fig. 45; also 2a.
> Smith, Mich. Acad. Sci., Arts & Letters 20, pl. 32 (as *H. squamulosus*).

Pileus 1.5–5 cm broad, obtuse to convex, the disc often slightly depressed, the margin incurved, color "flame scarlet," "grenadine red," to "orange chrome" (bright red to brilliant orange-yellow), margin yellowish at times, fading throughout to "ochraceous-salmon," finally becoming bright yellow over all, surface dry or only slightly moist, glabrous when young but very soon breaking up into minute or distinct fibrillose scales especially near the margin. Context thick and firm, concolorous with the surface and fading to yellow; odor and taste not distinctive.

Lamellae bluntly adnate or with a slight decurrent tooth, seceding quite readily, reddish to pale yellow, close to subdistant (18–22 reach the stipe, 2–3 tiers of short lamellulae), broad (4–6 mm), thick, edges even.

Stipe 3–5 cm long, 3–6 mm thick, "apricot yellow" or tinged with

Fig. 45. *H. squamulosus*

red, concolorous within except for the white pith, frequently compressed, equal, hollow, apex white-pruinose, glabrous elsewhere.

Spores 6–8(9) × 4–5 μ, subellipsoid, smooth, pale yellow in Melzer's reagent. Basidia 30–46 × 5–7(8) μ, 2- and 4-spored. Pleurocystidia none, cheilocystidia 40–50 × 3–6 μ, occasional, filamentous, often flexuous. Gill trama parallel to subparallel, hyphae 8–20 μ broad, yellowish in Melzer's reagent. Pileus trama homogeneous. Cuticle a turf-like covering of upright or subappressed, septate, more or less constricted hyphae, the terminal element often clavate. Clamp connections present on the cuticular hyphae.

HABIT, HABITAT, AND DISTRIBUTION—Scattered to gregarious, particularly around rotten stumps and very rotten logs, Ontario, Massachusetts, New Jersey, Pennsylvania, Michigan, Tennessee, and Washington, August–September.

MATERIAL STUDIED—MICHIGAN: Imshaug 3786; Smith 7045, 10958, 50099, 50482, Whitmore Lake, Aug. 13 and Sept. 1, 1929. NEW JERSEY: Ellis & Everhart, N. A. Fungi, 1912. PENNSYLVANIA: Kauffman, Mt. Gretna, Sept. 8 and 11, 1924, and Sept. 1, 1926. TENNESSEE: Sharp 4436; Sharp & Hesler 12761; Hesler 13873. WASHINGTON: Smith 49244. CANADA: Cain, Ontario, Sept. 5, 1936; Smith 26328. NETHERLANDS: Bas 694.

OBSERVATIONS—We have varied, from time to time, in our opinion as to the proper status of this species in our classification, but at present believe it should be recognized as a species distinct from *H. miniatus*, on the presence of the cheilocystidia, though these are scattered to rare, and its thicker and more squamulose pileus.

83
Hygrophorus subovinus, sp. nov.

Illustrations:
Fig. 46; also 2b, 2c.

Pileus 1.5–3 cm latus, convexus, cinereo-fuscus, hygrophanus, uvidus sub-ater; odore suavis, gustu alkalinus; lamellae adnexae, albidae vel cineraceae, contusae rufo-fuscae, latae, distantes; stipes 3–6 cm longus, 4–8 mm crassus, cineraceus, siccatus sub-ater; sporae 5–6(7) × 5–6 μ, globosae vel subglobosae; pleurocystidia 56–115 × 6–10 μ, cheilocystidia 46–52 × 2–3 μ. Specimen typicum in Herb. Univ. Tenn.; lectum in Cades Cove, Great Smoky Mts. National Park, Tenn., June 8, 1957, L. R. Hesler 22583.

Pileus 1.5–3 cm broad, convex, expanding more or less convex, gray-brown near "pale drab gray" (not matched), blackish when wet, some-

Fig. 46. *H. subovinus*

what fibrillose, disc becoming more or less squamulose, moist (not viscid), somewhat rimose, margin even. Context thick on disc, thin on margin, pallid to brownish, unchanging when bruised, brittle, fragile; odor fragrant, taste slightly alkaline.

Lamellae adnexed then emarginate, whitish to grayish, becoming pinkish to reddish brown when bruised, broad (up to 12 mm), distant, many short, edges even.

Stipe 3–6 cm × 4–8 mm, grayish (not matched), unchanging when handled, drying blackish, at times compressed, flexuous, base attenuated, hollow.

Spores 5–6(7) × 5–6 μ, globose, subglobose, subovoid, or rarely short-ellipsoid, smooth, white in deposit, pale yellowish in Melzer's reagent. Basidia 34–48 × 6–8 μ, 2- and 4-spored. Pleurocystidia 56–115 × 6–10 μ, scattered, cylindric to subfusoid, projecting; and pseudocystidia 88–96 × 4.5–6 μ with brownish contents, cheilocystidia 64–78 × (2.5)7–10 μ, cylindrical, few. Gill trama subparallel, hyphae 7–18 μ broad. Cuticle of more or less erect hyphae (turf), a trichodermium, or at times repent hyphae which are septate, pale fuscous, the terminal elements with rounded apices. Hypodermium none. Pileus trama of radially disposed hyphae. Clamp connections rare on the cuticular hyphae. Lactifers brown, in the trama of the gills and pileus.

HABIT, HABITAT, AND DISTRIBUTION—Gregarious on soil in deciduous woods, Massachusetts, North Carolina, and Tennessee, June–August.

MATERIAL STUDIED—MASSACHUSETTS: Bigelow 7542. NORTH CAROLINA: Hesler 13982. TENNESSEE: Campbell & Hesler 21824; Hesler 22683 (type, on soil in deciduous woods, Cades Cove, Great Smoky Mts. National Park, June 8, 1957), 24404, 24511 (from type station).

OBSERVATIONS—This is close to *H. ovinus*, differing in its globose to subglobose spores, and in the presence of cystidia on the gills. The brown lactifers in the trama of the pileus and gills are conspicuous, but no latex was exuded when the fresh fruiting bodies were injured. The ends of these elements occasionally extend into the hymenium as pseudocystidia.

84
Hygrophorus atro-olivaceus Sm. & Hes.
Sydowia 8: 326. 1954

Illustrations:
   Fig. 47; also 8b.

Pileus 1–3 cm broad, convex with a straight margin, soon convex-depressed, at times plano-depressed with a decurved margin, "mummy brown" (blackish brown) on disc and "buffy brown" (olive brown) on margin, fading to dingy gray-brown, moist and hygrophanous, squamulose (especially along the margin), when moist opaque to translucent striate, margin often crenate. Context brittle, soft, watery; odor and taste mild.

Lamellae arcuate to subdecurrent, in age at times with decurrent lines, near "drab gray" when young but margins pallid, subdistant, broad or medium broad, often intervenose to subporoid, edges even.

Fig. 47.
H. atro-olivaceus

Stipe 3–5 cm long, 5–12 mm diameter at apex, evenly colored and a paler gray-brown than the pileus, usually compressed, naked and moist.

Spores 5–6 × 3.5–4.5 μ, ellipsoid to subglobose, smooth, hyaline in KOH and Melzer's reagent. Basidia 28–34 × 6–7 μ, flexuous at base, 4-spored. Pleurocystidia and cheilocystidia none. Gill trama parallel, hyaline in KOH, in Melzer's reagent dark amber brown from granules within the cells which stain dark. Pileus trama similar to gill trama in color in KOH and Melzer's reagent, cuticle a trichodermium (the elements grouped to form fascicles which are the squamules). Pileus trama of interwoven hyphae, more or less radially disposed. Clamp connections none.

HABIT, HABITAT, AND DISTRIBUTION—Caespitose in woods, Michigan and Washington, July–September.

MATERIAL STUDIED—MICHIGAN: Smith 26159, 37561, 39418 (type, from Pellston, Mich., Aug. 10, 1952), 42092. WASHINGTON: Smith 31052, 31744, 40145.

OBSERVATIONS—The lack of clamp connections, the faded, squamulose pileus, dark gray-brown colors, and reaction of the contents of the hyphae to Melzer's reagent, along with the small spores, are distinctive.

85

Hygrophorus olivascens Sm. & Hes.
Sydowia 8: 328. 1954

Pileus 10–25 mm broad, obtuse with an incurved margin, expanding to plane or with a few flattened umbo, when young "chamois" with a smoky brown cast, becoming a clearly chamois color at maturity and then somewhat translucent, when faded opaque and pale buff, moist, hygrophanous, surface glabrous, becoming fibrillose squamulose as in *H. miniatus.* Context very waxy and brittle, pale watery yellow (paler than pileus) or concolorous with pileus surface, when broken staining brownish; odor sharp and fragrant, taste slightly acidulous.

Lamellae depressed-adnate, concolorous with edge of pileus, whitish in age, distant to subdistant, broad, edges with a tendency to stain olivaceous where bruised.

Stipe 4–6 mm long, 5–8 mm thick, concolorous with pileus or brownish spotted from handling, equal or narrowed below, glabrous and naked.

Spores 7–8.5 × 4.5–5.5 μ, ellipsoid, hyaline to pale yellowish in Melzer's reagent, smooth but as revived in KOH often appearing granulose but under oil immersion the granules or droplets are found to be just inside the wall. Basidia 30–48 × 7–9 μ, clavate, the lower half often flexuous, 4-spored. Pleurocystidia and cheilocystidia none. Gill trama parallel or nearly so, hyaline in KOH, hyphae 4–7 μ broad. Pileus trama hyaline and interwoven, with fascicles of hyphal end-cells projecting as the squamules. Clamp connections present in the cuticular hyphae.

HABIT, HABITAT, AND DISTRIBUTION—Gregarious on humus, in climax beech-maple forest, Michigan, July.

MATERIAL STUDIED—MICHIGAN: Smith 39276 (type, from Tahquamenon Falls State Park, July 24, 1952).

OBSERVATIONS—The smoky brown color of young caps, the sharp fragrant odor, and tendency of the gill edges to stain olivaceous are distinctive field characters. The species appears to be most closely related to *H. caespitosus* Murr. but differs in the olive-staining gills and tendency of the stipe to stain brownish where handled.

86

Hygrophorus caespitosus (Murr.) Murr.
Mycologia 6: 2. 1914

Hydrocybe caespitosa Murr., Mycologia 6: 2. 1914.
Camarophyllus caespitosus Murr., North Amer. Flora 9: 387. 1916.

Illustrations:
    Fig. 48; also 8g.
    Murrill, Mycologia 6, pl. 113, fig. 2 (as *Hydrocybe caespitosa* Murr.).

Pileus 1–6 cm broad, convex or the disc flattened, soon broadly or deeply depressed over the disc and with a spreading or turned-up margin, color usually "cream buff" to "honey yellow," sometimes bright yellow, covered with small scales over all, scales somewhat recurved and "old gold" to darker brownish, the tips often blackish, moist, soon dry, not viscid, margin even or wavy. Context fairly thick, yellowish to bright yellow; odor and taste not distinctive or slightly of raw Irish potato.

Lamellae broadly adnate-decurrent or developing a long tooth, at times slightly sinuate-decurrent, white becoming yellowish, broad, thick, occasionally forked, triangular, subdistant to distant.

Stipe 2–5 cm long, 3–7(10) mm thick, concolorous with the pileus or a more sordid olivaceous yellow-brown, tapering slightly downward, glabrous, often flexuous, moist or dry, spongy, becoming hollow.

Spores 6.5–9(10) × 4–6(7) μ, ellipsoid, smooth, not amyloid, white in mass. Basidia (31)40–60 × (6.5)7–9 μ, 4-spored, the sterigmata 8–10 μ long. Pleurocystidia and cheilocystidia none. Gill trama subparallel to slightly interwoven, hyphae (8–12)15–19(28) μ broad, yellowish in iodine. Pileus trama homogeneous beneath a turf-like covering of upright to appressed hyphae the free ends of which often bear a slightly enlarged clavate, ovoid, to ellipsoid cell, all parts golden yellow in iodine. Clamp connections rare on the gill trama hyphae; rare or none on the cuticular hyphae.

HABIT, HABITAT, AND DISTRIBUTION—Caespitose or in small groups of two or three individuals, in coniferous and deciduous woods, on clay banks, or on mossy soil, Alabama, Georgia, North Carolina, Tennessee, Maryland, New York, June–August.

MATERIAL STUDIED—ALABAMA: Burke 44. GEORGIA: Hesler 21928. NEW YORK: Murrill (type, east of Bronx Park, Sept. 26, 1909). MARYLAND: Kauffman, Cabin John, Aug. 22, 1919. NORTH CAROLINA: Totten 7041; Hesler 12258, 13948, 14421. TENNESSEE: Hesler & Sharp 8130, 12835, 14242; Norris 21929; Smith 10658; Stupka 17811.

OBSERVATIONS—Some of the specimens of the type are characterized by relatively long slender stipes in the dried condition. Murrill's dimensions of the fresh material, however, were 4–5 cm × 3–5 mm, and thus the stipe would seem to be fairly thick in relation to the length. In most of our collections the stipes are shorter, and the fruiting bodies have a squatty appearance. However, this is hardly a distinctive character. We have not found the species fruiting in abundance, but it

Fig. 48. *H. caespitosus*

may be more robust than Murrill's specimens indicate. It is closely related to *H. cantharellus*, both by the nature of the hyphae covering the pileus and by its slightly interwoven gill trama. The colors clearly distinguish them, however. *H. squamulifer* Boud. appears to be closely related.

Notes on the type: Spores 7–9(10) × 4–6(7) μ, ellipsoid, smooth, non-amyloid. Basidia 37–60 × 7–9 μ, 4-spored. Pleurocystidia and cheilocystidia none. Gill trama subparallel. Epicutis composed of erect or more or less appressed, tangled hyphae, the free ends of which are usually swollen. Clamp connections rare in gill trama; none found in epicutis.

87
Hygrophorus nitratus Fr.
Hymen. Eur., p. 421. 1874

> *Hygrocybe nitrata* (Fr.) Wünsche, Die Pilze, p. 112. 1877.
> *Camarophyllus nitratus* Ricken, Vademecum für Pilzfreunde, p. 197. 1920.

Illustrations:
  Fig. 49.
  Bresadola, Icon. Myc., tab. 353.
  Lange, Flora Agar. Dan. 5, pl. 165E.
  Ricken, Die Blätterp., pl. 7, fig. 7.

Pileus 2–5(7) cm broad, singly or subcaespitose, convex to obtusely conic, somewhat umbonate in age, very pale brownish at first, at times "snuff brown," usually becoming grayish to gray-brown (not matched), finally dark grayish brown to nearly blackish, moist or soon dry, at length fibrillose-squamulose, margin even, splitting readily. Context thin, brittle, pale to dark brownish gray, unchanging; odor nitrous, taste acidulous.

Lamellae emarginate, whitish, darkening somewhat in age, at times yellowish with a grayish tint, subdistant, broad (up to 10 mm), intervenose, alternating long and short, edges even.

Stipe 4–10 cm long, 2–10 mm thick, pale brownish at first, dark grayish in age, fragile, terete to compressed, glabrous, somewhat longitudinally striate, equal or slightly ventricose downward, base often white and pointed, hollow.

Spores 7.5–10 × 4.5–6 μ, subovoid to ellipsoid, smooth, white in mass, pale yellow in Melzer's reagent. Basidia 4-spored, 32–43 × 6–9 μ, mostly 4-spored, a few 2-spored. Pleurocystidia and cheilocystidia not differentiated. Gill trama subparallel, hyphae 7–25 μ broad, yellowish in Melzer's reagent. Cuticle of non-gelatinous, repent or more or less erect hyphae, 4–12 μ broad, which are brownish, the terminal elements with more or less rounded apices and cystidioid. No hypodermium. Pileus trama of radial, subparallel hyphae. Clamp connections on the cuticular hyphae.

HABIT, HABITAT, AND DISTRIBUTION—Gregarious to scattered, on soil in deciduous or coniferous woods, North Carolina, Tennessee, Maine, Massachusetts, Michigan, and Canada, June–August.

Fig. 49. *H. nitratus*

MATERIAL STUDIED—MAINE: Bigelow 3232, 3628, 3806. MASSACHU-
SETTS: Bigelow 7234, 9079; Davis, South Acton, Aug. 1916; Stow, Aug.
1916 and July 1917. MICHIGAN: Smith 37312; Thiers 3941. NORTH CARO-
LINA: Hesler & Sharp 12737; Hesler 14437, 21813, 22383; Smith 10149.
TENNESSEE: Hesler 18624, 19174, 20881. GREAT SMOKY MTS. NATIONAL
PARK: Smith 9930, 10647. CANADA: (Quebec) Bigelow 5515, 5516, 5517.
NETHERLANDS: Bas 1655.

OBSERVATIONS—The nitrous odor and gray-brown colors distinguish this species from its near relatives. It is closely related to
H. nitiosus which is characterized by a nitrous odor and a pinkish to
brownish color-change on bruising; and to *H. ovinus* in which the
odor is mild or at times faintly fruity and the color of the flesh, gills,
and stipe changes to pinkish to brownish where bruised.

88
Hygrophorus erinensis Dennis
Kew Bull. 2: 262. 1953

Illustration:
  Dennis, Kew Bull. 2, fig. 7.

Pileus 1.5 cm broad, convex then subumbilicate, cinnamon brown,
umbilicus minutely squamulose. Context white, thin.

Lamellae adnate, white, subdistant.

Stipe yellowish, shining, slender, cylindric, fistulose, glabrous.

Spores 8–11 × 6–7 μ, ellipsoid. Basidia 50 × 10 μ, 4-spored. Pleurocystidia and cheilocystidia none. Clamp connections present on the
cuticular hyphae.

HABIT, HABITAT, AND DISTRIBUTION—Solitary on bare soil, under
palms (*Bactris*), Trinidad.

MATERIAL STUDIED—TRINIDAD: Dennis 302 (type).

OBSERVATIONS—Dennis (1953) says that in habit this species suggests a brown variety of *H. firmus* Berk. & Br., but that the basidia are
not dimorphous. It also somewhat resembles *H. nitratus* var. *glauco-
nitens* (Fr.) Bres. (Bresadola Tab. 354, 1) which has spores 9–11 ×
5–6 μ but a brown stipe and a nitrous odor.

Notes on the type: Spores 8–11 × 6–7 μ, ellipsoid, smooth, yellowish in Melzer's reagent. Basidia 46–62 × 7–10 μ, 2- and 4-spored, sterigmata stout. Pleurocystidia and cheilocystidia none. Gill trama parallel,
hyphae broad (6–14 μ). Cuticle with surface hyphae repent, or on the
disc (which is minutely squamulose), the surface hyphae are thin-
walled, erect to semi-erect, broad (6–12 μ), fuscous, septate, more or
less constricted at septa, and with clamp connections.

89
Hygrophorus cokeri Sm. & Hes.
Lloydia 5: 34. 1942

> *Hygrophorus gomphidioides* Coker, Elisha Mitchell Sci. Soc. Jour. 45:
> 168. 1929. Non *H. gomphidioides* P. Henn. 1908.

Illustration:
   Coker, Elisha Mitchell Sci. Soc. Jour. 45, pl. 14.

Pileus 1.5–2.8 cm broad, convex, disc depressed, near "cinnamon rufous" to "tawny," slightly viscid, fibrous, the fibrils innate and separated forming interrupted radial grooves, the tips erect to form scattered, punctate squamules, margin incurved and drooping. Context about 1.5 mm thick at the disc, concolorous but paler, tender, not brittle; odor none, taste distinctly and persistently bitter-astringent.

Lamellae subdecurrent, deep chestnut or mahogany brown, slightly glaucous from the spores, rather close, narrow to medium, thick, waxy, veined, edges blunt, more or less uneven.

Stipe 1.5–3 cm long, 3–6 mm thick, nearly concolorous, subequal or tapering downward, base usually constricted, usually compressed and channelled, hollow, flesh fibrous, easily splitting, dry.

Spores (5.5)6.5–8(9) × 3.5–4.8 μ, ellipsoid, smooth, yellowish in Melzer's reagent. Basidia 34–48 × 5–6 μ, 4-spored. Pleurocystidia and cheilocystidia none. Gill trama subparallel to undulating-parallel. Cuticle of repent hyphae which loosen in bundles and then are more or less erect, hyphae slender, not constricted, not of the *miniatus*-type. Pileus trama of radially disposed hyphae. Clamp connections not found.

HABIT, HABITAT, AND DISTRIBUTION—On sandy soil, in mixed woods, North Carolina, April.

MATERIAL STUDIED—NORTH CAROLINA: Coker 4248 (type, collected by J. N. Couch, from near Meeting of the Waters, Chapel Hill, April 15, 1920).

OBSERVATIONS—The description of microscopic characters given above is based on our study of the type.

Regarding this species Coker states: "It seems to fall in the *miniatus-cantharellus* group, but it is not very close to any of these. It is a very peculiar and well-marked species, sharply distinguished by the conspicuously radiating fibrous lines on the cap, ending in delicate squamules, strongly depressed *Gomphidius*-like shape of the cap and the distinctive colors. The spores are smaller than others of the group."

SERIES COCCINEI (Fayod) stat. nov.
Subsection Coccinei Fayod, Ann. Sci. Nat. Ser. 7 (9): 308. 1889.
Characters as given in key to series, page 108.
Type species: *H. coccineus* Fr.

90

Hygrophorus aurantius (Murr.) Murr.
Mycologia 4: 332. 1912

> *Hydrocybe aurantia* Murr., Mycologia 3: 195. 1911.

Pileus 1.5 cm broad, obconic, aurantiacous, dry or moist, glabrous, margin smooth or slightly striate.

Lamellae adnate, subconcolorous, rather broad and distant.

Stipe 2.5 cm long, about 2 mm thick, aurantiacous, apex pruinose, elsewhere glabrous, slightly tapering downward.

Spores 4–5 × 3–5 μ, subglobose, ovoid, or short-ellipsoid, smooth, non-amyloid. Basidia 26–38 × 4–6 μ, 4-spored. Pleurocystidia and cheilocystidia none. Gill trama parallel to subparallel. Cuticle of repent hyphae, a cutis. No hypodermium. Pileus trama of radial hyphae. Clamp connections present on the gill trama hyphae; none found in the cuticular hyphae.

HABIT, HABITAT, AND DISTRIBUTION—On the ground in woods, Jamaica, December–January.

MATERIAL STUDIED—JAMAICA: Murrill 743 (type, from Morce's Gap, 5000 feet elevation, Dec. 29, 30, Jan. 2, 1908–09).

OBSERVATIONS—The microscopic characters given above are based on our study of the type. This species is related to *H. deceptivus*, but the pileus of the latter is brownish to buff.

Although the names *Agaricus aurantius* Sowerby and *Agaricus aurantius* Vahl. (Fl. Dan.) both are considered to be applied to *Hygrophori*, we have been unable to locate an actual combination of that species epithet with *Hygrophorus* prior to Murrill's publication. However, this is one of those combinations which are easily missed in a survey of the literature.

Hongo (1952a) describes *H. aurantius* from Japan.

91
Hygrophorus flavoluteus (Murr.) Murr.
Mycologia 4: 332. 1912

Hydrocybe flavolutea Murr., Mycologia 3: 196. 1911.
Illustration:
Fig. 2d.

Pileus 1.3 cm broad, 5 mm high, convex, luteous, with faint traces of red, polished, slightly viscid, radiate-striate.

Lamellae apparently free, but really connected by slender threads of tissue across the disc to which the stipe is attached, flavous, close, rather broad, slightly ventricose, several lamellulae.

Stipe 2.2 cm long, 1.5 mm thick, citrinous, whitish-tomentose and slightly enlarged at the base, equal above, smooth, glabrous.

Spores 5–7 × 5–6 μ, globose to subglobose, smooth, pale yellowish in Melzer's reagent. Basidia 40–52 × 7–8 μ, 4-spored. Pleurocystidia none; cheilocystidia 16–41 × 6–16 μ, versiform: vesiculose, pyriform, cuneiform, clavate. Gill trama subparallel. Cuticle composed of vesiculose cells, an epithelium, not a palisade. No hypodermium. Pileus trama very thin, of pseudoparenchyma. Pileus flesh extremely thin. Clamp connections none.

HABIT, HABITAT, AND DISTRIBUTION—On soil, on a bank, Jamaica and Mexico, December–January.

MATERIAL STUDIED—JAMAICA: Murrill 527 (type, from Cinchona, Dec. 25–Jan. 8, 1908–09).

OBSERVATIONS—The cellular cuticle of *H. flavoluteus* separates it at once from its seemingly near relatives. The microscopic characters described above are based on our observation and study of the type.

92
Hygrophorus earlei (Murr.) Murr.
Mycologia 4: 332. 1912

Hydrocybe earlei Murr., Mycologia 3: 196. 1911.
Illustration:
Fig. 8d.

Pileus 3 cm broad, convex, pale reddish yellow, glabrous, silky-shining, margin at times striate. Context yellow, mild.

Lamellae adnexed, whitish then cremeous, broad, crowded.

Stipe 5–6 cm long, 4–6 mm thick, cream or pale yellow, glabrous, shining, somewhat flattened, equal, hollow.

Spores 6–8(9) × 6–7.5 μ, globose to subglobose, smooth, pale yellowish in Melzer's reagent. Basidia 38–50 × 6–9 μ, mostly 2-spored, some 4-spored. Pleurocystidia and cheilocystidia none. Gill trama subparallel. Cuticle of repent, more rarely erect, irregularly-shaped, many more or less nodulose, broad (6–12 μ) hyphae. No differentiated hypodermium. Pileus trama of radial hyphae. Clamp connections none.

HABIT, HABITAT, AND DISTRIBUTION—On soil, in a pasture, Cuba and Antigua (Lesser Antilles), June–October.

MATERIAL STUDIED—CUBA: Earle 562 (type, from Herradura, June 16, 1907).

OBSERVATIONS—*Hygrophorus earlei* is related to *H. sphaerosporus*, but the types do not closely resemble each other. The latter is dark brown and its spores tend toward flat-sidedness; the former is reddish brown and its spore are slightly larger and show no tendency toward flat sides.

Dennis (1953) reports this species from Antigua. He found the pileus to be lemon to zinc orange, pellucid-striate in age; the flesh hygrophanous; the lamellae white at first then warm buff; the stipe-base white; the spores 7–8(11) × 5.5–7 μ; the basidia 4-spored; and cystidia none. Dennis (1953) also reports *H. earlei* from Trinidad, but we have studied his collections and conclude that his Nos. 50 and 161 from there might better be referred to *H. subflavidus*, because of spore size.

The description of the microscopic characters given above is based on our study of the type.

93
Hygrophorus deceptivus Sm. & Hes.
Lloydia 5: 45. 1942

Armillariella deceptiva (Sm. & Hes.) Singer, Lilloa 22: 216. 1951.
Illustrations:
    Fig. 50.
    Smith and Hesler, Lloydia 5, pl. 2a.

Pileus 10–40 mm broad, convex, becoming expanded and the margin slightly upturned and splitting, hygrophanous, "tawny-olive," "clay color," "ochraceous tawny," "cinnamon brown," to "fuscous" (when wet), disc usually darker, "pinkish buff" when faded, canescent to minutely fibrillose, margin thin, striate when wet, even when dry. Con-

Fig. 50. *H. deceptivus*

text thick on the disc, thin on the margin, whitish to pallid or con-colorous with the pileus; odor none or earthy, taste mild to acidulous.

Lamellae broadly adnate, arcuate and becoming slightly decur-rent, pale buff or concolorous with the pileus, broad and finally ventri-cose, close to subdistant, lamellulae numerous, venose, edges even.

Stipe (2)4–10 cm long, 3–10 mm thick, apex whitish, elsewhere concolorous, apex canescent or pruinose, elsewhere glabrous, tapering downward, dry, fragile, hollow.

Spores 3–5 × 3–4 μ, ovoid, short-ellipsoid, subglobose, or globose, smooth, white in deposit, yellowish brown in Melzer's reagent. Basidia 26–34 × 3–5 μ, 2- and 4-spored. Pleurocystidia and cheilocystidia none. Gill trama of elongated, subparallel cells, 4–7(12) μ broad, yellowish in Melzer's reagent. Cuticle of non-gelatinous hyphae which are fuscous, repent, probably erect at first, septate, often constricted, the terminal elements clavate-cystidioid. No hypodermium differentiated. Pileus trama homogeneous, interwoven, radially disposed. Clamp connections none.

HABIT, HABITAT, AND DISTRIBUTION—Gregarious on soil and humus, in deciduous and mixed woods, Alabama, North Carolina, South Carolina, and Tennessee; France; June–August.

MATERIAL STUDIED—ALABAMA: Burke 66. NORTH CAROLINA:

Hesler 10247 (type, from Indian Creek, near Bryson City, July 30, 1939), 19197, 24374; Sharp 14258. SOUTH CAROLINA: Hesler 23159. TENNESSEE: Sharp & Hesler 12738; Sharp 17670; Hesler 14227, 22588, 23075. FRANCE: Josserand (1937).

OBSERVATIONS—This species resembles *H. hymenocephalus* superficially but lacks the palisade of clavate cells over the surface of the pileus. It also differs in its closer gills which do not become dark gray or drab in age. Its minute spores and lack of odor separate it from *H. ovinus* and *H. nitratus*. In some respects it is very similar to *H. sphaerosporus*, but there is a distinct difference between the spores of these two species and between the colors of the fruiting bodies. In *H. deceptivus*, the spores tend to be slightly flat-sided, and are yellowish brown in Melzer's reagent; the pileus when fresh is tawny-olive to sayal brown, and retains these colors when dried. In *H. sphaerosporus* the spores are not flat-sided, and are pale yellow or almost colorless in Melzer's reagent; the pileus is whitish, inclining to reddish brown, and when dried is definitely a dark reddish brown. *H. schulzeri* Bres. sensu Josserand (1937) belongs here.

94
Hygrophorus subaustralis Sm. & Hes.
Lloydia 5: 46. 1942

Illustrations:
    Fig. 51; also 2e, 7g.
    Dennis, Kew Bull. 2, fig. 5.

Pileus 1–4(5) cm broad, more or less conic, then convex to plane, with a low conic umbo, margin incurved slightly at first, moist or dry, not viscid, at times atomate, densely matted-fibrillose (under lens), becoming rimose, shining white, disc at times slightly yellowish, opaque, margin even. Context white, unchanging, waxy; odor mild, taste bitter.

Lamellae adnexed to emarginate, pure white, finally cream-tinted, broad, close to subdistant, thin, distinctly waxy, edges even.

Stipe 2–7(11) cm × 2–6 mm, equal, shining white, white within, dry, appressed-fibrillose over all or the apex delicately pruinose, often curved, equal, stuffed becoming hollow.

Spores 5–6.5 × 3–4 μ, ellipsoid to more or less pip-shaped to subovoid (from deposits), smooth, hyaline, yellowish in Melzer's reagent, white in mass. Basidia 24–30 × 5–6 μ, 4-spored. Pleurocystidia scattered to abundant, fusoid-ventricose with obtuse apices, more rarely subcylindric, thin-walled, hyaline, 36–75 × 6–16 μ; cheilocystidia similar, few. Gill trama parallel to subparallel, hyphae 5–12 μ broad. Cuticle of repent hyphae, a cutis. No hypodermium. Pileus trama of radial hyphae. Clamp connections present on the cuticular and gill trama hyphae.

HABIT, HABITAT, AND DISTRIBUTION—On bare soil or in deep humus, in deciduous and mixed woods, Tennessee, North Carolina, and Trinidad, August and September.

MATERIAL STUDIED—NORTH CAROLINA: Smith 10844 (type); Hesler 14423, 17951, 18628, 20463. TENNESSEE: Hesler 22663, 23195, 23221, 24513; Hesler & Sharp 14423; Smith 14872. TRINIDAD: Dennis 51.

OBSERVATIONS—This is a handsome, small, white species with pleurocystidia and cheilocystidia. In the original description, a spore deposit was not available, and the spore measurements were erroneously reported to be 4–5 × 3–4 μ, subglobose. Subsequent collections yielded spore deposits in which the spores are 5–6.5 × 3–4 μ, ellipsoid to pip-shaped or subovoid. Spores from the lamellae are at times found to be immature and smaller than those from deposits. Although the basidia are short for an *Hygrophorus*, the obvious waxy consistency of the lamellae influences us to place it in this genus rather than in *Tricholoma*.

Dennis (1953) reports this species from Trinidad. He finds the spores subglobose, 4.5–7 × 4–5.5 μ; basidia 2- or 4-spored, 25–30 × 6–7 μ; pleurocystidia and cheilocystidia similar, delicate, ventricose, with long tapering apices, necks and pointed apices 45–60 × 8 μ below, 2–3 μ above.

Fig. 51. *H. subaustralis*

95

Hygrophorus pseudoparvulus, sp. nov.

Pileus 1 cm latus, convexo-depressus, glaber, uvidus, hygrophanus, striatus, aquoso-pallidus, deinde albus; lamellae distantes, angustae, decurrentes, albae, fere cinnamomo-ochreae siccae; stipes 1 cm longus, 1.5 mm crassus, albus, siccus, nullum velum; sporae 5.5–6.5(7) × 2.8–3.5 μ, anguste oblongae. Specimen typicum in Herb. Univ. Michigan; lectum Tahquamenon Falls State Park, Mich., July 23, 1951, A. H. Smith 37024.

Pileus about 1 cm broad, convex-depressed, glabrous, moist, hygrophanous, watery-pallid and translucent striate, fading to white and drying white. Context thin, white, odorless.

Lamellae distant, narrow, decurrent, white, near "cinnamon buff" as dried.

Stipe about 1 cm long, 1.5 mm thick, equal, white, unpolished and dry, no veil present.

Spores 5.5–6.5(7) × 2.8–3.5 μ, narrowly oblong, hyaline in KOH and Melzer's, smooth. Basidia 4-spored, 23–28 × 5–6 μ, narrowly clavate. Pleurocystidia and cheilocystidia none. Gill trama of subparallel hyphae the cells somewhat inflated. Epicutis of pileus of narrow (2–4 μ) hyaline non-gelatinous hyphae. Clamp connections present.

HABIT, HABITAT, AND DISTRIBUTION—Solitary on a very rotten log, Tahquamenon Falls State Park, Luce County, Mich. July 23, 1951.

MATERIAL STUDIED—MICHIGAN: Smith 37024.

OBSERVATIONS—This species is a true *Hygrophorus* of section *Hygrocybe*, and keys out nearest to *H. subaustralis* from which it differs in the decurrent gills and narrow oblong spores, in addition to lacking pleurocystidia. It is most closely related to *H. parvulus* from which it is readily separated by its narrower spores and lack of pigment. The very narrow spores preclude its being classified as an albino *H. parvulus*.

96

Hygrophorus brevipes Sm. & Hes.
Lloydia 5: 57. 1942

Pileus 2–2.5 cm broad, obtuse becoming broadly campanulate to plane with a low obtuse umbo, the margin sometimes flaring in age, pure white or tinged cream color on the disc, fading to a dead white and when dried white or very faintly cream color and shining, glabrous, hygrophanous to subhygrophanous, lubricous to subviscid. Context fragile, fairly thick, white; odor and taste not distinctive.

Lamellae adnate-decurrent with a pronounced tooth, white, unchanging, close, thickish, narrow.

Stipe 1.5–2 cm long, 6–8 mm thick, white, equal, solid, glabrous, dry.

Spores 7–12 × 4–5.5(6) μ, ellipsoid, a few oblong, smooth, yellowish in Melzer's reagent. Basidia 38–52 × 7–9 μ, 2- and 4-spored. Pleurocystidia and cheilocystidia none. Gill trama subparallel, hyphae 4–16 μ broad. Cuticle of appressed hyphae, at times with more or less erect free ends. No differentiated hypodermium. Pileus trama of radial hyphae. Clamp connections rare on the cuticular and gill trama hyphae.

HABIT, HABITAT, AND DISTRIBUTION—Gregarious on humus in oak woods, Michigan, October.

MATERIAL STUDIED—MICHIGAN: Smith 6056a (type, from Ann Arbor, Oct. 13, 1936).

OBSERVATIONS—Although *H. brevipes* has the stature of a small specimen of *H. pratensis*, it shrinks more than specimens of that species when dried and the pilei have a shining appearance. The colors and large spores give it some resemblance to *H. virgineus* in which we were at first inclined to place it. *H. virgineus* is a typical *Camarophyllopsis* with interwoven trama, however, and has an unpolished appearance when dried. It is very difficult to compare a species like this with those known for Europe because the gill trama of many of the more unusual European species has apparently not been critically studied. On the basis of stature alone *H. brevipes* could be referred either to section *Hygrophorus* or *Camarophyllopsis*, but one would not suspect that it is an *Hygrocybe*. *H. stenophyllus* Mont. is described as caespitose, but otherwise appears to be close to *H. brevipes*. However, it has not been recognized since it was described, and there is no information concerning its gill trama. It might be in section *Hygrophorus* or in *Camarophyllopsis*.

97

Hygrophorus roseus (Murr.) Murr.
Mycologia 4: 332. 1912

Hydrocybe rosea Murr., Mycologia 3: 197. 1911.

Pileus 1 cm broad, 5 mm high, convex with an umbilicate center, resembling *Omphalia* in shape, roseus to incarnate, glabrous, smooth, margin entire or rarely lobed, decurved. Context very thin, allowing the lamellae to show through on the upper side.

Lamellae decurrent, arcuate, white, stained red, medium broad, subdistant.

Stipe 1.5 cm long, 1 mm thick at base, much enlarged at apex, deep red at the apex, paler than the pileus below, smooth, cylindric.

Spores 8–13 × 6–9 μ, broadly-ellipsoid, smooth, pale yellow in Melzer's reagent. Basidia 33–48 × 8–10 μ, 4-spored, sterigmata 4–5 μ long. Pleurocystidia and cheilocystidia none. Gill trama parallel.

HABIT, HABITAT, AND DISTRIBUTION—In moss on a decayed log, Jamaica, January.

MATERIAL STUDIED—JAMAICA: Murrill 811 (type, from Sir John Peak, 6000 feet elevation, Jan. 5, 1909).

OBSERVATIONS—The microscopic characters given above are based on our study of the type.

The type is too meager to section; the structure of the cuticle was therefore not observed. A painting accompanies the type. Somewhat related to *H. subcaespitosus*, it differs in larger spores and colors.

98
Hygrophorus troyanus (Murr.) Murr.
Mycologia 4: 332. 1912

Hydrocybe troyana Murr., Mycologia 3: 198. 1911.

Pileus 1–1.5 cm broad, 3 mm high, subhemispheric to convex, ferruginous, not viscid, smooth.

Lamellae decurrent, violaceous, distant, rather broad, two or three times inserted.

Stipe 4 cm long, 2.5 mm thick, latericious above, paler below, changing to flavous at the base, glabrous, cylindric.

Spores 7–9(10) × 3.5–5 μ, more or less ellipsoid, many constricted much as in *H. subminiatus*, smooth, pale yellow in Melzer's reagent. Basidia 30–42 × 5–7 μ, 2- and 4-spored. Pleurocystidia and cheilocystidia none. Gill trama subparallel, hyphae 7–12 μ broad, clamp connections none. Cuticle poorly differentiated, hyphae repent or more or less erect, hyphae 3–5 μ broad, no gelatinous layer, a cutis. No hypodermium. Pileus trama of radial hyphae. Lactifers scattered in the gill trama. Clamp connections rare on the cuticular hyphae.

HABIT, HABITAT, AND DISTRIBUTION—On soil, Jamaica and Trinidad, September to January.

MATERIAL STUDIED—JAMAICA: Murrill & Harris 1078, 1090 (type, from Troy, Jan. 12–14, 1909). TRINIDAD: Dennis 74.

OBSERVATIONS—The description of microscopic characters given above is based on our study of the type.

Dennis (1953) reports having found this species in Jamaica and Trinidad. Without studying fresh material, we are unable to evaluate the meaning of the discrepancy between the violaceous gills reported by Murrill and salmon-orange gills described by Dennis. Murrill had a good eye for field characters, but was not always careful about observations of microscopic details. We agree that Murrill erred in describing the pileus as viscid. Dennis stated that the pileus surface is lubricous but not truly viscid. Our sections of the type showed a non-gelatinous cuticle. This confirms Dennis' observations. Dennis found the pileus up to 2.5 cm broad, scarlet shading to orange; context yellow; the spores 6–9 × 3–4 μ; the basidia 4-spored; cystidia none; the gill trama parallel. Further, he points out that *H. subcaespitosus* Murr. differs in its white to straw-colored gills and broader spores (9–10 × 4.5–5.5 μ).

99

Hygrophorus mexicanus (Singer), comb. nov.

Hygrocybe mexicana Singer, Sydowia 12: 225. 1958.

Pileus about 10 mm broad, convex, umbilicate, brightest scarlet red, glabrous, not viscid, margin sulcate and transparent striate halfway to disc. Context almost concolorus with the surface; odor none.

Lamellae very broadly adnate, a slightly decurrent tooth present or absent, or subdecurrent, yellow mixed with pinkish red, distant, very broad.

Stipe 21 mm long, 1.5 mm thick at apex, reaching 2.5 mm at base, bright scarlet red, not viscid, not striate, slightly tapering upwards.

Spores 7–9.5 × 4–7 μ, ellipsoid, rather variable but not falling into definite categories of size or shape, smooth, hyaline. Basidia 25–35 × 7.2–9.2 μ, 2- and 4-spored, clavate, not dimorphous but remarkably short as compared with spore size. Pleurocystidia and cheilocystidia none. Gill trama subregular. Clamp connections present.

HABIT, HABITAT, AND DISTRIBUTION—Gregarious, on soil and humus, Mexico (Oaxaca), July. Type, M1531, from Huautla de Jiménez, July 12, 1957.

OBSERVATIONS—Singer says that this species is closely related to the European *H. coccineus* sensu Smith & Hesler. The latter, he says, is rare in the United States and is larger than *H. mexicanus*. Singer also points out that it is close to *H. firmus* but lacks dimorphous spores. We have not seen the type.

100

Hygrophorus ravenelii B. & C.

Ann. Mag. Nat. Hist. II (12): 424. 1853

Pileus 4–6.5 cm broad, convex, orange-red, moist, smooth.

Lamellae deeply emarginate but attached, paler than the pileus, ventricose.

Stipe 10–12.5 cm long, 6 mm thick, yellow, whitish and attenuated below, brittle, fistulose.

Spores 8–9 × 4.5–5.5 μ, rather numerous, ellipsoid, smooth, colorless in Melzer's reagent. Basidia 41–49 × 4–8 μ. Pleurocystidia and cheilocystidia none. Gill trama composed of subparallel hyphae, 3.5–6 μ broad, many are collapsed and do not revive in 2% KOH, yellowish brown in Melzer's reagent. Pileus cuticle hyphae with a few clamp connections, repent to somewhat erect, not gelatinous. Pileus trama yellowish brown in Melzer's reagent.

HABIT, HABITAT, AND DISTRIBUTION—On wet soil, South Carolina.

MATERIAL STUDIED—SOUTH CAROLINA: Ravenel (type, on deposit in the Herbarium at Kew Gardens, 2889).

OBSERVATIONS—The description of microscopic characters given above is based on our study of the type.

Although there are two collections at Kew, only the type, No. 2889, according to Dr. G. Taylor at Kew, was definitely determined by Berkeley as *H. ravenelii.*

The single carpophore is dark red and is cemented to the sheet. There seems to be no umbo.

The second collection, Kew No. 3444, may be a different species. The spores are similar to those of the type, but the basidia are smaller, the pileus is pallid-brownish with very thin flesh, and the gills are thin.

Coker (1929) reported in some detail on an agaric from North Carolina which he described and figured under the name *H. ravenelii.* We have studied Coker's Nos. 3590, 3780, 3757, and 3790. In all of these the spores are 9–14 × 5.7–8 μ, the basidia 2- and 4-spored, clamp connections absent, and the pileus is strongly umbonate. In our opinion, Coker's specimens are *H. cuspidatus.* So far as we know, the type is the only reported collection of the true *H. ravenelii.* Further search may yield additional collections of it.

101

Hygrophorus subcaespitosus (Murr.) Murr.

Mycologia 4: 332. 1912

Hydrocybe subcaespitosa Murr., Mycologia 3: 197. 1911.

Pileus 2–3 cm broad, convex to plane or depressed, ruber when young, miniatous when colder, subcaespitose.

Lamellae adnate or slightly decurrent, white to stramineous, broad, almost distant, inserted.

Stipe 3 cm long, 5 mm or more thick, luteous or paler yellowish, cylindric to slightly flattened, smooth, glabrous.

Spores 7.5–10 × 4.5–6 μ, ellipsoid, smooth, yellowish in Melzer's reagent. Basidia 32–46 × 6–9 μ, 2-spored. Pleurocystidia and cheilocystidia none. Gill trama subparallel to slightly interwoven. Cuticle of repent hyphae (a cutis); at times with some free ends erect. No hypodermium differentiated. Pileus trama of radial hyphae. Clamp connections present on the cuticular hyphae.

HABIT, HABITAT, AND DISTRIBUTION—On rich soil under tree ferns, Jamaica, December–January.

MATERIAL STUDIED—JAMAICA: Murrill 750 (type, from Morce's Gap, 5000 ft. elevation, Dec. 29, 30, Jan. 2, 1908–09).

OBSERVATIONS—The microscopic characters given above are based on our study of the type.

This species is related to *H. coccineus* and *H. ravenelii*, but differs in its colors and habit of growth.

102
Hygrophorus coccineus (Fr.) Fr. sensu Ricken
Epicr. Myc., p. 330. 1838

Agaricus coccineus Fr., Syst. Myc. 1: 105. 1821.
Hygrocybe coccinea (Fr.) Kummer, Führ. in Pilzk., p. 112. 1871.
Illustrations:
Color photograph, front cover; fig. 52; also 6.
Bresadola, Icon. Myc., tab. 344.
Juillard-Hartmann, Icon. Champ., pl. 47, fig. 3.
Lange, Flora Agar. Dan., 5, pl. 168G (as *Hygrocybe*).
Murrill, Mycologia 2, pl. 27, fig. 7.
Pomerleau, Mushrooms of Eastern Canada and the U. S., fig. 16C, and pl. 2, fig. 6.
Ramsbottom, Mushrooms and Toadstools, pl. 13a.
Smith and Hesler, Lloydia 5, pl. 4.
Wakefield and Dennis, Common British Fungi, pl. 36, fig. 4.

Pileus 2–5 cm broad, obtusely conic with an incurved margin when young, obtusely umbonate, with a spreading margin in age, "Nopal red" to "spectrum red," fading somewhat, smooth, glabrous, moist or sublubricous to subviscid, lacking a well-defined gelatinous pellicle, margin opaque or faintly striatulate when moist. Context reddish to orange, waxy, fragile; odor none, taste mild.

Lamellae broadly adnate to adnexed, often with a decurrent tooth,

Fig. 52. *H. coccineus*

orange-red to yellowish orange, pallid yellowish when dried, close to subdistant, broad, thickish, intervenose, edges even.

Stipe 3–7 cm long × 3–8 mm thick, concolorous with the pileus above or throughout, soon becoming yellowish near the base which sometimes is whitish from a coating of mycelium, glabrous, glistening, uneven, equal, fragile, moist, not viscid, hollow.

Spores 7–10.5 × 4–5 μ, ellipsoid, smooth, white in mass, yellow in Melzer's reagent. Basidia 43–54 × 6–8 μ, 4-spored. Pleurocystidia and cheilocystidia not differentiated. Gill trama subparallel, hyphae (5)8–16 μ broad, yellowish in iodine. Cuticle of repent hyphae, or at times a few more or less erect (a cutis). No hypodermium differentiated. Pileus trama of radial, parallel to subparallel hyphae. Clamp connections on the hyphae of the cuticle, gill trama, and subhymenium.

HABIT, HABITAT, AND DISTRIBUTION—Gregarious on soil in deciduous, coniferous, and mixed woods, California, Oregon, Washington, Michigan, Tennessee, North Carolina, Alabama, Florida, Pennsylvania,

Maryland, New York, Maine, and Massachusetts; Canada (Ontario); also Greenland, Europe, and Japan; summer and autumn.

MATERIAL STUDIED—ALABAMA: Burke 84. CALIFORNIA: Smith 9360, 9415. FLORIDA: Hesler 21060. MAINE: Bigelow 3785, 4701; Rea 473. MARYLAND: Kauffman, Cabin John, Aug. 19, 1919. MASSACHUSETTS: Bigelow 8427, 9136. MICHIGAN: Kauffman, Marquette, Aug. 27, 1906, Rock River, Sept. 14, 1929, 285; Smith 38291; Thiers 3643, 3872. NORTH CAROLINA: Hesler 16437, 17074, 17151, 22111. OREGON: Kauffman, Mt. Hood, Oct. 10, 1922. PENNSYLVANIA: Overholts, Huntington Co., Sept. 3, 1933. TENNESSEE: Hesler 4462, 4463, 7873, 9566, 10925, 16576, 17671, 18287, 20188, 23526. WASHINGTON: Brown, Lake Quinnault, Oct. 1925; Smith, Mt. Rainier, Sept. 8, 1948; Stuntz, Mt. Rainier National Park, Sept. 18, 1948. CANADA (Ontario): Smith 4739. DENMARK: J. P. Jensen, five collections (Hesler 23931, 23932, 23933, 23934, 23935). NETHERLANDS: Bas 1675.

OBSERVATIONS—Material collected near Lyon, France, and identified as *H. coccineus* by Josserand was communicated to Smith. It is the same as the material described above from California. Ricken's description applies remarkably well to all of these specimens, and so we have used the name in the sense that he used it. Ricken emphasized that the cap was more moist than viscid. Fries, however, described the pilei of both *H. coccineus* and *H. puniceus* as viscid. Hence there appears to be a possibility that the *H. coccineus* of Ricken and that of Fries are different. The specimens from California failed to show a distinct gelatinous pellicle either fresh or when revived, and no such layer was found on those from Josserand. Specimens of *H. puniceus* sectioned and compared under the microscope showed a very well-developed pellicle even on the oldest fruiting bodies. In spite of its lack of a pellicle, *H. coccineus* may feel slightly viscid when moist, and this may account for the statements to that effect in the literature. The color of the base of the stipe is very likely to lead one into trouble if he attempts to put much emphasis upon it. In *H. puniceus* according to our experience, it may be either whitish or yellow, most often white. In *H. coccineus* it is usually orange, but may appear white because of a thin coating of white mycelium which develops under moist conditions; neither is there any appreciable difference in spore size. The specimens of *H. coccineus* from France had spores $7-10 \times 4-5$ μ. Ricken gives them as $7-9 \times 5$ μ, and in the California collection they were $7-9 \times 5$ μ. In *H. puniceus* they measure $8-10 \times 5-6$ μ. Kauffman gave them as $9-12 \times 4-5$ μ for *H. puniceus* and $7-9 \times 5-6$ μ for *H. coccineus*. These differences do not appear significant, and in addition it is possible that the larger spores in some of Kauffman's material came from 2-spored basidia. We believe that his descriptions (1918: 196–97), both apply to *H. puniceus.* Murrill (1916) described *H. coccineus* as viscid, and (Murrill, 1910) illustrated it as having much the same color as *H. puniceus.* Hence his report and the distribution given in the *North American Flora* are also questioned. According to our experience, *H. puniceus* is a very common and variable species in North America, whereas *H. coccineus* is very rare.

Hongo (1952c) has reported this species from Japan, and M. Lange (1955) has found it in Greenland. He also suggests that *H. puniceus* f. *minor* recorded by Christiansen (1941) from Iceland may belong here.

103
Hygrophorus parvulus Pk.
N. Y. State Mus. Ann. Rept. 28: 50. 1879

Hydrocybe parvula (Pk.) Murr., North Amer. Flora 9: 378. 1916.
Illustrations:
Fig. 53.
Peck, N. Y. State Mus. Ann. Rept., pl. 1, figs. 20–24.
Smith and Hesler, Lloydia 5, pl. 15b.

Pileus 1–3 cm broad, obtuse to convex, sometimes with a depressed disc, glabrous, moist, at times subviscid, hygrophanous, "amber yellow," "apricot yellow," "light cadmium," "straw yellow," or "wax yellow," opaque and a paler yellow when faded, sometimes "orange" to "cadmium yellow" moist, fading to "baryta-yellow," translucent striate. Context brittle, waxy, thin, concolorous with the surface, unchanging; odor and taste mild.

Lamellae decurrent, subdistant, broad, subtriangular, intervenose, whitish or pale yellowish to "wax yellow," edges even.

Stipe 3–6 cm long, 2–3 mm thick, "citron yellow" to "amber yellow," base frequently becoming tinged "grenadine red" or dull rufous, at times the lower half or more tinged rufous or ochraceous salmon, terete or compressed, narrowed at the base or equal, fragile, glabrous, dry or moist, not viscid, hollow.

Spores 5–7(8.5) $\times$ 3.5–5 μ, ellipsoid, smooth, pale yellow in Melzer's reagent. Basidia 26–40 $\times$ 5–7 μ, 2- and 4-spored. Pleurocystidia and cheilocystidia not differentiated. Gill trama of subparallel hyphae, the cells 8–20 μ long, 10–30 μ broad. Cuticle of repent hyphae, a few surface hyphae appearing slightly gelatinous, some free ends more or less erect. No hypodermium differentiated. Pileus trama of radial hyphae. Clamp connections present on the cuticular hyphae.

Fig. 53. *H. parvulus*

HABIT, HABITAT, AND DISTRIBUTION—Gregarious on soil and humus, in deciduous and mixed woods, and under rhododendron, Maine, Massachusetts, New York, Tennessee, North Carolina, Michigan, Oregon, California, and Canada, June–October. Dennis (1961) has reported it from Venezuela.

MATERIAL STUDIED—CALIFORNIA: Smith 8545. MAINE: Bigelow 3986, 4047, 4074, 4619, 4620, 4621, 4622; Rea 486; Rea & Woodbury, Denmark, Aug. 6, 1940. MASSACHUSETTS: Bigelow 7656, 7879, 8603, 8604, 8833, 8902, 9055. MICHIGAN: Kauffman, Bay View, July 19, 1905, and Marquette, Aug. 27, 1906; Mains 32628; Smith (Brooks 1290, 1304), 15216, 57133. NEW YORK: Peck (type, from Northville, August), also from Lake Pleasant, August. NORTH CAROLINA: Hesler 14349, 17948, 19351, 20513, 22302, 23209; Kauffman, Hot Springs, Aug. 22, 1924; Smith & Hesler 11324. OREGON: Kauffman, Mt. Hood, Oct. 14, 1922. TENNESSEE: Hesler 4453, 17695, 18602, 22409, 23504. GREAT SMOKY MOUNTAINS NATIONAL PARK: Hesler 17213; Smith 9844, 10745. CANADA: (Quebec) Bigelow 4846, 6065.

OBSERVATIONS—A noticeable feature in this species, as pointed out by Peck (1907), is found in the stipe which is often more highly colored (pinkish red) than the pileus.

Notes on the type follow: Spores 5–7 × 3.5–5 μ, ellipsoid, smooth, non-amyloid. Basidia 30–39 × 6–7 μ, 2- and 4-spored. Pleurocystidia and cheilocystidia none. Gill trama subparallel to parallel, hyphal cells 20–63 × 10–27 μ. Cuticle of appressed or a few more or less erect hyphae. Clamp connections present on the cuticular hyphae.

104

Hygrophorus mycenoides Sm. & Hes.

Lloydia 5: 42. 1942

Illustrations:
  Figs. 2f, 7d.

Pileus 6–12 mm broad, convex or conic at first, the margin in-curved, becoming convex to plane and with a slight umbo, disc at times depressed slightly and the margin spreading, "deep chrome" to "light orange-yellow" over the center, the margin "mustard yellow" to "Naples yellow" (orange-yellow around the disc, pale yellow toward the margin), finally fading to almost pure white, the yellow color occasionally persistent in various places, moist and lubricous (not truly viscid), striate to the disc at first. Context thin, waxy, fragile, bright yellow fading to white; odor and taste not distinctive.

Lamellae broadly adnate to subdecurrent, bright yellow at first, the faces fading to white or pale yellow before the edges, and hence the lamellae frequently appear marginate, whitish over-all in age, sub-distant, sometimes appearing close when the short gills are well developed, narrow or at late maturity rather broad.

Stipe 2.5–4 cm long, 1–1.5 mm thick, pale wax yellow or concolorous with the pileus, equal, slender, tubular.

Spores (5)6–7 × 2.5–3.5 μ, narrowly ellipsoid, smooth, hyaline, yellowish in Melzer's reagent. Basidia 18–30 × 4.5–6 μ, 4-spored. Pleurocystidia none; cheilocystidia (16)28–33 × (4)7–9 μ, abundant, sub-cylindric, the apices obtuse, thin-walled, with yellow contents at first, hyaline in age. Gill trama of subparallel to slightly interwoven hyphae, the cells 8–20 μ wide and 15–60 μ long, at first with pale yellow contents. Cuticle of repent hyphae (a cutis). No hypodermium differentiated. Pileus trama of radial hyphae. Clamp connections rare on the cuticular hyphae, none found on the hyphae of the stipe.

HABIT, HABITAT, AND DISTRIBUTION—Scattered on humus, in mixed woods, Tennessee, August.

MATERIAL STUDIED—TENNESSEE: Smith 9988 (type, from Cades Cove, Great Smoky Mts. National Park, Aug. 10, 1938), 10137 (paratype, same locality, Aug. 13, 1938).

OBSERVATIONS—In all respects, except its basidia, this species appeared to be a true *Hygrophorus*, and in fact is similar to *H. ceraceus* or *H. parvulus* in many respects. It is more *Mycena*-like than either, however, hence the specific name. It is also close to the very poorly known *H. aurantiacoluteus* B. & C. but is distinct from that species as described by its broadly adnate rather than long-decurrent gills. Both apparently have brilliant orange colors and slender stature. Our specimens showed no resemblance to *Omphalia fibula* in general appearance and lacked cystidia; and it is largely on this basis that we have considered them to represent a different species. *H. subceraceus* Murr. also appears to be closely related, but is described as having a viscid pileus. *H. wynniae* B. & Br. is close but is said to have much broader spores and narrow decurrent lamellae.

105
Hygrophorus mephiticus Pk.
Torrey Bot. Club Bull. 33: 213. 1906

Pileus 2–4 cm broad, convex becoming plane or nearly so, hygrophanous, yellowish brown when moist, ochraceous when dry, sometimes tinged green, margin striatulate when moist. Context whitish, sometimes tinged yellow; odor mephitic.

Lamellae sinuate, adnexed, grayish-violaceous or grayish purple, broad, thick, distant, at times connected by veins, often wavy, lamellulae present.

Stipe 3–5 cm long, 2–5 mm thick, concolorous with the pileus or paler, base often whitish-mycelioid, equal or tapering below, curved or flexuous, brittle, hollow.

Spores 8.5–12 × 5–7 μ, ellipsoid, smooth, pale yellowish in Melzer's reagent. Basidia 46–63 × 6–8 μ, 2- and 4-spored. Pleurocystidia and cheilocystidia none. Gill trama of undulating-subparallel, or very slightly interwoven hyphae, 4–9 μ broad. Cuticle of repent hyphae, a few with free ends. Clamp connections few in the gill trama.

HABIT, HABITAT, AND DISTRIBUTION—Among *Sphagnum* in swamps, Massachusetts, August.

MATERIAL STUDIED—MASSACHUSETTS: Davis (type, collected by Simon Davis, Stow, Aug. 25, 1905).

OBSERVATIONS—The microscopic characters given above are based on our study of the type.

Peck (1906) states that this is a peculiar and well-marked species, easily recognized by its unusual colors, odor of skunk, and habitat. The odor persists several days after the plants have been collected.

The dried specimens (type), especially their broad, more or less distant gills, remind one of *Laccaria laccata* (Fr.) Berk. & Br.

There is no reason to place *H. mephiticus* in synonymy with *H. auratocephalus* as was done by Murrill (1916). Although both species have a mephitic odor, the larger spores and violaceous gills will distinguish *H. mephiticus* at once. Bigelow's *H. purpureofolius* differs in pileus colors, gill attachment, and odor of the context.

Fig. 54.
H. nitiosus

106
Hygrophorus nitiosus Blytt
Norges Hymenomycetes. Videnskab Selskabets Skrifter. Math. Naturv.
Kl. 1904. No. 6. 1905

> *Hygrocybe ingrata* Jensen & Moeller, Fungi of the Faeröes, p. 136.
> 1945.
> *Hygrocybe nitiosa* (Blytt) Moser apud Gams, Kleine Kryptogamenfl.
> von Mitteleuropa, p. 37. 1953.

Illustration:
Fig. 54.

Pileus 2–5 cm broad, convex-umbonate, expanding slightly, near
"snuff brown," moist, soon dry, radiately appressed-fibrillose, margin
even. Context dingy-grayish, at times pinkish when cut, relatively thin;
odor nitrous, taste acidulous.

Lamellae deeply emarginate, whitish changing to pinkish, and at
times becoming blackish where bruised, broad, subdistant, edges
even.

Stipe 4–8 cm long, 3–8 mm thick, pallid brownish, becoming pinkish brown where bruised, drying blackish, at times ventricose below,
often compressed, glabrous, striate, dry, hollow.

Spores 7.5–10 × 4.5–6 μ, ellipsoid, smooth, yellowish in Melzer's reagent. Basidia 33–42 × 7–8 μ, mostly 4-spored, a few 2-spored. Pleurocystidia and cheilocystidia none. Gill trama of broad, subparallel hyphae. Cuticle of repent to more or less erect, brownish hyphae. Pileus trama of radial hyphae. Clamp connections on the cuticular hyphae.

HABIT, HABITAT, AND DISTRIBUTION—On soil, in deciduous wood, Tennessee, July–August; also Europe.

MATERIAL STUDIED—TENNESSEE: Hesler 12737, 22383. FRANCE: Bas 1112 (ex-Herb. Univ. Leiden).

OBSERVATIONS—This species is between *H. ovinus* (which turns pinkish where bruised, and the odor faint but not nitrous), and *H. nitratus* (the color of which is unchanging, but has a nitrous odor). *Hygrophorus nitiosus* shows the color change of *ovinus*, and the nitrous odor of *nitratus*.

Haller (1951a) discusses this species as known to him through his collections. In his material, the lamellae are cream; in our collections and that of Bas' collection from France, the lamellae are whitish, i.e., only slightly paler. In all these collections, however, the gills become reddish, pinkish, or brownish where bruised. It is Haller's opinion that *H. nitiosus* is included in the description which we (Smith and Hesler, 1942) give for *H. ovinus*. In the present studies, we have referred to *H. ovinus* those individuals of this complex which show a color change and a faint but fragrant (fruity) odor. In our earlier work (1942) we followed Bresadola (1928) in admitting to *H. nitratus* a collection in which there was a color change. That and similar collections we here refer to *H. nitiosus*. It is now known that *H. metapodius* differs from all of these in its amyloid spores.

107

Hygrophorus cinerascens Berk. & Br.
Journ. Linn. Soc. Bot. 11: 562. 1871. *Emend.* Petch, Ann. R. Bot. Gar. Peradeniya 6: 324. 1917

Illustration:
Dennis, Kew Bull. 2, fig. 6.

Pileus 4 cm broad, hemispherical, becoming campanulate, then expanded, with a small umbilicus which is perforated at a very early stage to connect with the cavity of the stipe, fuscous, very dark when young, paling and exposing the drab-gray flesh between the fibrils with age, drying black. Context thin, very hygrophanous.

Lamellae adnate-decurrent, drab-gray, subdistant, medium broad, wedge-shaped, thick.

Stipe whitish, finally drab, smooth, at first equal, becoming obconical as the pileus expands and the perforation enlarges.

Spores 8–11 × 4–5.5 μ, ellipsoid-cylindric, pure white in deposits, non-amyloid. Basidia 40 × 8 μ, 4-spored. Pleurocystidia and cheilocystidia none. Gill trama parallel, hyphae 14–20 μ broad. Cuticle of parallel hyphae with thin-walled cells 85–150 × 10–11 μ. Clamp connections present.

HABIT, HABITAT, AND DISTRIBUTION—On soil, under bamboos, Trinidad, October (Dennis 184).

MATERIAL STUDIED—TRINIDAD: Dennis 184.

OBSERVATIONS—Dennis (1953) states that this seems to be the West Indian representative of *H. ovinus* Fr. from which it differs in its slender stature and perforate pileus. Petch noted a strong nitrous odor not present in the Trinidad collection. We have studied Dennis' collection (No. 184) from Trinidad, and have recorded our observations as follows: Spores 8–11 × 5–6(7) μ, ellipsoid, smooth, pale yellowish in Melzer's reagent. Basidia 40–52 × 7–9 μ, 2- and 4-spored. Pleurocystidia and cheilocystidia none. Gill trama parallel, hyphae 7–16 μ broad. Lactifers in gill trama, 25–4 μ broad. Cuticle undifferentiated, surface hyphae erect to repent brown, 3–9 μ broad, terminal elements cystidioid. Clamp connections few.

108
Hygrophorus virescens, sp. nov.

Illustrations:
  Fig. 55; also 7a.

Pileus 2–4.5 cm latus, luteus obscuro-aurantio colore inmixtus, mox viridis, non viscidus, rimosus, lobatus; lamellae adnexae, pallido-virides, marginibus serratae; stipes 3–6 cm longus, 3–8 mm crassus, viridis; sporae 7–9(10) × 5–6.5 μ, ellipsoideae. Specimen typicum in Herb. Univ. Mich.; lectum prope Trinidad, Calif. Dec. 14, 1956, A. H. Smith 56649.

Pileus 2–4.5 cm broad, obtuse when young, becoming plane or nearly so, the margin often curved up in age; color variable: when young near honey yellow with dull orange variously present, soon becoming "lime green"; glabrous, moist but not viscid, in age the margin rimose, often variously lobed and splitting. Context lime green, unchanging where bruised, very fragile; odor and taste not distinctive.

Lamellae adnexed, attached to the stipe apex by a tooth, whitish with lime green tones near the pileus, edges paler, serrate.

Stipe 3–6 cm long, 3–8 mm thick, lime green, base whitish, moist or

Fig. 55. *H. virescens*

dry, somewhat striate in age. Tubular to hollow, terete or compressed.

Spores 7–9(10) × 5–6.5 μ, ellipsoid, smooth, yellow in Melzer's reagent. Basidia 40–55 × 7–10 μ, 2- and 4-spored. Pleurocystidia and cheilocystidia none. Gill trama parallel to subparallel, hyphae 8–20 μ broad. Cuticle of repent, non-gelatinous hyphae, not sharply differentiated from the pileus trama, a cutis. No hypodermium differentiated. Pileus trama of radial, parallel to subparallel hyphae, in tangential view the ends of the hyphae present a pseudoparenchyma-like appearance. Clamp connections present.

HABIT, HABITAT, AND DISTRIBUTION—Caespitose under redwood, California, December.

MATERIAL STUDIED—CALIFORNIA: Smith 56649 (type, from Trinidad, Dec. 14, 1956).

OBSERVATIONS—Although this species has been collected only once, it is very distinctive. Because of the non-gelatinous cuticle on both pileus and stipe, it cannot be placed in *H. psittacinus*. When dried, the pilei of *H. virescens* are near warm buff in color. Moreover, the green color develops as the carpophore matures, whereas in *H. psittacinus* the green pigment is present in young buttons.

109
Hygrophorus tahquamenonensis Sm. & Hes.
Sydowia 8: 331. 1954

Pileus 2.5–5 cm broad, obtusely conic with a flaring margin, color evenly pale ocher yellow and fading to "pinkish buff" or "pale pinkish buff," surface moist and hygrophanous, when faded minutely squamulose, margin opaque, soon blackish along the edge where bruised. Context thin, yellowish then dingy pallid; odor and taste nitrous.

Lamellae ascending, adnate to adnexed, pale yellow when young, fading to pale pinkish buff or near it, broad and ventricose, distant, edges even.

Stipe 4–5 cm long, 4–7 cm thick, pallid to yellowish-pallid, discoloring to brownish where handled, drying to more or less pale fuscous, equal or slightly enlarged below, soon hollow, glabrous and naked (including the apex).

Spores 7–9 × 5–5.5 μ, oblong to subovoid, smooth, hyaline, pale yellowish in Melzer's reagent. Basidia 45–50 × 8–9 μ, 4-spored. Pleurocystidia and cheilocystidia none. Gill trama subparallel, nearly hyaline in KOH, yellowish in Melzer's solution, and lacking any dark granules. Cuticle a trichodermium of more or less erect, to repent, septate hyphae, the apical cells not differentiated as to size and shape. No hypodermium differentiated. Pileus trama of radially disposed hyphae. Clamp connections present.

HABIT, HABITAT, AND DISTRIBUTION—Scattered to isolated in a mixed hardwood and conifer forest, Michigan, August.

MATERIAL STUDIED—MICHIGAN: Hesler & Smith 41821 (type, Upper Falls, Tahquamenon Falls State Park, Aug. 3, 1953); Smith 41982.

OBSERVATIONS—This species would be identified as *H. nitratus* if it were not for the yellow-ocher pileus and gills, and to some extent the stipe, as well as the staining cap-margin and stipe. *H. nitratus* is essentially a gray species. *H. helvella* Boud. is closely related in having ocher-gray colors and in blackening, but is described as having more or less globose spores and a farinaceous odor. Boudier's (1911) illustration is not at all suggestive of our fungus.

110
Hygrophorus ovinus (Fr.) Fr.
Epicr. Myc., p. 328. 1838

> *Agaricus ovinus* Fr., Syst. Myc. 1: 109. 1821.
> *Camarophyllus ovinus* (Fr.) Kümmer, Führ. in Pilzk., p. 117. 1871.
> *Hygrocybe ovina* (Fr.) Kühner, Le Botaniste 17: 44. 1926.

Illustrations:
  Fig. 56.
  Bresadola, Icon. Myc., tab. 336.
  Juillard-Hartmann, Icon. Champ., pl. 48, fig. 9.
  Lange, Flora Agar. Dan. 5, pl. 166E.
  Ricken, Die Blätterp., pl. 7, fig. 6.
  Smith and Hesler, Lloydia 5, pl. 3.

Pileus 2–5 cm broad, convex to hemispheric, becoming broadly convex to somewhat expanded in age, the disc often remaining obtuse or somewhat flattened, gray-brown to brownish-fuliginous, paler and more grayish when faded, at times "clay color" on the disc to "pinkish buff" on the margin, darkening in age, moist but soon dry and not viscid, silky when faded, rimose in age, at times disc cracked to form scales, margin even. Context thick on disc, thin toward, margin brittle, pallid, pinkish when bruised; odor faint, at times fruity, taste slightly alkaline.

Lamellae adnate, soon deeply emarginate, whitish, pinkish when bruised, finally spotted blackish, usually blackening when dried, broad, moderately close to subdistant.

Stipe 4–7 cm long, 5–10 mm thick, equal, the apex at times flared, terete or compressed, pallid or concolorous with the pileus, pinkish brown to vinaceous when handled, finally blackish, often curved, hollow.

Spores (6)7–9(10) × 4.5–6(7) μ, ellipsoid to subovoid, smooth, white in mass, yellowish in Melzer's reagent. Basidia 4-spored, 38–57 × 6–8(10) μ. Pleurocystidia and cheilocystidia none. Gill trama parallel to subparallel, hyphae 6–20 μ broad, pale sordid vinaceous brown in Melzer's reagent. Cuticle of repent to semi-erect, non-gelatinous, brownish hyphae which are radially disposed, the cells 40–125 × 8–20 μ, only slightly or not at all constricted at the septa. No hypodermium differentiated. Pileus trama hyphae radial, similar to those of the surface. Clamp connections rare on the cuticular hyphae.

Fig. 56. *H. ovinus*

HABIT, HABITAT, AND DISTRIBUTION—Gregarious on soil, in deciduous, mixed, and coniferous woods, Tennessee, North Carolina, and California, July–September; also Europe and Japan.

MATERIAL STUDIED—CALIFORNIA: Smith 9392, and Trinidad (Calif.), Jan. 1938. NORTH CAROLINA: Smith & Hesler 7457; Hesler 19123; Totten 4332 (as *H. metapodius*). TENNESSEE: Hesler 20889, 22003; R. F. Rodier 20122. AUSTRIA: Moser, Aug. 27, 1948 (Hesler 24120).

OBSERVATIONS—The dull colors, the odor (not nitrous, but at times fruity), equal stipe, the color change exhibited by the various parts, and the deeply emarginate gills distinguish our collections. Orton (1960) says the odor is none or nitrous. The vinaceous reaction to Melzer's reagent of the gill trama and flesh of the pileus, described above, is best observed on specimens which have not blackened on drying. The reaction is sporadic and weak, most of the tissue remaining sordid yellowish brown.

Singer (1951) lists *H. metapodius* as a synonym of *H. ovinus*. But, J. Lange (1935–40), Bresadola (1928), and Orton (1960) recognize both species. Orton (1960: 256) reports the amyloid character of the spores of *H. metapodius*, a feature which adequately separates it from *H. ovinus*. In our study of Moser's collection from Austria, we found pseudocystidia—structures we had not observed in *H. ovinus*.

Hongo (1958a) reports *H. ovinus* from Japan.

SUBSECTION PUNICEI Fayod

Ann. Sci. Nat. Ser. 7(9): 309. 1889.
Pileus viscid, stipe dry; pileus not sharply conic.
Type species: *H. puniceus* Fr.

SERIES PUNICEI

KEY TO SPECIES

1. Spores 11–16 × 8–12 μ; pileus white, stained pinkish at times . . . .
. . . . .111. *H. albicarneus*
1. Not as above 2
   2. Spores globose to subglobose, 5–7 × 4.5–7 μ; pileus whitish . . . . . .
   . . . . .112. *H. sphaerosporus*
   2. Spores 9–12 × 5–6.5 μ; pileus white, lamellae close and narrow
   . . . . .96. *H. brevipes*
    2. Not in either of above choices 3
3. Pileus white to whitish 4
3. Pileus at least distinctly colored over disc 5

111

Hygrophorus albicarneus, sp. nov.

Pileus 8–12 mm latus, convexus, albus demum rubicundulus, viscidus, glaber; caro albida, odore et gustu mitis; lamellae decurrentes demum adnato-decurrentes, pallido-rubicundulae, subdistantes, latae demum modice latae; stipes 2–3 cm longus, 2–3 mm crassus, pallidus, siccus, aequalis; sporae 11–16 × 8-12 μ, ellipsoideae. Specimen typicum in Herb. Univ. Mich.; lectum Mt. Hood, Ore., May 31, 1947, W. B. Gruber.

Pileus 8–12 mm broad, convex, expanding to broadly convex or shallowly depressed, white to pinkish, viscid, glabrous, margin even, drying pallid to dingy pinkish buff. Context whitish, thick on disc, thin elsewhere; odor and taste not distinctive.

Lamellae decurrent to adnate-decurrent, white becoming pale pink, transparent, subdistant, narrow to broad, edges even and not gelatinous.

Stipe 2–3 cm long, 2–3 mm thick, pallid to dingy, dry, equal, naked to appressed-fibrillose, unchanging when dried.

Spores 11–16 × 8–12 μ, ellipsoid, smooth, white in deposits, pale yellow or almost colorless in Melzer's reagent. Basidia 50–62 × 9–12 μ, 2- and 4-spored. Pleurocystidia and cheilocystidia none. Gill trama undulating parallel or subparallel hyphal cells 10–18 μ broad. Cuticle a broad (150–400 μ) gelatinous zone, an ixocutis, the hyphae 1.5–4 μ in diameter. No hypodermium differentiated. Pileus trama of periclinal hyphae. Clamp connections present.

HABIT, HABITAT, AND DISTRIBUTION—Singly to sparsely scattered on soil, next to patches of melting snow, Oregon, May.

MATERIAL STUDIED—OREGON: Gruber (type, from Mt. Hood, May 31, 1947); Crater Lake National Park, July 15, 1955. (R. McP. Brown 282).

OBSERVATIONS—This species differs from *H. brevipes* in its more viscid pileus, its close, narrower lamellae, and its much larger spores. The white to pinkish pileus and the unusually large spores constitute distinctive characters. No small basidia or small spores were found. The pileus is about as slimy as that of *H. unguinosus*.

112
Hygrophorus sphaerosporus Pk.
Torrey Bot. Club Bull. 22: 486. 1895

Camarophyllus sphaerosporus (Pk.) Murr., North Amer. Flora 9: 386. 1916.

Pileus 12–24 mm broad, subconic, convex, obtuse or slightly umbonate, whitish, inclining to reddish brown, the margin incurved viscid. Context thick at the center, firm, white; odor unpleasant in drying.

Lamellae adnate or slightly decurrent, white, broad, subdistant.

Stipe 2.5–5 cm long, 4–6 mm thick, colored like the pileus, glabrous, floccose above, flexuous, often slightly thickened at the base, solid.

Spores 5–7 × 4.5–7 μ, globose to subglobose, smooth, at times one or more sides faintly flattened, pale yellowish to colorless in Melzer's reagent. Basidia 28–38 × 6–8 μ, 4-spored. Pleurocystidia and cheilocystidia none. Gill trama parallel to subparallel, hyphae 5–14 μ broad. Cuticle a gelatinous zone, 40–150 μ thick, with scattered areas of brownish hyphae on the surface, the subjacent hyphae colorless. Cuticular hyphae radially disposed, 2–3.5 μ broad. No hypodermium differentiated. Pileus trama of radial hyphae. Clamp connections absent.

HABIT, HABITAT, AND DISTRIBUTION—Communicated to Peck by C. McIlvaine, from Iowa, October.

MATERIAL STUDIED—IOWA: McIlvaine (Peck's type).

OBSERVATIONS—The microscopic characters given above are based on our study of the type.

Peck says: "The fresh plant is said to have no decided odor, but when partly dried it emits a slight but rather unpleasant odor. It belongs apparently to the section *Camarophyllus*, and is related to *Hygrophorus peckii*." Murrill followed Peck in placing this species in *Camarophyllus*, but it clearly belongs in the section *Hygrocybe*.

113
Hygrophorus fornicatus Fr.
Epicr. Myc., p. 327. 1838

> *Camarophyllus fornicatus* (Fr.) Karsten, Bidr. Finl. Nat. Folk. 1: 227. 1879.
> *Hygrocybe fornicata* (Fr.) Singer, Lilloa 22: 152. 1951.

Illustrations:
> Lange, Flora Agar. Dan. 5, pl. 165C (as *Camarophyllus fornicatus* [Fr.] Karst.).
> Ricken, Die Blätterp., pl. 7, fig. 8.

Pileus 4–6 cm broad, obtuse when young, the margin incurved, becoming obtusely umbonate with an expanded plane margin, whitish, or tinged pale gray over the disc, unchanging when bruised, the margin finally somewhat wavy and splitting radially, glabrous, viscid (the pellicle separable as a thin skin), margin faintly translucent striate when moist. Context firm, thin, waxy; odor and taste none; no color change noted.

Lamellae sinuate to adnexed, white, not changing color when bruised, subdistant, broad, thickish, firm, rigid, waxy, intervenose, edges even.

Stipe 3–6 cm long, 10–15 mm thick at the mid-portion, flaring at the apex or equal, white over all, hollow or soon becoming so, surface moist but not viscid, with scattered innate appressed silky fibrils, apex somewhat fibrillose-scabrous.

Spores 7–9 × 4.5–5.5 μ, ellipsoid to subovoid, smooth, colorless in Melzer's reagent. Basidia 36–54 × 6–8 μ, 2- and 4-spored. Pleurocystidia and cheilocystidia none. Gill trama subparallel, hyphae 6–15(25) μ broad. Lactifers present in the gill trama, 4–7 μ broad. Cuticle of gelatinous hyphae forming a transparent zone 175–225 μ broad. Clamp connections present on the cuticular hyphae.

HABIT, HABITAT, AND DISTRIBUTION—Singly under redwoods, California, December; also Europe.

MATERIAL STUDIED—CALIFORNIA: Smith 9394, 9459. BELGIUM:

Heinemann 1220; Hesler 23807. DENMARK: J. P. Jensen (Hesler 23938, 23939). SWITZERLAND: Huijsman (Hesler 24003).

OBSERVATIONS—From the literature, and dried material from Europe, which we have seen, it is apparent that this is a variable species. According to Kühner and Romagnesi (1953), the pileus may be white, or horn-gray to gray-brown; and may, on drying, become dusky gray or brownish-alutaceous. In our collections, the pileus was white or tinged pale gray over the center, and on drying became brownish. Orton (1960) reports the pileus, in material from England, pallid gray, gray-clay, or gray-olive with a paler margin. He also reports that the gills and flesh slowly become pinkish when cut or handled. Finally, Moser also (1955) describes the pileus as pale gray, olive-gray, or brownish, the margin pale.

We have studied the microscopic characters of material from Belgium, Denmark, and Switzerland; and find some variation in pileus color (dried), but little in spore size. From Denmark, material from Jensen (Hesler 23938), the spores are 5.5–7.5 × 4–4.7 μ; from M. Lange (Hesler 23939), the spores are 6.5–8 × 4–5 μ. From Belgium (Hesler 23807), the spores are 6–8.5 × 4–5 μ. In our California collections, the spores are slightly larger. In spore size and pileus color, our material closely resembles a collection from Switzerland by Huijsman (Hesler 24003).

J. Lange (1935–40) treated this species as a *Camarophyllus*, despite his statement that the trama of the gills is almost parallel, but somewhat interwoven. He regards it as a transition to *Hygrocybe*.

This species appears to be very rare in North America. It is close to *H. acutus*, but readily distinct as is pointed out in our discussion of that species. Its relationships appear to be with *H. ovinus*, but is not likely to be mistaken for either that species or *H. nitratus*.

114
Hygrophorus huronensis Sm. & Hes.
Lloydia 5: 59. 1942

Hygrocybe huronensis (Sm. & Hes.) Singer, Lilloa 22: 153. 1951.
Illustrations:
Fig. 57.
Smith and Hesler, Lloydia 5, pl. 14.

Pileus 1–3 cm broad, convex, the margin incurved somewhat, the disc flattened but not appreciably depressed, becoming broadly convex to nearly plane in age, not umbonate, appearing glassy and shining watery white, sometimes with a watery-gray circle around the disc (similar in color to the radial striae), opaque when faded and snow white over all, glabrous, viscid, hygrophanous, at times the disc becoming irregularly cracked, conspicuously translucent striate when moist. Context thin, firm, very waxy, watery white, becoming snow white, not very brittle; odor and taste mild, no color change noted in age or where bruised.

Lamellae sharply adnexed, white, unchanging, subdistant (33–37 reach the stipe, 1–2 tiers of short individuals), broad (3–4.5 mm), thin but firm, edges even.

Stipe 3–5 cm long, 3–5 mm thick, translucent and appearing glassy when moist but not viscid, becoming opaque in age but color changing very slowly, snow white in age, not staining when bruised, equal or a bit enlarged above, stuffed, becoming hollow, firm and waxy in consistency, the pith when present fibrillose, surface glabrous.

Spores 7–9 × 4.5–6 μ, ellipsoid, smooth, yellowish in Melzer's reagent. Basidia 24–40 × 7–10 μ, mostly 4-spored, some 2-spored. Pleurocystidia and cheilocystidia none. Gill trama parallel to subparallel, hyphae 12–23 μ broad. Cuticle a thin zone of gelatinous repent hyphae (an ixocutis). No hypodermium differentiated. Pileus trama of radial hyphae. Clamp connections present on the cuticular hyphae. Lactifers in the pileus trama and gill trama, 4–6 μ broad.

Fig. 57. *H. huronensis*

HABIT, HABITAT, AND DISTRIBUTION—Gregarious on grassy soil, under brush, Michigan, September.

MATERIAL STUDIED—MICHIGAN: Smith 15376 (type, from along the Huron River, Ann Arbor, Sept. 15, 1940).

OBSERVATIONS—The convex viscid pileus, dry stipe, adnexed gills, and white color throughout amply characterize this species. It appears to be the counterpart of *H. flavescens* but is white instead of yellow. Singer (1951) says that white forms have been observed among groups of *H. flavescens* which are indistinguishable from *H. huronensis*. Another white species, *H. purus*, differs in its sharply conic pileus and viscid stipe. Lactifers are present in the flesh of the pileus and occasionally in the gill trama of *H. huronensis*, but are not as large as those of *H. flavescens*.

115

Hygrophorus subluridus Murr.
Torrey Bot. Club Bull. 66: 159. 1939

Illustration:
    Fig. 9d.

Pileus about 3 cm broad, convex to expanded, broadly umbonate, fuscous, slimy-viscid, glabrous, delicately reticulate in part, margin even. Context rather thin, white, unchanging; odor none.

Lamellae adnexed, rounded behind, narrow, ventricose, pallid to fuscous, crowded, inserted, entire.

Stipe 6 cm long, 4 mm thick, subconcolorous, equal, glabrous.

Spores 3–4.5 × 3–3.5 μ, globose to subglobose, smooth, pale yellow in Melzer's reagent. Basidia 24–37 × 4.5–7 μ, 4-spored. Pleurocystidia and cheilocystidia none. Gill trama subparallel, in some sections slightly interwoven. Cuticle of closely interwoven hyphae bearing an ixotrichodermial turf, or palisade, 75–110 μ high, and composed of narrow, non-septate hyphae, 2–5 μ broad; pileus trama interwoven, the hyphae more or less radially disposed. Clamp connections present.

HABIT, HABITAT, AND DISTRIBUTION—Solitary on soil, under oak, Florida, September.

MATERIAL STUDIED—FLORIDA: Murrill F18292 (type, from Hunter's Station, near Gainesville, Sept. 6, 1938); Hesler 18457, from Gainesville, Aug. 16, 1944.

OBSERVATIONS—The description of microscopic characters given above is based on our study of the type.

Sections of the stipe of the type showed no gelatinous hyphae on the surface, despite Murrill's statement which accompanies the specimens that the stipe is viscid.

Murrill states that this species suggests *H. subpratensis*, a Cuban species, but the gills are not sinuate and the pileus does not fade. Murrill correctly interpreted *H. subpratensis* as a member of the section *Hygrophorus*. The globose spores of *H. subluridus* sharply separate it from *H. unguinosus* Fr., as does the dry stipe.

116
Hygrophorus subceraceus (Murr.) Murr.
Elisha Mitchell Sci. Soc. Jour. 55: 372. 1939

> *Hydrocybe subceracea* Murr., Elisha Mitchell Sci. Soc. Jour. 55: 371. 1939.

Pileus 1–3 cm broad, convex to subexpanded, at times with a small, broad umbo, viscid, glabrous, hygrophanous, "buff yellow" to "apricot yellow," flavous, tinged luteous when young and at the center when mature, pale chrome yellow when faded, margin even to translucent-striate when moist, entire to slightly lobed. Context very thin, flavous, unchanging; odor none, taste mild.

Lamellae short-decurrent to adnate, arcuate, broad or medium broad, inserted, medium distant, pale yellow, unchanging, edges even.

Stipe 2–4 cm long, 2–4 mm thick, concolorous with the pileus or paler yellow, base at times slightly orange chrome, glabrous, not viscid, subequal, flattened, hollow.

Spores 5–7.5 × 2.5–3.5 μ, ellipsoid, smooth, pale yellow in Melzer's reagent. Basidia 30–42 × 4.5–7 μ, mostly 4-spored, a few 2-spored. Pleurocystidia and cheilocystidia none. Gill trama subparallel, hyphae 4–8(10) μ broad. Cuticle of repent to more or less erect, somewhat gelatinous hyphae. No hypodermium differentiated. Pileus trama of radial hyphae. Clamp connections present on the cuticular hyphae.

HABIT, HABITAT, AND DISTRIBUTION—On soil, under hardwoods, Florida, Michigan, and Oregon; also Quebec, Canada and the Netherlands, July–November.

MATERIAL STUDIED—FLORIDA: West & Murrill F18374 (type, from Newnan's Lake, Nov. 15, 1938). MICHIGAN: Smith 58053. OREGON: Gruber & Smith 20118. CANADA: (Quebec) Bigelow 5512. NETHERLANDS: Geesteranus 13478.

OBSERVATIONS—The stipe of the type lacks a gelatinous layer, and its surface is therefore dry. The dry stipe and narrower spores separate this species from *H. ceraceus* Fr. In the Michigan collection (Smith 58058) the carpophores (dried) are somewhat brighter yellow than those of the type; otherwise there is agreement.

Notes on the type: Spores 5–7 × 2.5–3.5 μ, ellipsoid, smooth, pale yellow in Melzer's reagent. Basidia 30–40 × 5.5–7 μ, 4-spored. Pleurocystidia and cheilocystidia none. Gill trama subparallel, hyphae 4–8 μ broad. Cuticle of more or less gelatinous hyphae. Clamp connections present on the cuticular hyphae.

117
Hygrophorus caerulescens B. & C.
Ann. Mag. Nat. Hist. III (4): 292. 1859

Pileus 1–5 cm broad, flat, color a delicate blue-drab, viscid when wet, shining when dry. Context thick on the disc.

Lamellae decurrent, few, medium broad, subdistant, darker than the pileus, rather thick and fleshy, intervenose.

Stipe 3–6.4 cm long, 10 mm thick, pale blue, firm then soft and hollow, attenuated downwards.

Spores 5–7 × 3.5–4.5(5) μ, ellipsoid, smooth, very pale yellow in Melzer's reagent, numerous. Basidia 38–50 × 4–5 μ. Pleurocystidia and cheilocystidia none. Gill trama subparallel, hyphae slender (2–4 μ broad). Cuticle of more or less repent, gelatinous hyphae. Clamp connections not found.

HABIT, HABITAT, AND DISTRIBUTION—Among dead leaves and sticks in woods, New England.

MATERIAL STUDIED—Sprague (type, collected in New England).

OBSERVATIONS—The microscopic characters given above are based on our study of the type (consisting of one carpophore).

Murrill (1916) places this species under the heading "Doubtful Species," appended to his treatment of those *Hygrophorus* species with divergent gill trama. He says: "Described from specimens collected by Sprague among dead leaves and sticks in woods in New England. Like all Sprague's collections at Kew, this is accompanied by excellent notes and a beautiful sketch, which is very similar to *Camarophyllus fulvosus* in shape. The pileus is described as 'delicate blue-drab,' the lamellae as 'much decurrent, of a deeper color than the pileus,' and the stipe as 'white with a light blue tint.'"

118
Hygrophorus laetissimus Sm. & Hes.
Lloydia 5: 63. 1942

Hygrocybe laetissima (Sm. & Hes.) Singer, Lilloa 22: 153. 1951.
Illustrations:
   Fig. 58.
   Smith and Hesler, Lloydia 5, pl. 12.

Pileus 6–8 cm broad, obtuse, becoming nearly plane, color "spectrum red" over the disc (more brilliant than scarlet red), the margin

Fig. 58. *H. laetissimus*

orange to yellowish and opaque, not fading appreciably, margin incurved at first, spreading in age, viscid, glabrous. Context dull yellow
except for a thin red subseparable pellicle; odor and taste not distinctive.

Lamellae narrowly adnate to adnexed "peach red" (rufous with a
tinge of pink) near the margin, "orange chrome" near the stipe (brilliant orange), broad (up to 8–10 mm), subdistant (50 more or less
reach the stipe), thick but the edges thin.

Stipe 4–6 cm long, 10–30 mm thick, white, the base splashed with
scarlet or yellow, equal above a constricted base, hollow, fragile surface somewhat furfuraceous above, glabrous below.

Spores 7–10 × 4–5 μ, mostly ellipsoid, some subovoid or at least one
end broader, smooth, yellowish in Melzer's reagent. Basidia 40–60 ×
6–9 μ, mostly 4-spored, some 2-spored. Pleurocystidia and cheilocystidia none. Gill trama subparallel, hyphae 4–10 μ broad. Cuticle a conspicuous gelatinous zone, 100–125 μ thick, with imbedded interwoven
hyphae, an ixocutis. No hypodermium differentiated. Pileus trama of
radial hyphae. Clamp connections on the cuticular hyphae few, often
small and inconspicuous.

HABIT, HABITAT, AND DISTRIBUTION—Scattered under redwoods,
California, November.

MATERIAL STUDIED—CALIFORNIA: Smith 9148 (type, Prairie Creek State Park, Orick, Nov. 27, 1937), 9419.

OBSERVATIONS—The outstanding features of this species are its exceptionally brilliant red, viscid pileus and white stipe. In its other characters it closely resembles *H. puniceus* and *H. coccineus*. Both of these have colored stipes and were collected along with *H. laetissimus* so that a comparison of fresh specimens of all three species was made. There is also a rather distinct difference in color between dried specimens. Those of *H. laetissimus* are a bright fiery orange compared to the duller colors of both the others. *H. marchii* Bres. is also close to *H. laetissimus* but the former has a highly colored, more slender stipe.

119

Hygrophorus subminiatus (Murr.) Murr.
Mycologia 4: 332. 1912

Hydrocybe subminiata Murr., Mycologia 3: 198. 1911.

Pileus 1.5 cm broad, convex to plane, at length irregular, miniatous, varying slightly in places, viscid, smooth, margin undulate.

Lamellae decurrent, whitish to ochraceous, medium broad to narrow, subdistant.

Stipe 3 cm long, 2 mm thick, luteous, terete, crooked, slightly enlarged above, glabrous.

Spores 7–9 × 3.5–5 μ, subcylindric to more or less allantoid, at times slipper-shaped, more or less constricted, ends obtuse, smooth, pale yellowish in Melzer's reagent. Basidia 26–37 × 6–8 μ, 2-spored. Pleurocystidia and cheilocystidia none. Gill trama subparallel. Cuticle a narrow gelatinous zone (20–40 μ thick), the hyphae repent, an ixocutis, or at times more or less erect. No hypodermium differentiated. Pileus trama of radial hyphae. Clamp connections present on the cuticular hyphae.

HABIT, HABITAT, AND DISTRIBUTION—On soil on a shaded bank, Jamaica, December–January; possibly from Cuba, and from North Carolina, Michigan, and Washington, July–September.

MATERIAL STUDIED—JAMAICA: Murrill 369 (type, from Chester Vale, 3000 ft. elevation, Dec. 23, 1908). MICHIGAN: Sawyer, Gorge UBS, July 14, 1955; Smith 18681. NORTH CAROLINA: Hesler 12316. WASHINGTON: Smith 17170, 17421, 17928, 29510.

OBSERVATIONS—The description of microscopic characters given above is based on our study of the type. This species differs from *H. miniatus* in its viscid pileus, decurrent, gills, and more or less constricted spores. Actually, it is more closely related to *H. laetissimus* and *H. puniceus* than to *H. miniatus*.

120

Hygrophorus puniceus (Fr.) Fr.

Epicr. Myc., p. 331. 1838

Agaricus puniceus Fr., Syst. Myc. 1: 104. 1821.
Hygrocybe punicea (Fr.) Kummer, Führ. in Pilzk., p. 112. 1871.

Illustrations:
Fig. 59.
Böhme, Norsk Soppbok, pl. 2, fig. 13.
Bresadola, Icon. Myc., tab. 345.
Fries, Sv. Aetl. Svamp., pl. 77.
Juillard-Hartmann, Icon. Champ., pl. 47, fig. 2.
Kauffman, Agar. Mich., pl. 30 (as *H. coccineus*).
Lange, Flora Agar. Dan. 5, pl. 167B.
Murrill, Mycologia 2, pl. 27, fig. 5.
Peck, N. Y. State Mus. Bull. 5, pl. 58, figs. 1–7.
Peck, N. Y. State Mus. Mem. 3, 52, figs. 1–7.
Ramsbottom, Mushrooms and Toadstools, pl. 12.
Ricken, Die Blätterp., pl. 8, fig. 2.
Smith and Hesler, Lloydia 5, pl. 11.
Thomas, Field Book of Common Gilled Mushrooms, pl. 10, fig. 62.
Wakefield and Dennis, Common British Fungi, pl. 36, fig. 2.

Pileus 2–4(7) cm broad, obtusely conic and the margin incurved when young, becoming umbonate to plane, the margin sometimes remaining decurved and sometimes spreading or recurved, color deep blood red over all at first, fading in streaks (as if hygrophanous) to near "zinc orange," in age pale orange over all, glabrous, viscid, margin sometimes translucent striate. Context thin, fragile, waxy, sordid watery-reddish orange, becoming pale orange-yellow, unchanging; odor and taste mild.

Lamellae bluntly adnate with a decurrent tooth at first, becoming adnexed and sometimes seceding in age, reddish orange to pale yellow, subdistant, broad, edges even.

Stipe 2–7 cm long, (5)10–15 mm thick, reddish but soon fading to orange or yellow, base white or yellowish, yellow to orange within, more or less fibrillose-striate, equal or narrowed slightly at the base, sometimes slightly ventricose, stuffed to hollow.

Spores (7)8–11(12) × (3.5)4–6 μ, subellipsoid to oblong, smooth, yellowish in Melzer's reagent. Basidia 32–65 × 6–11 μ, usually 4-spored, at times 1-, 2-, 3-spored. Pleurocystidia and cheilocystidia none. Gill trama subparallel, hyphae 8–20 μ broad, the cells long and cylindric, basidia, subhymenium, and trama all yellow in Melzer's reagent. Cuticle a gelatinous pellicle, which is 125–175 μ thick, the hyphae 3–5 μ broad. No hypodermium differentiated. Pileus trama of radial hyphae. Clamp connections present on the cuticular hyphae.

HABIT, HABITAT, AND DISTRIBUTION—Gregarious to scattered under hardwoods and conifers, Nova Scotia to Manitoba in Canada, Maine,

Massachusetts, New York, Pennsylvania, Virginia, North Carolina, Tennessee, Alabama, Michigan, Washington, Oregon, and California, June–December; also Europe.

MATERIAL STUDIED—ALABAMA: Burke 84, 2075. CALIFORNIA: Smith 3803, 3867, 3930, 8358, 8508, 9013, 9170, 9416. MAINE: Bigelow 4675. MASSACHUSETTS: Davis, Stow, Sept. 19, 1911. MICHIGAN: Kauffman 381; Bigelow 8523, 8705; Smith 1203, 1448, 6049, 7689, 15447, 32478, 33090, 33244, 33554, 33937, 37086, 38696, 50243, 58285; Thiers 3310, 3556, 3585, 4234, 4289. NEW YORK: Kauffman & Mains, Adirondack Mts., Sept. 12, 1914; House, Newcomb, Sept. 21, 1924; Smith 418. NORTH CAROLINA: Smith & Hesler 7404, 10198. GREAT SMOKY MOUNTAINS

Fig. 59. *H. puniceus*

NATIONAL PARK: Smith 10220. OREGON: Gruber, Eugene, Jan. 25, 1944. PENNSYLVANIA: Kauffman, Mt. Gretna, Sept. 7, 1924; Overholts 16018. TENNESSEE: Hesler 4393, 4394, 4395, 7848, 10944; Rice 4438; Smith & Hesler 7450, 11332. VIRGINIA: Kelly 1559. CANADA: Bowerman 45188; Burlingham, Ontario, Aug. 1920; Groves & Hoare 27619; Smith 675, 814, 4738. AUSTRIA: Moser, Sept. 15, 1948 (Hesler 24133). DENMARK: J. P. Jensen (Hesler 23948, 23949, 23950).

OBSERVATIONS—The viscid pileus, its deep blood red color, and the somewhat fibrillose striate margin are the important diagnostic characters of the species. We have not been able to verify the differences between *H. coccineus* and *H. puniceus* as pointed out by Kauffman. For a critical comparison of these two see *H. coccineus* (page 183). The spore size varies considerably in specimens with 4-spored basidia. This added to the fact that 2-spored forms are also known to occur (also 1- and 3-spored), makes spore size a rather poor character to use in distinguishing this species from its close relatives.

121
Hygrophorus marchii Bres.
Icon. Myc. 7: 343. 1928

Hygrocybe marchii (Bres.) Singer, Lilloa 22: 153. 1951.
Illustrations:
    Fig. 60.
    Bresadola, Icon. Myc., pl. 343.

Pileus 3–6 cm broad, convex with an incurved margin, expanding to plane or the margin uplifted and somewhat crenate, blood red to scarlet when young but soon fading to orange-red and finally to yellow (orange-yellow to yellow dried), glabrous, viscid but soon dry. Context yellowish; odor and taste not distinctive.

Lamellae adnate to adnexed, orange-yellow to pale yellow, moderately broad, subdistant, edges even.

Stipe 4–6 cm long, 3–6 mm thick, concolorous with pileus, equal or nearly so, often becoming compressed, glabrous and naked, moist.

Spores 7–10 × 3.5–5 μ, narrowly ellipsoid, at times faintly constricted, smooth, pale yellow in Melzer's reagent. Basidia 34–41 × 5–7 μ, 2- and 4-spored. Pleurocystidia and cheilocystidia not seen. Gill trama parallel or nearly so, hyphae 7–14 μ broad. Cuticle a thin gelatinous pellicle of narrow hyphae (an ixocutis). No hypodermium differentiated. Pileus trama of radial hyphae. Clamp connections present on the hyphae of the cuticle, gill trama, and subhymenium.

Fig. 60. *H. marchii*

Habit, Habitat, and Distribution—Gregarious under hardwoods and in mixed forests, Alabama, Michigan, and California, July–October; also Iceland, the Faeröes, and Europe.

Material Studied—alabama: Burke 78. california: Smith 56213. michigan: Smith 25974, 25975, 25976, 25978, 25991, 30985, 32421, 37486, 57360, 58155; Thiers 969. denmark: J. P. Jensen (Hesler 23940).

Observations—This species has been a puzzle to us. It is very close to *H. flavescens;* in fact it differs in color from that species in much the same way that *H. cuspidatus* differs from *H. acutoconicus.* *H. marchii* was reported by Möller (1945) from the Faeröes, but he did not describe the pileus as viscid, and we are inclined to question his identification on that basis. His species, by virtue of the non-viscid pileus and somewhat curved-apiculate spores, may possibly be the same as *H. quietus* Kühner. Perhaps *H. marchii* should be regarded as a variety of *H. puniceus,* but this is not the impression one gets from seeing both in the fresh condition. *H. puniceus* has a characteristic appearance. It seems to be a fleshier species than *H. marchii.* It differs from *H. laetissimus* in its much more slender stipe (3–6 mm thick), in its fading pileus, and orange-yellow to pale yellow lamellae. On the other hand, in *H. laetissimus* the stipe is 10–30 mm thick, the pileus scarcely fades, and the lamellae are peach red.

Favre (1955) records this species from Switzerland, and Hongo (1951c) reports it from Japan (a first report). Morten Lange (1955) has found it in Iceland, and Lundell (1932) reports it from Sweden.

122

Hygrophorus mucilaginosus B. & C.

Jour. Bot. & Kew Misc. 1: 98. 1849

Pileus 12–18 mm broad, convex, at length plane, pale reddish yellow, darker in the center, very mucilaginous, margin striate.

Lamellae subdecurrent, flesh-colored, unequal, medium broad, distant, fleshy.

Stipe 2.5–5 cm long, 2 mm or more thick, pale yellow or carneous, composed of longitudinal fibers, brittle, subpellucid, fistulose.

Spores 5–7 × 3–4.5 μ, ellipsoid, smooth, yellowish in Melzer's reagent. Basidia 40–52 × 5–6 μ 4-spored. Pleurocystidia and cheilocystidia none. Gill trama subparallel. Subhymenium indistinct. Cuticle of the pileus fibrillose, the surface hyphae gelatinous. Clamp connections not found.

HABIT, HABITAT, AND DISTRIBUTION—On low ground, South Carolina.

MATERIAL STUDIED—SOUTH CAROLINA: The type, borrowed and studied through the courtesy of Kew Gardens.

OBSERVATIONS—The microscopic characters given above are based on our study of the type.

The cuticular hyphae of the stipe are non-gelatinous, and the stipe is therefore not viscid. The species is near *H. subminiatus*, the spores of which are larger and of different shape. It differs from *H. subceraceus* in its broader spores; from *H. nitidus* in its subdecurrent, flesh-colored lamellae, its dry stipe, and its smaller spores; and from *H. parvulus* in its pileus colors, its subdecurrent lamellae, its much larger basidia, and slightly smaller spores.

123

Hygrophorus flavescens (Kauff.) Sm. & Hes.

Lloydia 5: 60. 1942

> *Hygrophorus puniceus* var. *flavescens* Kauff., Mich. Acad. Sci. Rept. 8: 34. 1906.
> *Hygrocybe flavescens* (Kauff.) Singer, Lilloa 22: 154. 1951.

Illustrations:
> Fig. 61.
> Smith and Hesler, Lloydia 5, pl. 13.

Pileus 2.5–6(7) cm broad, broadly convex with an incurved margin when young, then flattened or slightly depressed on the disc, the margin remaining somewhat decurved, "cadmium orange" to "Mikado orange," or "mustard yellow," fading to "light orange-yellow" to "amber yellow," glabrous, viscid, soon dry and shining, margin striatulate when moist. Context thin, waxy, yellowish; odor and taste not distinctive.

Lamellae adnexed, "mustard yellow" to "pinnard yellow," broad, close to subdistant, edges even.

Stipe 4–7 cm long, (5)8–12(16) mm thick, base whitish, midportion orange, apex more or less concolorous with lamellae, equal or attenuated below, often compressed and grooved on one side, fragile and easily splitting, glabrous or faintly fibrillose at first, lubricous to moist or dry (not viscid), hollow.

Spores 7–8(9) × 4–5 μ, ellipsoid, smooth white in deposits, yellow in Melzer's reagent. Basidia 26–40 × 6–10 μ, 2- and 4-spored, clavate and base not prolonged. Pleurocystidia and cheilocystidia not differentiated. Gill trama parallel, hyphae 8–22 μ broad. Lactifers present in both pileus and gill trama, 60–150 × 4–10 μ, golden yellow in Melzer's reagent. Pileus trama homogeneous. Cuticle a narrow zone of gelatinous repent hyphae (an ixocutis). No hypodermium differentiated. Pileus trama of radial hyphae. Clamp connections on the hyphae of the cuticle and subhymenium.

HABIT, HABITAT, AND DISTRIBUTION—Gregarious on soil and humus, in deciduous, coniferous, and mixed woods, Canada, Maine, Massachusetts, New York, Pennsylvania, Virginia, North Carolina, Tennessee, Texas, Michigan, Washington, and California, January and June–November; also Scotland, Switzerland, and Japan.

MATERIAL STUDIED—CALIFORNIA: Lanphere 62; Newhall, Woodside, Jan. 1934; Smith 3512, 3886, 9168, 9464; Smith 56512. MAINE: Bigelow 3296, 3336, 3337, 3338, 3339, 3340, 3783, 4101; Rea 521. MASSACHUSETTS: Bigelow 6583, 6654, 6688, 7223, 8062, 8161, 8249, 8314, 8869, 8913, 9261; Darker 5708 (Farlow Herb.). MICHIGAN: Iltis, Douglas Lake, July 24, 1947; Imshaug 3488; Kauffman, Marquette, Sept. 1, 1906, 202; Smith 1365, 1420, 1935 (type, Whitmore Lake, June 22, 1935), 6380, 6580, 15562, 21492, 21908, 22097, 32556, 33128, 36503, 37081, 37273, 39465, 41724, 41753, 50081; Smith & Brooks 1038, 1207, 1289, 21696, 21857; Thiers 1912, 3028, 3207, 3260, 3414, 3495, 3554, 3646. NEW YORK: Bigelow 5065, 5084; Smith 203. NORTH CAROLINA: Hesler 8053, 11326, 12328; Sharp 9319. PENNSYLVANIA: Kauffman, Mt. Gretna, Sept. 10, 1924. TENNESSEE: Bain 7901; Campbell 22124; Hesler 4369, 4370, 4373, 4374, 4375, 4429, 7326, 11433, 12240, 17486, 19700, 20892, 21321; McCarroll 4372; Sharp 4371; Underwood 4406. TEXAS: Thiers 4727. WASHINGTON: Imshaug 1106; Smith 16707, 29908, 31044, 49246. CANADA: (Ontario) Hoare, Aug. 22, 1951, 28934; Smith 26416; (Quebec) Bigelow 5017, 5019, 5501.

OBSERVATIONS—According to our experience this is a common species and both of us, as well as other American mycologists, have probably called it *H. chlorophanus*. After handling specimens of this species, the stipe often feels subviscid to lubricous. However, if one observes the condition of the stipe carefully before damaging it, he will see that it is not covered by a gelatinous or viscid coating. The texture of the stipe is soft and delicate, thus causing it to bruise easily. Kauffman, in his unpublished notes, recognized the fungus as a distinct species and separated it from *H. chlorophanus* by the character of the stipe emphasized above. In addition he also recognized *H. chlorophanus*. Ricken (1915) described the stipe of *H. chlorophanus* as "glanzlos, fast glatt, fast troken" and so may have had *H. flavescens* instead. *Hygrophorus marchii* Bres. is very close but differs, according to its description, in the brighter red colors. The colors of *H. flavescens*, of which we have observed many collections, are not red. The variation is to pale yellow, and forms which are almost pale sulphur yellow are not uncommon.

Favre (1955) reports this species from Switzerland, and Hongo (1952d) has found it in Japan (June and October).

Fig. 61. *H. flavescens*

SUBSECTION PSITTACINI Bataille

Flore Monogr. Hygrophores, p. 50. 1910.
Characters as given in key, p. 108.
Type species: *Hygrophorus psittacinus* Fr.

KEY TO SERIES

1. Pileus sharply conic .... Series *Puri,* below
1. Pileus obtuse to depressed 2
    2. Pileus color gray to dull brown, deep vinaceous brown or dull yellow-brown .... Series *Inolentes,* p. 218
    2. Pileus in red, yellow, blue, or green series . . . Series *Psittacini,* p. 224

SERIES PURI ser. nov.

Pileus conicus vel acute conicus.
Type species: *Hygrophorus purus* Pk.

KEY TO SPECIES

1. Pileus white ....124. *H. purus*
1. Pileus colored 2
    2. Blackening when cut or bruised ....a
        a. Lamellae yellow to orange .... 125. *H. singeri* var. *singeri*
        b. Lamellae whitish .... 126. *H. singeri* var. *albifolius*
    2. Not blackening as above; pileus red .... 127. *H. ruber*

124
Hygrophorus purus Pk.
N. Y. State Mus. Ann. Rept. 26: 63. 1874

    Hydrocybe pura (Pk.) Murr., North Amer. Flora 9: 377. 1916.

Illustrations:
    Fig. 62.
    Smith and Hesler, Elisha Mitchell Sci. Soc. Jour. 56, pl. 9, below.

Pileus (2.5)4–7.5 cm broad, conic, conic-campanulate, broadly conic, or with the margin recurved in age, white, tinged pinkish red where wounded, glabrous, viscid, finely rivulose, margin pellucid-striate. Context thin, white, very waxy; odor and taste mild.

    Lamellae uncinate, snow white, subdistant, rather broad, ventricose, edges even.

    Stipe 4–8 cm long, 3–8 mm thick, white and shining, base tinged pinkish red where wounded, equal or tapered slightly either way, sometimes flexuous or curved at the base, glabrous, glutinous, hollow.

    Spores 7–9 × 4–5 μ, ellipsoid, smooth, pale yellow in Melzer's

Fig. 62. *H. purus*

reagent, white in deposit. Basidia 37–58 × 6–7(8) μ, 4-spored, rarely 2-spored. Pleurocystidia and cheilocystidia not differentiated. Gill trama subparallel to very slightly interwoven, hyphae 8–13 μ broad, yellowish in Melzer's reagent. Cuticle of colorless, gelatinous hyphae, 3–6(10) μ broad. No hypodermium differentiated. The pileus trama is of broad, 6–10(20) μ, hyphae which are loosely and radially disposed. Even though radial, the hyphae tend to be interwoven. Clamp connections present on the cuticular hyphae.

HABIT, HABITAT, AND DISTRIBUTION—In deep humus, mixed woods, New York, North Carolina, and Alabama, August–October.

MATERIAL STUDIED—ALABAMA: Burke 86. NEW YORK: Peck (type, from Crogham, Lewis County). NORTH CAROLINA: Hesler 12290.

OBSERVATIONS—Notes on the type: Spores 7–9 × 4.5–5.5 μ, ellipsoid, smooth, pale yellow in Melzer's reagent. Basidia 41–53 × 7–8 μ, 2- and 4-spored. Gill trama subparallel to very slightly interwoven, hyphae 4–8(12) μ broad. Cuticle of gelatinous hyphae. Clamp connections rare on the cuticular hyphae. Hesler's No. 12290, from North Carolina, agrees with the type.

In section the stipe shows a thick outer coating of slender, gelatinous hyphae similar to that found in *H. psittacinus*. Similar hyphae project from the surface of the pileus and become matted together forming the viscid pellicle. *H. purus* has much the stature of *H. calyptraeformis,* but its white pileus and glutinous stipe at once distinguishes it. Peck (1907) says that *H. calyptraeformis* var. *niveus* Cke. scarcely differs from *H. purus,* but we found no cystidia on Peck's type.

125
Hygrophorus singeri Sm. & Hes. var. **singeri**
Sydowia 8: 331. 1954

Hygrocybe singeri (Sm. & Hes.) Singer, Sydowia 11: 355. 1957.

Pileus 1–3 cm broad, conic, becoming broadly conic, color reddish orange to yellow, translucent-striate to disc, blackening in age, glabrous, slimy-viscid. Context very soft, greenish yellow, blackening when cut or bruised; odor and taste not distinctive.

Lamellae ascending and attached at very apex of stipe, pale orange when young and finally greenish yellow, blackening where bruised, close, broad, 2 tiers of lamellulae.

Stipe 4–6 cm long, 3–5 mm thick, equal, pale orange-yellow becoming greenish yellow, blackening where bruised, slimy-viscid over entire length (as in *H. laetus*).

Spores 9–12 × 5–6 μ, elliptic in face view, in side view slightly bean-shaped, smooth, yellowish in Melzer's solution. Basidia 36–42 × 9–11, 4-spored. Pleurocystidia and cheilocystidia none. Gill trama parallel. Cuticle a gelatinous zone of narrow, repent hyphae (an ixocutis). No hypodermium differentiated. Pileus trama of radial hyphae. Clamp connections present. Stipe with narrow hyphae (3–5 μ), gelatinous in KOH and present as an outer layer. Clamp connections present.

HABIT, HABITAT, AND DISTRIBUTION—Scattered on a wet bank under herbaceous plants, Oregon, Washington, Michigan, Mexico, and Argentina.

MATERIAL STUDIED—MICHIGAN: Smith 43520, 43618, 49825. OREGON: Smith 19162 (type, from East Fork, Salmon River, Mt. Hood, about 4300 ft.), 19606. WASHINGTON: Stuntz, Mt. Rainier National Park, Oct. 2, 1952. MEXICO: Singer M1538a. ARGENTINA: Singer M15.

OBSERVATIONS—This species is obviously in the *H. conicus* series, but the character of the viscid stipe is so unusual and striking that it cannot be regarded as other than a major character. One frequently finds specimens of *H. conicus* in which the stipe is soft to the touch and hence subviscid (or even doubtfully viscid in wet weather). These forms, however, are not to be confused with *H. singeri.* The latter often fruits during dry weather and yet the stipe is as viscid as in *H. laetus,* so slimy that it is difficult to hold. The disjunctive distribution of this species, so far as now known, is interesting and peculiar.

126
Hygrophorus singeri var. *albifolius,* var. nov.

Pileus 2–5 cm latus, conicus, deinde conico-umbonatus, glutinosus, ochraceo-luteus, se obscurans deinde virescens, nigrescens siccus; lamellae albae, sub-caeruleae denique nigrae siccae, angustae; stipes 10–12 cm longus, 4–6 mm crassus, glutinosus, omnino flavus vel apice luteus, sub-viridis deinde nigrescens siccus; sporae 9–13 × 6–7.5 μ, ellipsoideae demum oblongae. Specimen typicum in Herb. Univ. Mich.; lectum Willamette, Ore., Nov. 16, 1947, Frank P. Sipe 1057.

Pileus 2–5 cm broad at base, conic, conic-umbonate when expanded, glutinous, ochraceous orange beneath the gluten, becoming darker and then greenish, blackening in drying.

Lamellae white, bluish and finally black when dried, narrow ascending.

Stipe 10–12 cm long, 4–6 mm thick, equal, glutinous, yellow over all or orange at apex, smooth, greenish, and then blackening when bruised.

Spores 9–13 × 6–7.5 μ, elliptic to oblong, hyaline in KOH or content pale bister (from darkening process), yellowish hyaline in Melzer's solution. Basidia 2-spored, 38–50 × 9–14 μ, content often bister in KOH. Pleurocystidia and cheilocystidia none seen. Epicutis of gelatinous narrow interwoven hyphae. Clamp connections absent.

HABIT, HABITAT, AND DISTRIBUTION—Oregon, under fir, Willamette area, Nov. 16, 1947. Frank P. Sipe 1057.

OBSERVATIONS—The specimens had been pressed, which very likely accounts for their completely blackened condition. There are no clamps at the base of the basidium or on the cuticular hyphae. The floccose tissue of the cap revived poorly, and the apparent absence of clamps could be a failure to find them due to the condition of the material.

127
Hygrophorus ruber Pk.
N. Y. State Museum Bull. 116: 32. 1907

Hydrocybe ruber (Pk.) Murr., North Amer. Flora 9: 379. 1916.

Pileus 1.5–5 cm broad, thin, conic, usually not expanded, acute or subobtuse, cuspidate or narrowly umbonate, bright red, not turning black in drying, viscid or glutinous.

Lamellae adnexed, yellow or yellowish brown, narrow, ascending, subdistant.

Stipe about 2 cm long, 2 mm thick, colored like the pileus, equal, viscid, hollow.

Spores 7–9 × 4.5–6 μ, ellipsoid, smooth, pale yellow in Melzer's reagent. Basidia 31–44 × 6–8 μ, 4-spored. Pleurocystidia and cheilocystidia none. Gill trama subparallel to parallel, with scattered lactifers. Cuticle of gelatinous, more or less repent hyphae, 2.5–5 μ broad. No hypodermium. Pileus trama of radially disposed hyphae, lactifers present, 3–4(5) μ broad. Clamp connections present on the cuticular hyphae. Surface hyphae of stipe gelatinous.

HABIT, HABITAT, AND DISTRIBUTION—On soil among moss, in swampy woods, Massachusetts and Florida, September and October.

MATERIAL STUDIED—FLORIDA: Murrill F18739. MASSACHUSETTS: Morris (Peck's type, from Ellis, September).

OBSERVATIONS—This species is distinct from *H. conicus*, which it resembles in shape, more viscid pileus, bright-red stipe, and persistent, unchanging color on drying; and from *H. cuspidatus* by its viscid stipe and small spores. Although in the Florida collection the spores tend to be slightly larger, and some basidia were 2-spored, it otherwise closely resembles the type.

The microscopic characters given above are based on our study of the type. In the original description Peck (1907) gives the spores as 6–7.5 × 4–5 μ, but we found them larger.

SERIES INOLENTES (Bataille) stat. nov.

Subsection Inolentes Bataille, Flore Monogr. Hygrophores, p. 57. 1910.

Characters as given in key to series, page 214.

Type species: *Hygrophorus unguinosus* (Fr.) Fr.

KEY TO SPECIES

1. Pileus dark yellow-brown to deep vinaceous brown fading to pinkish tan ....128. *H. perplexus*
1. Pileus drab to lead color 2
   2. Clamp connections present; pileus near lead color ....
      ....129. *H. unguinosus* var. *unguinosus*
   2. Clamp connections absent; pileus olive brown ....
      ....130. *H. unguinosus* var. *subaromaticus*

128

Hygrophorus perplexus Sm. & Hes.

Sydowia 8: 328. 1954

Illustration:
Fig. 63.

Pileus 1–3 cm broad, obtusely conic with the margin curved in against the gills at first, expanding to broadly campanulate or plane with an obtuse umbo, "Prout's brown" to near "Rood's brown" and slowly developing an olivaceous to orange tinge on margin and also becoming translucent-striate, gradually changing to pale orange-tan or

Fig. 63.
    H. perplexus

pinkish tan, hygrophanous and fading to buff-pink ("light ochraceous salmon" to "light ochraceous buff"), very slimy-viscid. Context very thin and fragile, concolorous with cap and fading like it; odor and taste none.

Lamellae ascending and adnate with a tooth or when full, expanded depressed-adnate (never decurrent), "amber yellow" young, finally "apricot yellow," broad, close to subdistant, edges even.

Stipe 3–5 cm long, 2–5 mm thick at apex, slightly thicker below or equal, slimy-viscid over all, "ochraceous buff" at base, pallid watery-grayish above, finally yellow over all (never seen to have olive tints).

Spores 6–8 × 4–5 μ, ellipsoid to ovoid, smooth, hyaline in KOH, yellowish in Melzer's reagent. Basidia 36–44 × 7–9 μ, 4-spored. Pleurocystidia and cheilocystidia none seen. Gill trama subparallel to very slightly interwoven, hyphae 6–12 μ broad, subhymenium not distinctive. Pileus trama homogeneous beneath a gelatinous cuticle (an ixotrichodermium) of narrow, branched hyphae arranged in a turf 75 to 100 μ high, composed of slender hyphae (1.5–2.5[6] μ broad). No hypodermium differentiated. Pileus trama of interwoven, radially disposed hyphae. Clamp connections present on the cuticular hyphae, but small and difficult to demonstrate.

HABIT, HABITAT, AND DISTRIBUTION—Gregarious to subcaespitose under aspen and beech on thin sandy soil, Michigan, June.

MATERIAL STUDIED—MICHIGAN: Brooks & Smith 21491 (type, Univ. of Mich. Biological Station, Cheboygan County, June 26, 1946); McKnight, Pellston, July 2, 1953; Singer, Cheboygan Co., July 1, 1953; Smith 21615, 32279, 34029, 36442, 39000; Smith & Brooks 1098, 1099.

OBSERVATIONS—This species has the stature of *H. psittacinus* and the colors of the dried fruiting bodies are similar, but is not to be considered a color-form of that species. The dark brown to vinaceous brown young pilei are significantly different as species go in this group. This agaric has been observed in the Great Lakes Region for the last twenty years, but it was not until the mycological program was started at the University's Biological Station that localities were found where the fungus fruited regularly and could be observed from season to season. Some investigators would probably refer this species to *H. sciophanus*, but we believe that there is a fundamental difference between it and the true *H. sciophanus*. Fries (1874) placed the latter between *H. colemannianus* and *H. laetus* in his subsection containing species with "Lamellis decurrentibus," whereas *H. psittacinus* was placed in the following section with gills adnexed to somewhat seceding. *H. perplexus* is so like *H. psittacinus* in gill characters that Fries certainly would have placed it beside that species if he had seen it. J. Lange's (1935–40) account of *H. sciophana* establishes a concept closely in line with that of Fries, and to us indicates a species different from *H. perplexus*. Confusion may have been caused by the description of Fries (1863) in his "Monographia" where (p. 18) the gills are described as "attenuato-adnatae, primities leviter adscendentes," but even here he placed the species next to *H. laetus*. In the same description he described the stipe of *H. sciophanus* as "lubricus," but this should not be misinterpreted as he applied the same term to the stipe of *H. laetus* in the following description. The *H. sciophanus* of Kühner and Romagnesi (1953) is probably *H. perplexus* since they arranged it next to *H. psittacinus*—but they omitted any reference to the type of gill attachment.

129

Hygrophorus unguinosus (Fr.) Fr. var. unguinosus
Epicr. Myc., p. 332. 1838

> *Hygrophorus luridus* B. & C. sensu Coker, Elisha Mitchell Sci. Soc. Jour. 45: 168. 1929.
> *Hygrocybe unguinosa* (Fr.) Karst. 1879.

Illustrations:
Fig. 64.
Coker, Elisha Mitchell Sci. Soc. Jour. 45, frontispiece and p. 23.
Bresadola, Icon. Myc., tab. 352.
Juillard-Hartmann, Icon. Champ., pl. 48, fig. 3 (as *H. irrigatus* var.
unguinosus).
Lange, Flora Agar. Dan. 5, pl. 168I (as *Hygrocybe*).
Smith and Hesler, Lloydia 5, pl. 15a.
Wakefield and Dennis, Common British Fungi, pl. 33, fig. 2.

Pileus 2–5 cm broad, hemispheric becoming convex and finally nearly plane, occasionally obtusely conic, slightly umbonate when expanded, hygrophanous, blackish to umber or dark grayish brown, near "drab," "pale smoke gray," glabrous, at times minutely rivulose, glutinous to slimy-viscid when moist, shining when dry, becoming smoke gray on the disc and pallid along the margin in age, translucent striate. Context thin, soft, fragile, grayish or white; odor none, taste mild.

Lamellae adnate to slightly adnexed, at times emarginate, with a decurrent tooth, broad (up to 10 mm), at times subventricose, thick, subdistant, intervenose, white or shaded pale gray, at times "cinereous," edges even.

Stipe 3–9 cm × 2–5 mm, concolorous with or paler than the pileus, equal and flexuous, fragile, glabrous, slimy or viscid when moist, varnished when dry, tubular.

Spores $(6)7–10 \times 4–5(6)$ μ, ellipsoid, smooth, white in mass, yellowish in Melzer's reagent. Basidia $36–55 \times 5–8$ μ, 1-, 2-, and 4-spored. Pleurocystidia and cheilocystidia none. Gill trama subparallel to slightly interwoven, hyphae 7–20 μ broad, yellowish in Melzer's reagent. Lactifers numerous in the pileus and gill trama. Cuticle an ixotrichodermium composed of a zone of repent, brownish hyphae bearing more or less erect and tangled, almost colorless hyphae 2–4 μ broad (not a palisade). Hypodermium rather distinct. Pileus trama of radial hyphae. Clamp connections present but rare, of the medallion type.

Habit, Habitat, and Distribution—Gregarious to scattered on humus and soil, in coniferous and mixed woods, in swamps, Nova Scotia and Ontario in Canada, Maine, Massachusetts, New York, North Carolina, South Carolina, Tennessee, Florida, Michigan, Washington, and California, June–December; also Europe.

Material Studied—california: Smith 3781, 9376, 9406. florida: Murrill F17268. maine: Bigelow 3696, 3870, 4306. massachusetts: Bigelow 8417, 9117. michigan: Brooks 1251; Saunders 32547; Smith 4983, 6723, 6828, 9619, 18472, 18616, 21859, 25953, 26050, 33590, 37806,

Fig. 64. *H. unguinosus* var. *unguinosus*

37773, 39221, 39273, 39333, 39578, 39653, 42610; Thiers 1117, 1238, 3327. NEW YORK: Bigelow 5060, 5066. NORTH CAROLINA: Hesler 8199, 10874, 12361, 17045; Holland 3353; Sharp & Hesler 9320; Smith 9767; Smith & Hesler 7440. TENNESSEE: Hesler 12170, 12757; Smith 9903, 10084; Smith & Hesler 7452, 11333, 13734. WASHINGTON: Smith 17965. CANADA: (Ontario) Cain, Sept. 7, 1936; (Nova Scotia) Smith 875. BELGIUM: Heinemann, near Brussels, Nov. 1, 1960. DENMARK: J. P. Jensen (Hesler 23954). AUSTRIA: Moser, Aug. 27, 1948 (Hesler 24126).

OBSERVATIONS—This is a striking species because of its contrasting gray to dark umber colors and whitish to pale-gray gills. It appears to be rare but widely distributed. Bresadola (1928) found a 2-spored form with spores 8–9 × 7 μ. *H. irrigatus* was placed by Fries in section *Camarophyllus*, but Konrad (1936) places it in synonymy with *H. unguinosus*, a disposition which, in accordance with its gill trama structure, is correct. *H. luridus* B. & C. sensu Peck (1907) and sensu Coker (1929) does not appear to be distinct from *H. unguinosus*. Both are characterized by their dark colors, very viscid stipes, and whitish to pale-grayish gills. Neither Coker nor Peck discussed *H. luridus* in relation to *H. unguinosus*. Our specimens are all referable to the Friesian species.

Josserand (1959) reports clamp connections. We have found them to be very rare.

130
Hygrophorus unguinosus var. subaromaticus Sm. & Hes.
Lloydia 5: 81. 1942

Pileus 2–5 cm broad, convex with an incurved margin, becoming plane or nearly so, color "buffy brown" on the disc, "pale olive-buff" near the whitish margin (a dull olive grayish brown to pallid), glabrous, slimy-viscid, margin striatulate. Context thin, very soft and fragile, whitish; odor faint but disagreeably subaromatic, taste mild to slightly disagreeable.

Lamellae bluntly adnate with decurrent tooth, white with a faint gray cast, broad, subdistant, edges even.

Stipe 5–6 cm long, 6–10 mm thick, concolorous with the gills when fresh but drying pale gray like the pileus, equal, hollow, fragile, slimy-viscid as in *H. laetus*, glabrous.

Spores 7–9 × 4–5.5 μ, ellipsoid, smooth, pale yellow in Melzer's reagent. Basidia 42–55 × 7–9 μ, 2- and 4-spored. Pleurocystidia and cheilocystidia not differentiated. Gill trama subparallel, hyphae 7–14 μ broad, yellow in Melzer's reagent. Cuticle a thick (180–300 μ), gelatinous zone, the hyphae narrow, colorless, more or less interwoven (an ixotrichodermium). Hypodermium a rather well-defined brownish zone. Pileus trama of radial hyphae. Clamp connections absent or *very* rare.

HABIT, HABITAT, AND DISTRIBUTION—On soil under redwoods, California, November.

MATERIAL STUDIED—CALIFORNIA: Smith 9167 (type, from Prairie Creek State Park, Orick, Nov. 28, 1937).

OBSERVATIONS—The faint but disagreeably subaromatic odor and almost complete lack of clamps on the hyphae distinguish this variety from the type.

SERIES PSITTACINI

Key to Species

1. Pileus white to whitish 2
1. Pileus colored 3
   2. Lamellae adnexed; stipe 5–10 mm thick .... 131. *H. westii*
   2. Lamellae decurrent; stipe 2–3 mm thick . . 135. *H. laetus* f. *pallidus*
3. Pileus green to blue at first, fading to yellow or vinaceous 4
3. Not as above 5
   4. Pileus green, fading to yellow . . 132. *H. psittacinus* var. *psittacinus*
   4. Pileus blue, then red, finally yellow ....
   .... 133. *H. psittacinus* var. *californicus*
5. Pileus often multicolored—olive, yellow, and reddish intermingled or
   a blend of these, becoming pinkish-vinaceous in age or when dried;
   often with an odor of fish .... 134. *H. laetus*
5. Not fading as in above 6
   6. Pileus yellow when young 7
   6. Pileus red when young 15
7. Pileus convex-depressed young; bright yellow fading to whitish; lamellae typically long-decurrent .... 136. *H. nitidus*
7. Not as above 8
   8. Lamellae adnexed to emarginate or at times becoming free 9
   8. Lamellae broadly adnate to decurrent 10
9. Pileus at maturity deep lemon yellow .... 137. *H. chlorophanus*
9. Pileus at maturity scarlet to orange .... 144. *H. luteistipes*
   10. Cheilocystidia present, cylindric to filamentose 11
   10. Cheilocystidia absent 12
11. Pileus, lamellae, and stipe yellow and remaining so dried ....
   .... 138. *H. hondurensis*
11. Fruit body pinkish-vinaceous when faded or dried ..... 134. *H. laetus*
   12. Stipe white; clamp connections none on hyphae of fruiting body . .
   .... 139. *H. flavifolius*
   12. Stipe colored 13
13. Stipe orange-red at first .... 140. *H. subminutulus*
13. Stipe yellow from the beginning 14
   14. Spores fusoid .... 141. *H. citrinopallidus*
   14. Spores ellipsoid to ovoid .... 142. *H. ceraceus*
15. Taste of pellicle bitter .... 143. *H. reai*
15. Taste mild 16
   16. Spores 5–7 μ long; lamellae broad; stipe red, slowly fading ......
   .... 140. *H. subminutulus*
   16. Spores 7–10 μ long 17
17. Lamellae whitish; stipe yellow; gills nearly free .... 144. *H. luteistipes*
17. Not as above 18
   18. Epicutis of pileus an ixotrichodermium .... 128. *H. perplexus*
   18. Epicutis of pileus of appressed gelatinous hyphae ....
   .... 145. *H. minutulus*

131

Hygrophorus westii Murr.

Lloydia 5: 139. 1942

Pileus 2.5–4 cm broad, convex, expanding-convex, slightly umbili-cate, slimy-viscid, glabrous, pallid with a yellowish tint, disc slightly darker, margin involute, even. Context white, thin; odor somewhat disagreeable, taste mild.

Lamellae adnexed, arcuate, white, close, narrow, tapering behind.

Stipe 2–3 cm × 5–10 mm, white, slimy-viscid, apex white-floccose, enlarged above or below.

Spores (5.5)6–8 × 3.5–4 μ, ellipsoid to subpyriform, smooth, non-amyloid. Basidia 40–48 × 5–9 μ, 4-spored. Pleurocystidia and cheilo-cystidia none. Gill trama composed of parallel to subparallel hyphae. Cuticle an ixotrichodermium, 250–400 μ thick, the hyphae more or less erect, densely tangled, 2–4 μ broad. No hypodermium differentiated. A few lactifers present. Clamp connections on the cuticular hyphae, and occasionally on the lactifers.

HABIT, HABITAT, AND DISTRIBUTION—On soil under oaks, Florida, January.

MATERIAL STUDIED—FLORIDA: West, F19307 (type, from near Hogtown Creek, Gainesville, Jan. 11, 1940).

OBSERVATIONS—The description of microscopic characters given above is based on our study of the type.

In appearance, the dried carpophores resemble those of *H. dis-coideus* (which has divergent gill trama), and Murrill erroneously regarded it as a member of the section *Hygrophorus* (*Limacium*). The pilei of the type (dried) are "ochraceous tawny" to "buckthorn brown," and the lamellae "cinnamon."

132

Hygrophorus psittacinus (Fr.) Fr. var. **psittacinus**

Epicr. Myc., p. 332. 1838

Agaricus psittacinus Fr., Syst. Myc. 1: 102. 1821.
Hygrocybe psittacina (Fr.) Kummer, Führ. in Pilzk., p. 112. 1871.
Illustrations:
Fig. 65.
Boudier, Icon. Myc., pl. 42.
Bresadola, Icon. Myc., tab. 346, fig. 1.
Bulliard, Herb. Fr., pl. 545, fig. 1 (as *Agaricus cameleon*).
Gillet, Champ. Fr., pl. 137 (346).
Hussey, Ill. Brit. Myc., 1. pl. 49.
Juillard-Hartmann, Icon. Champ., pl. 47, fig. 4.
Lange, Flora Agar. Dan. 5, pl. 168D (as *Hygrocybe*).

Murrill, Mycologia 2, pl. 27, fig. 4.
Ricken, Die Blätterp., pl. 8, fig. 6.
Schaeffer, Fung. Bavar., pl. 301.
Smith, Mushrooms in their Natural Habitats, Reel 12, No. 79.
Sowerby, Engl. Fungi, pl. 82.
Wakefield and Dennis, Common British Fungi, pl. 34, fig. 5.

Pileus 1–3 cm broad, conic to campanulate or finally convex to plane, sometimes remaining umbonate, glutinous or viscid, appearing as if varnished when dry, color dark green or "parrot green" when young and fresh, soon fading or changing color to ochraceous buff, rufous, tawny, pinkish flesh color, yellow ocher, sordid yellowish, or olivaceous orange, usually drying bright pale incarnate, translucent striate at first, opaque when faded. Context thin, concolorous with the surface, fragile (but somewhat tenacious because of the thick pellicle); odor and taste not distinctive.

Lamellae adnate, "light celandine green" at first, soon reddish or "cadmium yellow" to "light cadmium," narrow to broad, subdistant, edges even.

Stipe 3–7 cm long, 2–5 mm thick, green above or almost over all when very young, soon changing to yellow or orange, in age pinkish like the pileus, slimy-viscid throughout its entire length, equal or tapering upward slightly, hollow.

Spores 6.5–8(10) × 4–5(6) μ, ellipsoid, smooth, pale yellow in Melzer's reagent. Basidia 28–46 × 6–8 μ, 2- and 4-spored. Pleurocystidia and cheilocystidia not differentiated. Gill trama subparallel or very slightly interwoven, hyphae 5–12(20) μ broad, yellowish in Melzer's reagent. Cuticle (an ixotrichodermium) of narrow (1.2–2.5 μ) hyphae. No hypodermium differentiated. Pileus trama of radial hyphae. Clamp connections none or rare on hyphae of epicutis, more frequently present at base of basidium.

HABIT, HABITAT, AND DISTRIBUTION—Gregarious to scattered in coniferous and deciduous woods, in pastures, and along roadsides; Nova Scotia, Ontario, and British Columbia in Canada; Maine, Massachusetts, New York, Maryland, North Carolina, Tennessee, Michigan, Washington, Oregon, and California; Europe; spring, summer, and autumn. Singer (1950) reports it from Argentina.

MATERIAL STUDIED—CALIFORNIA: Smith 3688, 8898, 9174, 9429, 56916. MAINE: Bigelow 3433; Rea 990. MARYLAND: Kelly 1003. MASSACHUSETTS: Bigelow 7133, 7198, 8420, 9011. MICHIGAN: Imshaug 4804, 4851; Kauffman, Ann Arbor, July 29, 1927; Mains 32767; Smith 1208, 1355, 1412, 1425, 1469, 1499, 6813, 7126, 21320, 25680, 33755, 36456, 37519, 41599; Thiers 2755, 2943, 3288, 3330, 3415, 3625. NORTH

Fig. 65.
H. psittacinus
var. *psittacinus*

CAROLINA: Coker 5110; Sharp & Hesler 9315, 10720; Smith & Hesler 7409, 11774. OREGON: Gruber 39. TENNESSEE: Hesler 4440, 11512, 12426, 13841, 14175, 17493, 18292, 23070; Kauffman, Elkmont, Sept. 19, 1916; Sharp & Hesler 9127, 12818. WASHINGTON: Imshaug 1015, 1089; Smith 3106, 14243, 16517, 17366, 17966, 29817, 29894. CANADA: Bigelow 5541; Smith 660, 4890. BELGIUM: Heinemann 2971. DENMARK: J. P. Jensen (Hesler 23944), 23945, 23946, 23947). NETHERLANDS: Bas 2304.

OBSERVATIONS—Spore measurements vary in collections from one region to another. Kauffman (1918) finds them 6–7.5 × 4–5 μ, J. Lange (1935–40) reports 8 × 5.5 μ, and Bresadola (1928) 8–12 × 4.5–6 μ. There is little possibility that *H. psittacinus* var. *psittacinus* would be confused with any other species or variety if the young stages are found. After the carpophores have changed color, they might be confused with *H. laetus,* or *perplexus,* and dried specimens of these two species are macroscopically indistinguishable. The collector is reminded that in age, or particularly on being dried, all traces of the typical parrot green color disappear.

133
Hygrophorus psittacinus var. *californicus,* var. nov.

Pileus 2–4 cm latus, caeruleus demum ruber, disco fuscus, glutinosus, margine striatus; lamellae adnatae, vinaceo-coriaceae, caeruleo tinctae, deinde ostendunt hinnuli colorem, demum basi flavae, subdistantes, latae; stipes 6–9 cm longus, 3.5–6 mm crassus, apex subcaeruleus, luteus demum infra pallido-aurantius, glutinosus; sporae

8–9(10) × 4–5(5.5) μ, *ellipsoideae. Specimen typicum in Herb. Univ. Mich.; lectum in Prairie Creek State Park, Calif., Dec. 5, 1956, A. H. Smith 56310.*

Pileus 2–4 cm broad, obtusely conic with an incurved margin, expanding to plano-umbonate, "Gobelin blue" on margin and disc "Hay's brown," becoming "mineral red" with a paler disc, "Pompeian red" at times fading out to yellowish, some olive showing at times, entirely glutinous, margin striate when moist. Context thin; odor and taste none.

Lamellae depressed-adnate to nearly free, vinaceous buff with a bluish cast when young, soon "light vinaceous fawn" to "fawn color," gradually yellowish, subdistant, broad, ventricose.

Stipe 6–9 cm long, 3.5–6 mm thick, apex bluish to bluish-vinaceous, pale orange downward but first passing through yellowish, equal or slightly enlarged downward, glutinous, tubular, and cartilaginous.

Spores 8–9(10) × 4–5(5.5) μ, ellipsoid, smooth, pale yellowish in Melzer's reagent. Basidia 42–60 × 7–9 μ, 2- and 4-spored. Pleurocystidia and cheilocystidia none. Gill trama subparallel to slightly interwoven, hyphae 6–15 μ broad. Cuticle (an ixotrichodermium) of narrow (2–3.5 μ) gelatinous. No hypodermium differentiated. Pileus trama of radial hyphae. Clamp connections none or rare and small, on the cuticular hyphae.

Habit, Habitat, and Distribution—Gregarious under conifers, California, December.

Material Studied—california: Smith 56310 (type, Prairie Creek State Park, Dec. 5, 1956), 56523.

Observations—This variety is distinguished from the typical *H. psittacinus* by its blue colors and larger basidia. Smith has collected a form (57304) from Michigan which is blue in age and which may belong here.

134
Hygrophorus laetus (Fr.) Fr.
Epicr. Myc., p. 329. 1838

> *Agaricus laetus* Fr., Syst. Myc. 1: 102. 1821.
> *Hygrocybe laeta* (Fr.) Kummer, Führ. in Pilzk., p. 112. 1871.
> *Hygrophorus peckii* Atk., Jour. Myc. 8: 114. 1902.
> *Hygrophorus davisii* Pk., Torrey Bot. Club Bull. 33: 214. 1906.
> *Hydrocybe davisii* (Pk.) Murr., North Amer. Flora 9: 382. 1916.
> *Hydrocybe roseiceps* Murr., Lloydia 5: 138. 1942.
> *Hygrophorus roseiceps* Murr., Lloydia 5: 157. 1942.

Illustrations:
> Figs. 66 and 67; also 2g.
> Bresadola, Icon. Myc., tab. 340.

Fries, Icon. Hymen., pl. 167, fig. 2.
Gillet, Champ. Fr., pl. 132 (338).
Juillard-Hartmann, Icon. Champ., pl. 50, fig. 16.
Lange, Flora Agar. Dan. 5, pl. 168 F & F¹ (as *Hygrocybe*).
Malencon, Bull. Trimest. Soc. Mycol. France 45, pl. 37.
Ricken, Die Blätterp., pl. 8, fig. 8.
Smith and Hesler, Lloydia 5, pl. 16a.
Wakefield and Dennis, Common British Fungi, pl. 33, fig. 1.

Pileus 1–3.5 cm broad, convex, then plane or depressed, the margin sometimes turned up giving the cap a subinfundibuliform appearance, color variable, when young "pale violet gray" to "light vinaceous gray," often sordid olivaceous orange becoming "Mars orange" to "orange-rufous" at maturity, sometimes "tawny olive," "buff orange," "pinkish buff" or "onion skin pink," glabrous, slimy-viscid, translucent-striate. Context thin, tough, concolorous with the surface or paler; odor none or faintly disagreeable (fishy), taste not distinctive.

Lamellae adnate to decurrent, variously colored (like the pileus), pinkish, pale violet-gray or light vinaceous gray and becoming "buff-pink," edges at times pinkish purple, tough, subdistant, narrow to moderately broad.

Stipe 3–12 cm long, 2–4(6) mm thick, more or less concolorous with the pileus, apex often "pale violet-gray," slimy-viscid, equal, hollow, fairly pliant, glabrous.

Fig. 66. *H. laetus*

Spores 5–7(8) × 3–4(5) μ, broadly ellipsoid, smooth, yellowish in Melzer's reagent. Basidia (25)38–66 × 4–7 μ, 2- and 4-spored. Pleurocystidia none; cheilocystidia 25–52 × 1.5–2.5 μ, slender-filamentous, at times branched, projecting. Gill trama parallel or subparallel, hyphae 7–20 μ broad, the subhymenium usually more or less gelatinizing. Pileus trama homogeneous beneath a thick gelatinous pellicle. Cuticle (an ixotrichodermium) of more or less erect, gelatinous, narrow (1–3 μ) hyphae. No hypodermium differentiated. Pileus trama radial. Clamp connections present on the cuticular hyphae, at times rare.

HABIT, HABITAT, AND DISTRIBUTION—Gregarious on damp soil in woods and on moss in bogs, Canada, Maine, Massachusetts, New York, Maryland, Pennsylvania, West Virginia, North Carolina, Tennessee, Alabama, Florida, Ohio, Michigan, Texas, Idaho, California, Oregon, and Washington; Belgium; May–December. Singer (1951) reports it from South America and Hongo (1951b) from Japan.

MATERIAL STUDIED—ALABAMA: Burke, Montgomery, Dec. 26, 1920, 72, 76, 77, 87. CALIFORNIA: Smith 9146, 9171, 56410. FLORIDA: Singer F490; Murrill F18737 (type of *H. roseiceps*, Feb. 13, 1939). IDAHO: Kauffman, Copeland, Sept. 7, 1922; Wehmeyer, Copeland, Sept. 8, 1922. MAINE: Bigelow 3638, 3784, 4056; Rea, Raymond, Aug. 2, 1940. MASSACHUSETTS: Bigelow 6205, 7018, 7034, 7132, 7222, 8345, 8976; Simon Davis (type of *H. davisii*, from Stow, Aug. 29, 1905). MICHIGAN: Imshaug 4810; Smith 1305, 1560, 1569, 1570, 1607, 6563, 6665, 7698, 9620, 18420, 21853, 21901, 25088, 33166, 33211, 33613, 33624, 44131, 49800, 50112; Thiers 815, 2944, 3239, 3277, 3493, 3552, 3661, 3882. NEW YORK: Cornell Univ. Herb., as *H. peckii* Atk.; Atkinson 20311; Bigelow 5075; Bradfield 13040; Mencke 24239; C. O. Smith 9649, 9733, 9759; Whetzel 9870; A. H. Smith 410 (Univ. Mich. Herb.). NORTH CAROLINA: Coker 2796, 3112; Hesler 4407, 8058, 12268, 24346; King & Hesler 9456; Sharp 4412, 4413; Sharp & Hesler 8249, 9249, 9311, 12747, 14259; Smith & Hesler 7392, 9766, 11726. OHIO: Walters, Cleveland, Aug. 22, 1934. OREGON: Smith 19064, 19218. PENNSYLVANIA: Krieger 1660. TENNESSEE: Bain & Hesler 7904; Hesler 4381, 4430, 4435, 9153, 11543, 12883, 24494; Sharp 7965, 8149; Sharp & Hesler 4404; Sharp & Underwood 7929. TEXAS: Thiers 1816. WASHINGTON: Imshaug 1019, 1792, 1793; Slipp 1167; Smith 2670, 16478, 16652, 29419, 30010, 30446, 30578, 40646; Smith & Bigelow 49085. WEST VIRGINIA: Sharp 12735. CANADA: Bigelow 5870; Groves & Hoare 28859; Jackson, Aug. 28, 1936; Smith 565. BELGIUM: Heinemann 2970.

OBSERVATIONS—The following notes are based on eight collections of *H. peckii* Atk., determined by Atkinson (the type not specified): Spores 5.5–8 × 3.5–5 μ, ellipsoid, smooth, yellowish in Melzer's reagent.

Fig. 67. *H. laetus*

Basidia (25)38–66 × 4–7 μ, 2- and 4-spored. Pleurocystidia none; cheilocystidia filamentous, 26–52 × 1.7–2.5 μ. Gill trama parallel to subparallel. Cuticle of loosely arranged, gelatinous hyphae. Clamp connections rare.

Notes on the type of *H. roseiceps* Murr.: Spores (4.5) 5.5–7 × 4–4.8 μ, ellipsoid to subovoid, smooth, yellowish in Melzer's reagent. Basidia 36–41 × 4–6 μ. Pleurocystidia none; cheilocystidia 34–42 ×

1.5–2 μ. Gill trama of subparallel hyphae. Cuticle of loosely interwoven, gelatinous hyphae, 1.5–2 μ broad. Clamp connections rare on the cuticular hyphae.

Notes on the type of *H. davisii* Pk.: Spores 5.5–7 × 3.5–4.5 μ, ellipsoid, smooth, yellowish in Melzer's reagent. Basidia 29–48 × 5.5–7 μ 2- and 4-spored. Pleurocystidia none; cheilocystidia 32–65 × 1–2 μ, clustered, cylindric-filamentous, at times slightly branched. Gill trama subparallel, hyphae 4–10 μ broad. Cuticle of gelatinous hyphae. Clamp connections present on the cuticular hyphae.

H. laetus is variable in many characters. On material from Michigan the spores from deposits measure 5–6 × 3–3.5 μ. On specimens from Tennessee they were 6–8.5 × 4–5 μ. An examination of a series of specimens, however, showed considerable intergradation; consequently we do not regard difference in spore size as significant. Fresh specimens vary in color, but there is intergradation, and when dried all collections are uniformly and characteristically a beautiful "flesh color" to "orange pink," and all exhibit the typical filamentous cheilocystidia.

Orton (1960) has described *H. xanthochrous* from England, a species which is related to *H. laetus*, but differs in its colors and in its lack of cheilocystidia. *Hygrophorus houghtonii* Berk. & Br. is listed as a synonym by Dennis, Orton, and Hora (1960).

135

Hygrophorus laetus f. pallidus Sm.
Papers Mich. Acad. Sci., Arts and Letters, 38: 59. 1953

Pileus white. Lamellae decurrent, distant, pallid. Stipe glutinous, pallid, same size as in type variety.

HABIT, HABITAT, AND DISTRIBUTION—On soil, Michigan, August.

MATERIAL STUDIED—MICHIGAN: Smith 37616 (type from Pellston, Aug. 11, 1951; collected by Harry Thiers).

OBSERVATIONS—The microscopic characters all agree with those of *H. laetus*, and the typical disagreeable odor was also present. Young stages were found, and the pallid pileus, gills, and stipe were characteristic, so that there is no possibility of the carpophores being merely faded fruiting bodies.

136

Hygrophorus nitidus B. & C.
Ann. Mag. Nat. Hist. II (12): 424. 1853

Hydrocybe nitida (B. & C.) Murr., North Amer. Flora 9: 378. 1916.

Illustrations:
  Fig. 68.
  Smith and Hesler, Lloydia 5, pl. 16b. 1942.

Pileus 1–4 cm broad, when young broadly convex or flattened and with an incurved margin, disc very soon becoming depressed, in age deeply infundibuliform, the margin either spreading or remaining decurved, "primuline yellow" to "apricot yellow," over all at first, fading to whitish or pale cream color, glabrous, viscid, striatulate when moist. Context soft, fragile, very thin, yellowish, fading to white; odor and taste not distinctive.

Lamellae arcuate at first, soon long-decurrent, pale yellow, edges often deeper yellow, subdistant to distant, narrow, moderately broad in age, intervenose, very fragile and easily broken, edges even.

Stipe 3–8 cm long, 2–5 mm thick, concolorous with the pileus at first, fading to whitish, fragile, equal or slightly enlarged above, flexuous at times, surface viscid and glabrous, glistening when dry, hollow.

Spores 6.5–8(9) × (3.5)4–5(6) μ, ellipsoid to subovoid, smooth very pale yellow in Melzer's reagent. Basidia 34–45 × 5–7 μ, 4-spored. Pleurocystidia and cheilocystidia not differentiated. Gill trama of subparallel to slightly interwoven hyphae of very large cells (40–135 × 10–32 μ). Cuticle (an ixocutis) a zone of gelatinous, repent hyphae. No hypodermium differentiated. Pileus trama of radial hyphae. Clamp connections present on the hyphae of the cuticle and pileus trama.

HABIT, HABITAT, AND DISTRIBUTION—Gregarious to scattered on humus, on wet soil, and in bogs; Nova Scotia and Ontario in Canada, and Maine, Massachusetts, New Jersey, New York, Pennsylvania, Michigan, Washington, North Carolina, South Carolina, Florida, Alabama, Tennessee, July–October.

MATERIAL STUDIED—ALABAMA: Burke 81. MAINE: Bigelow 3408, 3490, 3782; Rea 470, 537, 642. MASSACHUSETTS: Bigelow 7671, 8289, 8303, 9131. MICHIGAN: Bigelow, Emmet Co., 1955; Kauffman 328, Bay View, Aug. 24, 1905; Mains 32–107, 32111; Potter 3909; Povah P306; Smith 1259, 7030, 9621, 18404, 18764, 21856, 32575, 33586, 37074, 37791, 49997, 50100; Thiers 3268, 3343, 3438, 3635, 3897, 4017, 4042, 4204, 4291. NEW JERSEY: Ellis & Everhart, N. A. Fungi 22. NEW YORK: Ellis, Aug. 17, 1882. NORTH CAROLINA: Coker 5624; Hesler 12190, 13951, 14260, 16324; Sharp & Hesler 9312, 12745; Smith 10148. PENNSYLVANIA: Kauffman, Mt. Gretna, Sept. 4, 1924. TENNESSEE: Smith 9832, 10864. WASHINGTON: Kauffman, Cascade Mts., Sept. 18, 1915. CANADA: Bigelow 5664, 5882; (Ontario) Cain, Sept. 3, 1936; Kelly 884, 1180, 1231; Krieger 1709; Smith 632.

Fig. 68. *H. nitidus*

OBSERVATIONS—We have not seen the type, which is from South Carolina, but have studied Ellis' collection at the New York Botanical Garden which Murrill, in turn, found to agree with the type at Kew. M. Lange (1955) reports *H. vitellinus* Fr. sensu Möller, from Greenland, and believes it to be different from *H. nitidus*. In the latter, he points out, the hyphae of the gill trama are much broader than those of *H. vitellinus*, and the stipe is more slender.

137
Hygrophorus chlorophanus (Fr.) Fr.
Epicr. Myc., p. 332. 1838

> *Agaricus chlorophanus* Fr., Syst. Myc. 1: 103. 1821.
> *Hygrocybe chlorophana* (Fr.) Wünsche, Die Pilze, p. 112, 1877.

Illustrations:
  Boudier, Icon. Myc., pl. 41.
  Bresadola, Icon. Myc., tab. 341, fig. 1.
  Fries, Icon. Hymen., pl. 167, fig. 4.
  Gillet, Champ. Fr., pl. 139 (329).
  Juillard-Hartmann, Icon. Champ., pl. 50, fig. 13.
  Lange, Flora Agar. Dan. 5, pl. 166 B & D
  Lucand, Champ. Fr., pl. 94.
  Murrill, Mycologia 2, pl. 27, fig. 3.

Peck, N. Y. State Mus. Mem. 3, pl. 51, figs. 13–20.
Thomas, Field Book of Common Gilled Mushrooms, pl. 10, fig. 58.
Wakefield and Dennis, Common British Fungi, pl. 35, fig. 1.

Pileus 2–4 cm broad, convex then expanded, deep lemon yellow, disc at times orange-yellow, viscid, margin striate. Context thin, yellowish; odor and taste mild.

Lamellae adnexed, becoming emarginate, whitish to yellowish, rather close, narrow in front.

Stipe 3–7 cm long, 4–8 mm thick, viscid, concolorous with the pileus, hollow, glabrous, equal, at times more or less compressed.

Spores 6–8 × 4–5 μ, ellipsoid, smooth, yellow in Melzer's reagent. Basidia 34–48 × 5–8 μ, 4-spored. Pleurocystidia and cheilocystidia none. Gill trama parallel, hyphae 8–11(21) μ broad. Lactifers numerous, conspicuously yellow in Melzer's reagent, 3–5 μ broad. Cuticle (an ixocutis) in the form of a thin zone of gelatinous, repent hyphae. No hypodermium differentiated. Pileus trama of radial hyphae. Clamp connections rare on the cuticular hyphae.

HABIT, HABITAT, AND DISTRIBUTION—On soil, in open woods, Maine, Massachusetts, Michigan, Tennessee, Idaho, and Washington; Denmark; April–October.

MATERIAL STUDIED—IDAHO: Smith 54397. MAINE: Bigelow 3142, 3526. MASSACHUSETTS: Bigelow 8162. MICHIGAN: Smith 57351. TENNESSEE: Smith & Hesler 21351. WASHINGTON: Smith 49129. DENMARK: J. P. Jensen, four collections (Hesler 23925a, 23926, 23927, 23928).

OBSERVATIONS—In our previous studies (Smith and Hesler, 1942, p. 68), it was stated that we had not seen fresh material. Since then, fortunately, collections have been made by us as indicated above.

138
Hygrophorus hondurensis (Murr.) Murr.
Mycologia 4: 332. 1912

Hydrocybe hondurensis Murr., Mycologia 3: 197. 1911.

Illustrations:
Fig. 69; also 2h.
Smith and Hesler, Lloydia 5, pl. 17.
Dennis, Kew Bull. 2, fig. 9.

Pileus 1–1.5 cm broad, convex to plane, slightly depressed, red to luteous, very viscid, radiate-striate. Context deep yellow, thin.

Lamellae short-decurrent, ivory yellow, rather narrow, subdistant, inserted.

Stipe 3–4 cm long, 1–2 mm thick, lemon to deep chrome, very viscid, equal.

Spores 5–7 × 3–4.5 μ, ellipsoid, smooth, pale yellowish in Melzer's reagent. Basidia 34–43 × 5–6 μ, 2- and 4-spored. Pleurocystidia none; cheilocystidia abundant or rare, 28–36 × 1.5–2.3 μ, cylindric. Gill trama subparallel. Cuticle gelatinous, fibrillose, the hyphae repent to more or less erect. Clamp connections present on the cuticular hyphae.

HABIT, HABITAT, AND DISTRIBUTION—On soil, British Honduras, Trinidad, Florida, Michigan, and Washington, August–October.

MATERIAL STUDIED—BRITISH HONDURAS: Morton E. Peck (type, deposited in New York Bot. Gard. Herb., 1906). FLORIDA: Singer F560A. MICHIGAN: Smith 57505. TRINIDAD: Dennis 91, 91B (Kew Herb.). WASHINGTON: Smith 18021.

OBSERVATIONS—The type consists of one carpophore in which the lamellae have in part been devoured, and the pileus is slightly moldy. The description of the microscopic characters given above is based on our study of the type.

Dennis (1953) has compared the type with his two collections from Trinidad (No. 91, September 29, 1949; and No. 91B, October 27, 1949). He reports the pileus in his collections grenadine red to light cadmium; the context hygrophanous, deep yellow; the lamellae ivory yellow, subdistant; the spores 5.5–8 × 3–4.5 μ; a cystidia none. There is

Fig. 69. *H. hondurensis*

a possibility that the collections by Dennis represent an undescribed species, as the red pileus, in contrast to the colors as Murrill described them, could be significant.

A form intermediate between *H. laetus* and *H. hondurensis* was found in a pasture at Cape Flattery, Washington, Oct. 19, 1941 (Smith 18021). It is much more cartilaginous than *H. laetus,* dries a dull yellow instead of pink, has gelatinous cheilocystidia, a thick gelatinous subhymenium, and also thick gelatinous layers over both pileus and stipe. The fresh fruiting bodies are clear pale yellow and faded, as if hygrophanous to nearly white. When dried, however, all pilei regained their yellow color. In all probability these specimens should be classified in *H. hondurensis.* We believe it likely that future studies of *H. hondurensis* from the American tropics will reveal that it characteristically has the filamentous cheilocystidia.

139
Hygrophorus flavifolius Sm. & Hes.
Lloydia 5: 72. 1942

Hygrocybe flavifolia (Sm. & Hes.) Singer, Lilloa 22: 154. 1951.

Pileus (1)2–4 cm broad, obtusely conic, becoming convex to nearly plane, color evenly "apricot yellow" (a full bright yellow), soon fading to whitish over the disc, in age yellowish only along the margin, pallid over all when dried, glabrous and translucent striate to the disc, entire surface slimy-viscid. Context whitish, thin, fragile; odor and taste mild, no color change on bruised portions.

Lamellae broadly adnate, "cadmium yellow" (brilliant orange-yellow) and retaining their color when dried, not fading in age, subdistant, broad, veined at the base, edges even.

Stipe 4–5 cm long, 3–7 mm thick, white at all stages, equal or narrowed below, hollow, very slimy-viscid (as in *H. laetus*).

Spores 7–9 × 4–5 μ, ellipsoid, smooth, yellowish in Melzer's reagent. Basidia 32–46 × 5–6(8) μ, 4-spored. Pleurocystidia and cheilocystidia not differentiated. Gill trama subparallel to somewhat interwoven, hyphae 10–25 μ broad; lactifers present. Cuticle a zone of gelatinous repent hyphae, an ixocutis. Hypodermium not differentiated. Pileus trama of radial hyphae.

HABIT, HABITAT, AND DISTRIBUTION—Gregarious under redwoods, California, November.

MATERIAL STUDIED—CALIFORNIA: Smith 9164 (type, from Prairie Creek State Park, Orick, Nov. 28, 1937).

OBSERVATIONS—This very distinct species is well characterized by its obtuse, yellow, glutinous pileus, persistently bright-colored gills and very glutinous stipe. It is closely related to *H. psittacinus* but differs in color at all stages.

140
Hygrophorus subminutulus (Murr.) Orton
Trans. Brit. Mycol. Soc. 43: 176. 1960

> *Hydrocybe subminutula* Murr., Torrey Bot. Club Bull. 67: 233. 1940.

Pileus 7–10 mm broad, convex to subexpanded, rarely depressed, gregarious, viscid, glabrous, red, soon fading to yellow but often retaining the red color in the center, margin even.

Lamellae arcuate-decurrent, pale yellow, distant, broad, inserted.

Stipe 1.5–2.5 cm long, 1–2 mm thick, red, not soon fading, viscid, glabrous, tapering downward.

Spores 5–7 × 2.5–3.5 μ, ellipsoid, smooth, yellowish in Melzer's reagent. Basidia 28–35 × 5–7 μ, 4-spored. Pleurocystidia and cheilocystidia none. Gill trama subparallel. Cuticle of gelatinous hyphae which are subparallel radially (with several free ends). Clamp connections few.

HABIT, HABITAT, AND DISTRIBUTION—On soil, under hardwoods, Florida, November. Orton (1960) reports it from England.

MATERIAL STUDIED—FLORIDA: Murrill F18392 (type, from Gainesville, Nov. 7, 1938).

OBSERVATIONS—The description of microscopic characters given above is based on our study of the type. Murrill states that the short stipe and small spores separate it from near relatives. Aside from spore size, there is little by which to distinguish it from *H. minutulus* Pk. Additional collections are needed to ascertain whether or not it can always be separated from *H. minutulus* on spore size. Orton (1960) gives a full description of British collections and points out that the stipe-apex nearly always is persistently red, as Murrill (1940) observed. Orton gives the spores as 5–7(8) × 2.5–3.5(4) μ. We find those of *H. minutulus* to be 7.5–9(10.3) × 4–5(6) μ. This difference in width is probably significant.

141
Hygrophorus citrinopallidus Sm. & Hes.
Sydowia 8: 327. 1954

Pileus 8–12 mm broad, convex, becoming broadly convex to turbinate, lemon yellow fading to white, somewhat striate both before and after fading, viscid, margin often very irregular. Context yellow, fading to white; odor and taste not distinctive.

Lamellae long-decurrent, close to subdistant, broad in mid-portion, faces cream color in young caps but lemon yellow in age and unchanging when the cap has faded to whitish.

Stipe 10–15 mm long, 2–3 mm thick at apex, lemon yellow like the pileus and fading to white, narrowed downward, glabrous, and shining, viscid.

Spores 7–9(10) × 4.5–5 μ, broadly fusoid in face view, inequilateral in side view, smooth, hyaline, yellowish in Melzer's reagent. Basidia 40–45 × 6–8 μ, 4-spored, with a dense content of oil globules (hymenium yellow in section). Pleurocystidia and cheilocystidia none seen. Gill trama interwoven to almost cellular because of the broad short cells (as seen in sections), yellow in water mounts of fresh material and when revived in KOH. Cuticle a thin ixocutis of gelatinous, repent hyphae. No hypodermium differentiated. Pileus trama of radial hyphae. Clamp connections.

HABIT, HABITAT, AND DISTRIBUTION—Scattered on tundra-like bank, 5000 ft. elevation, Washington, September–October.

MATERIAL STUDIED—WASHINGTON: Smith 40851 (type, from Mt. Rainier National Park, Oct. 12, 1952), 48071, 48070, 47734; Stuntz 30608.

OBSERVATIONS—This species would be identical with *H. vitellinus* Fr. were it not for the fusoid spores. Rea (1922) describes the spores of the specimens he found as broadly elliptical, 8–9 × 6 μ. Nüesch (1922) gives the dimensions as 5–8 × 3–5 μ and also describes them as ellipsoid. Since the spores of the Mt. Rainier collection are clearly broadly fusoid in face view and inequilateral in side view, we believe the American collection represents a distinct species. J. Lange (1940) comments on the confusion between *H. ceracea* and *H. vitellina*. His *Hygrocybe citrina* (Rea) Lange, however, does not have sufficiently decurrent, bright-yellow gills to represent our species. There is, of course, the possibility that we have the "true" *H. vitellinus*, but this should be proven from examination of spores from authentic material before trying to change existing concepts. Möller (1945) has given what we consider to be the best account of *Hygrocybe vitellina* and figures and describes the spores as ellipsoid and 6–8 × 4.5–5 μ. M. Lange (1955) reporting *Hygrophorus vitellinus* from Greenland gives the spores as subcylindric, 7.5–9 × 4–5 μ.

142

Hygrophorus ceraceus (Fr.) Fr.

Epicr. Myc., p. 330. 1838

Agaricus ceraceus Fr., Syst. Myc. 1: 102. 1821.
Hygrocybe ceracea (Fr.) Kummer, Führ. in Pilzk., p. 112. 1871.
Hygrocybe nitida var. lutea Murr., Torrey Bot. Club Bull. 66: 159.
    1939.
Illustrations:
    Boudier, Icon. Myc., pl. 39.
    Jacquin, Misc. Austr. 2, pl. 15, fig. 2.
    Juillard-Hartmann, Icon. Champ., pl. 50, fig. 9.
    Murrill, Mycologia 2, pl. 27, fig. 2.
    Sowerby, Engl. Fungi, pl. 20.
    Wakefield and Dennis, Common British Fungi, pl. 34, fig. 4.

Pileus 1–4 cm broad, convex, becoming broadly convex or obtuse, at times the disc flattened or slightly depressed, "light orange-yellow" to "wax yellow," fading to "straw yellow," glabrous, slightly viscid, hygrophanous, translucent striate to the disc when moist. Context yellowish, very soft and fragile; odor and taste not distinctive.

Lamellae broadly adnate to subdecurrent, pale yellow to nearly white, broadest at base, at times almost triangular, subdistant, thickish, edges even.

Stipe 2–5 cm long, 2–4 mm thick, concolorous with the pileus, equal, terete or compressed, glabrous, slightly viscid but soon dry, often undulating, hollow.

Spores 5.5–8 × 4–5 μ, broadly ovoid to subellipsoid, smooth, yellowish in Melzer's reagent. Basidia 30–45 × (4)5–7 μ, 4-spored. Pleurocystidia and cheilocystidia not differentiated. Gill trama of subparallel to slightly interwoven hyphae, cells 8–12(24) μ broad. Cuticle of repent hyphae, a few of the surface hyphae gelatinous, forming a thin ixocutis. No hypodermium differentiated. Pileus trama of radial hyphae. Clamp connections rare on the cuticular hyphae of the stipe and pileus.

HABIT, HABITAT, AND DISTRIBUTION—Scattered to gregarious on moss and soil, Massachusetts, New York, Pennsylvania, North Carolina, Tennessee, Alabama, Florida, Michigan, Washington, Oregon, and California, July–January; also Canada and Europe.

MATERIAL STUDIED—ALABAMA: Burke, Montgomery Co., Dec. 21, 1921. CALIFORNIA: Lewis, Santa Barbara, Jan. 6, 1939. FLORIDA: Murrill (type of H. nitidus var. luteus, Gainesville, Aug. 13, 1938). MASSACHUSETTS: Bigelow 8315. MICHIGAN: Smith 7261, 21534, 33745, 37021, 37056, 41761, 41777, 42263, 42663; Thiers 1108, 3309, 3348, 3637. NEW YORK: Bigelow 5049; Kauffman, Ithaca, Aug. 19, 1904, and North Elba,

Sept. 1, 1914; Smith 1064; Snell 8178. NORTH CAROLINA: Sharp & Hesler 9318. OREGON: Wehmeyer, Mt. Hood, Oct. 10, 1922. PENNSYLVANIA: Kauffman, Mt. Gretna, Sept. 1 and 10, 1926. TENNESSEE: Hesler 9512, 10929; Smith & Hesler 7403, 7406, 10080, 10155, 10734. WASHINGTON: Smith 3197. CANADA: Hoare 21895; Smith 678, 4011, 4124; (Quebec) Bigelow 5736, 5814.

OBSERVATIONS—The viscid pellicle is very difficult to demonstrate in dried material because of its poor organization. The same is true for the gelatinous layer over the stipe. In studying only dried material one would very likely conclude that neither the pileus nor the stipe was viscid. The less depressed pileus, the more adnate gills, and the failure of the pileus to fade to white distinguish *H. ceraceus* from *H. nitidus*. Murrill's *Hygrocybe nitida* var. *lutea* is the same as *H. ceraceus*.

143
Hygrophorus reai Maire
Trans. Brit. Mycol. Soc. 3 (3): 170. 1910

> *Hygrocybe reai* (Maire) J. Lange, Studies in Agarics of Denmark, V. Dansk Bot. Arkiv. 4: 25. 1923.

Illustrations:
    Fig. 70.
    Lange, Flora Agar. Dan. 5, pl. 168A (as *Hygrocybe*).
    Wakefield and Dennis, Common British Fungi, pl. 36, fig. 3.
    Wakefield and Dennis, Trans. Brit. Mycol. Soc. 3, tab. 11.

Pileus 1–3 cm broad, convex when young, becoming broadly convex in age, "grenadine red" to "flame scarlet" (brilliant red) on the disc, "deep chrome" (brilliant orange) toward the margin, in age fading to "deep chrome" over all, glabrous, viscid, faintly translucent striate toward the minutely crenate margin. Context concolorous with the surface and fading with it, brittle, thin (1.5–2.5 mm near the stipe); odor none, taste very bitter.

Lamellae bluntly adnate and soon seceding, "light buff" when young, becoming "straw yellow" (whitish and becoming pale yellow), subdistant (18–24 reach the stipe), 2 tiers of short individuals, broad (4–6 mm), edges even.

Stipe 3–5 cm long, 1.5–3.5 mm thick, concolorous with pileus or paler, usually narrowed below, very fragile, glabrous, viscid, shining, often translucent, surface undulating.

Spores 6.5–8(9) × 4–5.5 μ, ellipsoid, many irregular and variable in shape in dried carpophores, smooth, pale yellow in Melzer's reagent. Basidia 34–43 × 6–8 μ, mostly 4-spored, some 2-spored. Pleurocystidia and cheilocystidia none. Gill trama subparallel, hyphae 6–15 μ broad.

Fig. 70.
H. reai

Cuticle of a thin layer of gelatinous repent hyphae, an ixocutis. Hypodermium none differentiated. Pileus trama of radial hyphae. Clamp connections on the cuticular hyphae.

HABIT, HABITAT, AND DISTRIBUTION—Gregarious under conifers, New York, Michigan, and Washington, July–October; also Europe.

MATERIAL STUDIED—MICHIGAN: Porter & Smith 21149; Smith 32918, 42670. NEW YORK: Stewart, Adirondack Mts., Sept. 1921. WASHINGTON: Imshaug 775, 1286; Smith 18009. DENMARK: J. P. Jensen (Hesler 23951, 23952, 23953). AUSTRIA: Moser, Summer, 1956 (Hesler 24126).

OBSERVATIONS—The bitter pellicle of the pileus distinguishes this species from *H. minutulus*. In other characters they are similar. Further search may reveal its occurrence in areas additional to those given above.

144
Hygrophorus luteistipes Dennis
Kew Bull. 2: 264. 1953

Illustration:
    Dennis, Kew Bull. 2, fig. 10.

Pileus 2 cm broad, hemispheric to campanulate, then expanded, obtusely umbonate, viscid, scarlet to orange, yellowish, striate.

Lamellae adnexed then free, white then eburneous (near cartridge buff), 2 mm broad, edges denticulate.

Stipe citrine-luteous, cylindric, undulate, viscid, solid.

Spores 5–8 × 3–4(6) μ, ellipsoid. Basidia 4-spored. Pleurocystidia and cheilocystidia none. Gill trama parallel, hyphae thin-walled, broad. Cuticle of slender hyphae, embedded in mucilage.

HABIT, HABITAT, AND DISTRIBUTION—Gregarious on soil, in woods, Trinidad.

MATERIAL STUDIED—TRINIDAD: Dennis 424 (type, from Morne Bleu).

OBSERVATIONS—This species, according to Dennis (1953), differs from *H. hondurensis* Murr., *H. minutulus* Pk., *H. subminutulus* Murr., and *H. mucilaginosus* Berk. & Curt. in its almost free gills.

Notes on type: Spores 5.5–8 × 3–5 μ, ellipsoid, smooth, pale yellow in Melzer's reagent. Basidia 32–38 × 5–7 μ, 2-, mostly 4-spored. Pleurocystidia and cheilocystidia none. Gill trama parallel, hyphae 8–16(25) μ broad, thin-walled. Cuticle a gelatinous zone, with tangled hyphae which are colorless, 3–6 μ broad. Clamp connections few.

145
Hygrophorus minutulus Pk.
N. Y. State Mus. Bull. 1 (2): 9. 1887

Hydrocybe minutula (Pk.) Murr., North Amer. Flora 9: 380. 1916.
Illustration:
Fig. 71.

Pileus 5–15 mm broad, convex, then broadly convex to plane, the disc not depressed, "scarlet," "flame scarlet," to "Mars orange," hygrophanous, fading to "antimony yellow," glabrous, appearing silky on drying, distinctly viscid or glutinous, margin striatulate when fresh. Context thin, fragile, concolorous with the surface; odor and taste mild.

Lamellae adnate to adnexed or with a decurrent tooth, "orange buff" to "bittersweet orange," close to subdistant, broad and somewhat ventricose, edges even.

Stipe 1.5–5 cm long, 1–3 mm thick, at first red above, yellowish or whitish below, fading to yellow over all in age, fragile, equal or tapering downward, glutinous or viscid, stuffed, becoming tubular.

Spores 7–10.3 × 4–5(6) μ, ellipsoid, smooth, yellowish in Melzer's reagent. Basidia 30–45 × 5–8 μ, 4-spored. Pleurocystidia and cheilocystidia none. Gill trama of parallel to subparallel hyphae, yellow in Melzer's reagent, cells 6–15 μ broad. Cuticle an ixocutis, of repent, colorless hyphae, at times the surface hyphae are more or less erect. Hypodermium none. Pileus trama of radial hyphae. Clamp connections present on the cuticular hyphae.

Fig. 71. *H. minutulus*

HABIT, HABITAT, AND DISTRIBUTION—Gregarious to scattered on grassy soil, Nova Scotia, New York, Massachusetts, North Carolina, Tennessee, Alabama, Michigan, Texas, Montana, and Oregon, May–October; also Japan (Hongo, 1951a).

MATERIAL STUDIED—ALABAMA: Burke 61, 89. MASSACHUSETTS: Bigelow 6766, 8854. MICHIGAN: Brooks 1255; Smith 18714, 22072, 61296. MONTANA: Kauffman, Echo Lake, July 14, 1928. NEW YORK: Peck (type, from Sandlake, July). NORTH CAROLINA: Coker 8197; Hesler 7332, 8197, 13721, 14387, 22356; Smith 10158. OREGON: Smith 28356. TENNESSEE: Hesler 11556, 12908, 13799, 14429, 19637; Sharp 4399, 19695. TEXAS: Thiers 1862. CANADA: (Nova Scotia) Harrison 44494.

OBSERVATIONS—The following notes have been recorded for the type: Spores 8–10 × 4–5 μ, ellipsoid, smooth, faintly yellow in Melzer's reagent. Basidia 34–48 × 5–7 μ, 4-spored. Pleurocystidia and cheilocystidia none. Gill trama parallel to subparallel, hyphae 4–8 μ broad. Cuticle of more or less repent, gelatinous hyphae 4–8 μ broad. Clamp connections present on the cuticular hyphae.

Hygrophorus subminutulus is similar but has smaller spores. Apparently Coker's material (No. 2791), reported from North Carolina as *H. sciophanus*, is not different from *H. minutulus*.

SECTION HYGROASTER (Singer) Hes. & Sm. stat. nov.

Hygroaster Singer, Sydowia 9: 370. 1955.

Hymenophore waxy; spores nodulose; hymenophoral trama sub-parallel with only a slight divergence toward the subhymenium.

Type species: *Hygrophorus nodulisporus* Dennis.

146
Hygrophorus nodulisporus Dennis

Hygroaster nodulispora (Dennis) Singer, Sydowia 9: 370. 1955.
Illustration:
Dennis, Kew Bull. 2, fig. 4.

Pileus 2.5 cm broad, convex, subumbilicate, silky, black. Context black, thin, hygrophanous.

Lamellae adnato-decurrent, grayish, subdistant, narrow, thick, often forked.

Stipe grayish, cylindric, glabrous, fistulose.

Spores 7–10 × 6–8 μ, ellipsoid, nodulose, nodules obtuse, 1 × 1 μ, non-amyloid. Basidia 48–58 × 7–11 μ, 4-spored, cylindric-clavate. Pleurocystidia and cheilocystidia none. Gill trama of subparallel to woven hyphae which tend to diverge toward the hymenium, permeated by a few dark-staining, vermiform hyphae. Cuticular hyphae 4–11 μ broad.

HABIT, HABITAT, AND DISTRIBUTION—On soil, Trinidad.

MATERIAL STUDIED—TRINIDAD: Dennis 385 (type, from Upper Caura Valley).

OBSERVATIONS—Dennis (1953) states that although this species has spores like those of a *Mycenella*, its whole aspect is that of an *Hygrophorus*. He cites the long basidia and absence of cystidia to indicate an affinity with *Hygrophorus*.

Singer (1955) studied the type at Kew and found the gill trama to have a central strand of fuscous, non-gelatinous, slightly interwoven hyphae, and a hyaline lateral stratum consisting of thin filamentous hyphae, more or less diverging toward the hymenium and imbedded in a gelatinous mass. All hyphae are without clamp connections.

Singer (1955) observed that this is a very distinctive species, undoubtedly a representative of the *Hygrophoraceae* but differing from all other known members of the group by its stellate spores. It also has another unique correlation of characters, viz., bilateral trama and hyphae without clamp connections. Thus, he proposes (1955, p. 370) a new genus, *Hygroaster*.

We are not at all convinced that the amount of divergence observed on the hyphae of the hymenophoral trama is sufficient to place this species in section *Hygrophorus*, a group characterized by divergent gill trama hyphae.

Notes on the type: Spores 7–10 × 6–8 μ, ellipsoid, nodulose, nodules 1–2 × 1–2 μ, blunt. Basidia (40)50–62 × 9–12 μ, 2- and 4-spored. Pleurocystidia and cheilocystidia none. Gill trama of somewhat woven to subparallel hyphae of relatively short cells, tending to diverge toward the hymenium. Lactifers present in the gill and pileus trama. Cuticle of repent or semi-erect hyphae, which are septate, pale fuscous, and 5–10 μ broad. Clamp connections none.

SECTION AMYLOHYGROCYBE sec. nov.

Sporis amyloideis; tramate hymenophorali subregulari.
Species typica: H. metapodius Fr.

OBSERVATIONS—This section is at a level with section *Hygroaster* and *Hygrotrama*, i.e., based on a single character which is out of line with the great majority of the species of *Hygrophorus*. The two species included are more closely related to other species in *Hygrocybe* than to each other, but this hardly invalidates the section as similar situations occur throughout the classification of the *Agaricales*.

KEY TO SPECIES

1. Pileus umbrinous; context reddish where injured; stipe 2–2.5 cm thick . . . . .147. *H. metapodius*
1. Pileus white; stipe 1.5 mm thick; context not changing . . . . .148. *H. translucens*

147

Hygrophorus metapodius Fr.
Epicr. Myc., p. 328. 1838

> *Camarophyllus metapodius* (Fr.) Wünsche, Die Pilze, p. 115. 1877.
> *Hygrocybe metapodia* (Fr.) Moser apud Gams, Die Röhrlinge, Blätter- und Bauchpilze, p. 42. 1955.

Illustrations:
> Bresadola, Icon. Myc., tab. 335.
> Lange, Flora Agar. Dan., pl. 166G.

Pileus 6–8 cm broad, convex to expanded, umbrinous, rufescent, with fuscous squamules, becoming widely areolate-rimose, margin smooth. Context gray, rubescent where bruised, drying black; odor subfarinaceous, taste none.

Lamellae sinuate-adnate, uncinate-decurrent, whitish-cinereous to cinereous-subrufescent, broad, distant, faces venose.

Stipe 4–5 cm long, 2–2.5 cm thick, cinereous-fuscescent, reddish-spotted where bruised, attenuated below, subfibrillose to pruinose.

Spores 6–8 × 3–3.5 μ, obovate-elongate to subcylindric, hyaline. Basidia 28–35 × 6–8 μ, clavate.

HABIT, HABITAT, AND DISTRIBUTION—On soil, Europe and boreal America (Bresadola 1928).

MATERIAL STUDIED—DENMARK: Jensen (Hesler 23966).

OBSERVATIONS—Although reported from North America by Bresadola, we have not seen material of this species from North America. It probably has been confused with *H. ovinus*, which has larger, non-amyloid spores.

The description given above is based on Bresadola (1928). Our notes on the Danish collection, kindly communicated to us by Dr. Morten Lange and Mr. J. P. Jensen, are as follows: Spores 6–7 × 3–3.5(4) μ, ellipsoid to phaseoliform, smooth, amyloid. Basidia 42–50 × 6–7 μ, 4-spored. Pleurocystidia and cheilocystidia none. Gill trama subparallel, hyphae (5)10–16 μ broad. Cuticle a cutis of fuscous, nongelatinous hyphae. Pileus trama of more or less radial hyphae.

Apparently the odor varies from faint to strongly farinaceous.

148
Hygrophorus translucens (Murr.) Murr.
Mycologia 35: 433. 1943

> *Camarophyllus translucens* Murr., Mycologia 35: 424. 1943.
> *Hydropus translucens* (Murr.) Singer, Lloydia 9: 118. 1946.

Illustrations:
  Figs. 2i, 2j.

Pileus 1 cm broad, umbilicate, moist but not viscid, white, translucent, glabrous, margin deflexed, entire. Context membranous, pallid; odor none.

Lamellae decurrent, white, few, distant, broad, inserted, entire.

Stipe 1.5 cm long, 1.5 mm thick, white, translucent, glabrous, subequal, not viscid.

Spores 5.5–6.5 × 4.5–5.5 μ, subglobose, or ovoid, smooth, amyloid. Basidia 32–50 × 5.5–8 μ, 2- and 4-spored. Pleurocystidia 40–50 × 7–18 μ, versiform: clavate, ventricose, dumbbell shaped, apices rounded more or more rarely capitate to mucronate, scattered; cheilocystidia

36–52 × 7–12 μ clavate, apices rounded. Gill trama slightly interwoven to subparallel. Clamp connections on the cuticular hyphae. Epicutis a palisade or fascicles of pilocystidia, 58–88 × 9–18 μ, versiform (clavate, cylindric).

HABIT, HABITAT, AND DISTRIBUTION—On soil, under hardwood, Florida, August.

MATERIAL STUDIED—FLORIDA: Murrill F18045 (type, from near Gainesville, Aug. 13, 1938).

OBSERVATIONS—We have not seen fresh material. The above description of macroscopic characters is taken from Murrill (1943); that of the microscopic characters is based on our study of the type.

The nearly globose, amyloid spores, the pleurocystidia, cheilocystidia, and pilocystidia are distinctive characters of *H. translucens*. Under Singer's arrangement (1951), this is called *Hydropus translucens* (Murr.) Singer. The amyloid spores place it *Amylohygrocybe*. A re-study of this species from fresh material may dictate a change in its taxonomic position. It might be a *Mycena*, but since we have not seen it fresh we have no basis for transferring it. The moderately long basidia indicate *Hygrophorus*.

SECTION HYGROPHORUS

Section Limacium Fr. (as "Tribus"), Epicr. Syst. Myc., p. 320. 1838.

Subgenus Limacium Bataille, Flore Monogr. Hygrophores, p. 28, 1910.

Section Colorati Bataille, Flore Monogr. Hygrophores, p. 32. 1910.

Genus Limacium (Fr.) Kummer, Führ. in Pilzk., p. 118. 1871.

Spores smooth; hymenophoral trama of divergent hyphae from a thin to distinct central strand; clamp connections present or absent on hyphae of fruiting body; spores non-amyloid.

Type species: *H. eburneus* Fr.

KEY TO SUBSECTIONS

1. Stipe viscid to slimy from the remains of an outer veil ....Subsection *Hygrophorus*, below
1. Stipe dry; veil if present fibrillose and not gelatinous ....Subsection *Camarophylli*, p. 309

SUBSECTION HYGROPHORUS

Characters as given in Key to Subsections.

149

Hygrophorus chrysodon (Fr.) Fr.
Epicr. Myc., p. 320. 1838

> *Agaricus chrysodon* Fr., Syst. Myc., p. 32. 1821.
> *Limacium chrysodon* (Fr.) Kummer, Führ. in Pilzk., p. 118, 1871.

Illustrations:
  Fig. 72.
  Atkinson, Mushrooms, Edible, Poisonous, etc., fig. 112.
  Batsch, Elench. Fung., fig. 212.
  Bresadola, Icon. Myc., tab. 301.
  Gillet, Champ. Fr., pl. 330.
  Güssow and Odell, Mushrooms and Toadstools, pl. 45.
  Juillard-Hartmann, Icon. Champ., pl. 50, fig. 17.
  Lange, Flora Agar. Dan. 5, pl. 164G.
  Ricken, Die Blätterp., pl. 6, fig. 4.
  Smith and Hesler, Lloydia 2, pl. 3.
  Wakefield and Dennis, Common British Fungi, pl. 19, fig. 4.

Pileus 3–8 cm broad, convex, expanding, subumbonate or obtuse, white and unicolorous except for superficial numerous golden yellow ("apricot yellow") floccose granules on the margin or over all at first, viscid when moist, shining when dry, margin at first involute and white floccose-tomentose. Context white, thick, soft; odor and taste not distinctive.

Lamellae decurrent, white or with yellow powder on the edges, intervenose, distant, moderately broad.

Stipe 3–8 cm long, 6–12(18) mm thick, white, apex with yellow floccules which may form an imperfect zone or ring, equal, viscid, stuffed.

Spores 7–9(10) × 3.5–4.5(5) μ, ellipsoid, often inequilateral, at times curved at the apiculus, smooth, pale yellow in Melzer's reagent, white in mass. Basidia 40–54 × 6–8 μ, 4-spored. Pleurocystidia and cheilocystidia none. Gill trama of divergent hyphae, 4–10 μ broad. Cuticle an ixocutis, a zone of gelatinous hyphae 120–200 μ thick, hyphae 3–5 μ broad, more or less repent, periclinally disposed and parallel, but at intervals exhibiting erect columns of hyphae (the floccose granules). No distinct hypodermium differentiated. Pileus trama compactly interwoven, hyphae both periclinally and radially disposed. Clamp connections present on the cuticular hyphae.

HABIT, HABITAT, AND DISTRIBUTION—On soil, in conifer woods, general in the United States, Canada, and Europe, July–January.

MATERIAL STUDIED—ARIZONA: Lowe 9262. CALIFORNIA: Pusateri 7; Smith 8411, 8846. COLORADO: Cotner, Tolland, Aug. 26, 1920; Smith 52287, 52359, 52518, 52800, 52949. IDAHO: Gruber 525; Smith 15913, 16019, 44621, 44599, 47066, 53332, 53399, 53456, 54547, 58443, 59038, 60203; Smith & Bigelow 42002, 46555; Westerdale & Smith 59652. MICHIGAN: Bailey 142; Smith 1138, 43068, 43975. MONTANA: Smith 57069. NEW MEXICO: Barrows 215. NEW YORK: Kauffman, Ithaca, Oct. 17, 1902; Smith 973. OREGON: Sipe 85; Smith 8013, 8112, 8126, 8901, 9121, 20046, 27947, 28139. TENNESSEE: Hesler 16575, 19472, 20189.

Fig. 72. H. chrysodon

WASHINGTON: Smith 3303, 3357, 14828, 17624, 40586, 40943, 49138; Stuntz 31431. WYOMING: Smith 35373, 35751. SPAIN: Singer, Cabalunya, 1934. BELGIUM: Heinemann 1917.

OBSERVATIONS—This is a widely distributed and easily recognized species. We have not found *H. chrysodon* var. *leucodon* Alb. & Schw. which is said to be characterized by white instead of yellow granules. *H. chrysodon* is very abundant at least during certain seasons in California, Oregon, and Washington, but appears to be rare in Michigan, in the Southeast, and in New York.

SERIES HYGROPHORUS

Subsection Candidi, Bataille, Flore Monogr. Hygrophores, p. 28. 1910.

Characters as given in key to series, page 249.

KEY TO SPECIES

1. Lamellae sinuate ....150. *H. eburneiformis*
1. Lamellae broadly adnate to decurrent 2
  2. Odor distinctly fragrant; pileus and stipe becoming pale dingy pinkish buff in age ....152. *H. cossus*
  2. Odor not distinctive, if basidiocarp discolors 3
3. Stipe typically short and thick (15–35 mm thick); pileus 5–14 cm broad ....156. *H. ponderatus*
3. Stipe (3)5–10(15) mm thick, tapered downward to equal 4
  4. Lamellae brownish in age, when dried they become dark reddish brown ....153. *H. chrysaspis*
  4. Not as above, gills merely dingy-ochraceous as dried 5
5. Spores 10–14 × 6.5–7.5 μ ....155. *H. albiflavus*
5. Spores 7–10 μ long 6
  6. Pileus becoming yellowish in age and when dried the stipe with red-brown punctate at apex ....154. *H. glutinosus*
  6. Pileus remaining white and stipe not punctate with red-brown points in age or when dried ....151. *H. eburneus*

150

Hygrophorus eburneiformis Murr.
Mycologia 30: 364. 1938

Pileus reaching 6 cm broad, convex, umbonate to expanded and irregular, white, smooth, slimy-viscid, margin undulate to lobed. Context white, unchanging, thin, taste mild.

Lamellae sinuate, moderately broad, distant, interveined.

Stipe 4 cm long, 10–20 mm thick, with a satiny sheen, viscid, glabrous, subequal, hollow.

Spores 7–9(10) × 4.2–5(6) μ, ellipsoid, at times somewhat irregular (in dried material), smooth, tinged yellowish in Melzer's reagent. Basidia 37–56 × 6–8(9) μ, 4-spored. Pleurocystidia and cheilocystidia none. Gill trama (in dried material) only slightly or not at all divergent, often slightly interwoven, hyphae 3–10 μ broad. Cuticle of repent, narrow, gelatinous hyphae, 1.5–4 μ broad, the gelatinous zone 100–140 μ thick. No hypodermium differentiated. Pileus trama interwoven, hyphae radially disposed. Clamp connections not found.

HABIT, HABITAT, AND DISTRIBUTION—In leaf mold, under magnolia, Florida, January.

MATERIAL STUDIED—FLORIDA: Murrill 16030 (type, from Alachua Co., Jan. 9, 1938).

OBSERVATIONS—The description of macroscopic characters above is taken from Murrill's (1938) original account. We have studied the type; the description of microscopic characters given above is based on these type studies.

In his Latin description, Murrill (1938) states that the stipe is viscid, although he omits this point in the English version. Sections of dried material do not revive well, and the gill trama does not show the typical divergent condition. A study of revived material of other species of section *Hygrophorus* which were known to have divergent gill trama was made as a comparison, and it was found that in the less robust species the trama does not always revive in such a manner as to show the original arrangement of the hyphae. For this reason further studies of fresh material are desirable on Murrill's species.

151
Hygrophorus eburneus (Fr.) Fr.
Epicr. Myc., p. 321. 1838

> *Agaricus eburneus* Fr., Syst. Myc., p. 33. 1821.
> *Limacium eburneum* (Fr.) Kummer, Führ. in Pilzk., p. 119. 1871.

Illustrations:
> Fig. 73.
> Atkinson, Mushrooms, Edible, Poisonous, etc., fig. 113.
> Bresadola, Icon. Myc., tab. 303.
> Bulliard, Herb. Fr., pl. 551, fig. 2.
> Dufour, Atl. Champ., pl. 19, fig. 41.
> Gillet, Champ. Fr., pl. 122 (335).
> Güssow and Odell, Mushrooms and Toadstools, pl. 46, fig. 2.
> Krieger, Mushroom Handbook, fig. 93.
> Lange, Flora Agar. Dan. 5, pl. 164 E & E^1.
> Murrill, Mycologia 6, pl. 131.
> Ricken, Die Blätterp., pl. 6, fig. 5.
> Schaeff., Fung. Bavar., pl. 39 (as *Agaricus laetus*).
> Smith and Hesler, Lloydia 2, pl. 1.
> Wakefield and Dennis, Common British Fungi, pl. 34, fig. 3.

Pileus 2–7(10) cm broad, obtuse to convex, then plane or umbonate, in age the margin sometimes elevated and the disc depressed, pure white over all, drying whitish or yellowish, glutinous to viscid, glabrous or with a whitish-shining silkiness, margin even and at first involute and floccose-pubescent. Context white, thick on the disc, thin toward the margin; odor and taste mild.

Lamellae somewhat arcuate at first, soon decurrent, subdistant to distant, moderately broad, broadest near the stipe, narrowed in front, pure white, slightly yellowish or buff in age and when dried.

Stipe 4.5–15(18) cm long, 2–8(15) mm thick, equal to somewhat tapered downward or with a greatly attenuated almost vermiform base, flexuous, glutinous, silky beneath the gluten, apex fibrillose, punctate or minutely squamulose, pure white, at times becoming sordid in age, stuffed, then hollow.

Spores 6–8(9) × 3.5–5 μ, ellipsoid, smooth, pale yellow in Melzer's reagent, white in mass. Basidia 42–52 × 6–8 μ, 4-spored. Pleurocystidia and cheilocystidia none. Gill trama of divergent hyphae, 7–12 μ broad.

Fig. 73. *H. eburneus*

Cuticle of gelatinous, narrow (3–6 μ) hyphae which are repent but often with a few to many erect or ascendant free ends. No hypodermium differentiated. Pileus trama of interwoven hyphae, radially disposed. Clamp connections present.

HABIT, HABITAT, AND DISTRIBUTION—On soil, mostly in coniferous woods, thickets, and grassy areas, Canada, Massachusetts, New York, North Carolina, Tennessee, Michigan, Colorado, Idaho, California, Oregon, and Washington, August–January; also Europe.

MATERIAL STUDIED—CALIFORNIA: Eastwood 2, 3; McMurphy 58, 139; Pusateri 61; Smith 8303, 8630. IDAHO: Smith 54348. MASSACHUSETTS: Bigelow 8773; Murrill & Thompson, Stockbridge, Oct. 1911. MICHIGAN: Bailey 105; Smith, Oct. 14, 1931, 1146, 4968. NORTH CAROLINA: Beardslee 15214. OREGON: Gruber 229; Murrill 832, 887; Morton E. Peck, Salem, Jan. 1911; Sipe 87, 88, 465, 8788; Smith 8089, 8909, 9087, 9098, 55423. TENNESSEE: Hesler 9578, 10907, 13052, 17253. WASHINGTON: Smith 2759, 18012, 31843, 40182, 40187, 40573, 40925. CANADA: (Ontario) Kelly 746; Smith 4634; (Quebec) Groves F8764; (British Columbia) Waugh *DAOM* 39340. EUROPE: Bresadola, Oct. 1899; Romell, Sept. 19, 1912. NETHERLANDS: Bas, Oct. 5, 1953. DENMARK: J. P. Jensen (Hesler 23955). BELGIUM: Heinemann 2959. SWITZERLAND: Huijsman, July 9, 1960.

OBSERVATIONS—This is perhaps the commonest species of the section in the United States. In Michigan it has been collected in beech woods, and in addition Kauffman (1918) reported it from thickets and grassy areas. In Tennessee, it grows in both conifer and hardwood forests, and in Oregon and California the same wide range of variability has been observed. In southern Oregon it has been found in exceptionally large quantities in mixed forests of oak and pine. Murrill (1912a) and Zeller (1922) have both commented on the abundance of this species on the West Coast, and it is reported in most of the floristic studies on agarics in this country. The numerous descriptions in the literature agree very well on the important diagnostic characters.

Ordinarily pilei which are not overmature will remain almost pure white if properly dried. Occasionally old specimens may become yellowish or sordid in drying, and if any material is overheated a change in color is almost certain to take place. The base of the stipe nearly always dries darker, especially if water-soaked. Kauffman (1918) recognized *H. eburneus* var. *unicolor* (Pk.) Kauff., but it is believed that this is *H. chrysaspis* Métrod. *H. eburneus* var. *decipiens* (Pk.) Kauff. we have not seen. Kühner (see Kühner and Romagnesi, 1953, p. 58) has described a new variety, var. *carneipes,* which is distinguished by a slightly flesh tint of the lamellae and stipe. *H. eburneus* should not be confused with *H. chrysaspis* Métrod, in which, on drying, the lamellae become reddish brown and the pileus brownish, often the disc blackish. We feel certain that chemical tests will enable these two, and others, to be readily distinguished when fresh, but as yet we have not had an opportunity to apply the tests.

152
Hygrophorus cossus Fr.
Epicr. Myc., p. 321. 1838

> *Limacium cossus* (Sow. ex Fr.) Wünsche, Die Pilze, p. 118, 1877.
> *Hygrophorus eburneus* var. *cossus* (Sow. ex Fr.) Quél., Flore Myc.
>   Fr., p. 482, 1888.
> *Limacium eburneum* var. *cossus* (Sow. ex Fr.) J. Lange, Dansk Bot.
>   Arkiv. 4: 16. 1923.

Illustrations:
> Fig. 74.
> Bresadola, Icon. Myc., tab. 304.

Pileus 3–7 cm broad, obtuse with an incurved margin expanding to broadly convex to nearly plane, surface glutinous and glabrous, whitish or evenly "pale pinkish buff," at maturity becoming slightly more ochraceous or flushed salmon color and retaining either tint in drying.

Fig. 74. *H. cossus*

Context white, no color change on bruising, fairly soft; odor distinctly aromatic, taste not distinctive.

Lamellae broadly adnate to decurrent, close to subdistant, narrow to broad, white and clean at first, soon flushed salmon-buff, edges even.

Stipe 4–9 cm long, (3)8–12 mm thick, equal or tapered at the base, white, flavescent, fibrillose-punctate to scabrous at apex, lower two-thirds covered by a gelatinous sheath representing the gluten, with a thin inner white-fibrillose veil; lower part salmon-buff to sordid cinnamon-buff in age.

Spores 7–9 × 4–4.5 μ, ellipsoid, smooth, hyaline, hyaline to yellowish in Melzer's reagent. Basidia 38–46 × 7–8 μ, 4-spored. Pleurocystidia and cheilocystidia none seen. Gill trama of divergent hyphae, 2.5–6 μ broad. Cuticle a gelatinous zone, 200–400 μ thick, the hyphae 2–4 μ in diameter and nearly hyaline, closely interwoven (an ixocutis). No hypodermium differentiated. Pileus trama of radial hyphae. Clamp connections present.

HABIT, HABITAT, AND DISTRIBUTION—Gregarious around an old oak stump, Ann Arbor, Mich., September–October (and under conifers, Smith 63312), Idaho; also Europe. Although Peck (1874) reported it from New York, he later (1907) doubted his identification.

MATERIAL STUDIED—IDAHO: Smith 54207. MICHIGAN: Smith 20681, 51016. ENGLAND: Reid, Sept. 18, 1952 (as *H. eburneus* var. *cossus*).

OBSERVATIONS—By virtue of the odor and whitish pileus which later develops an ochraceous tone, our collections are referred to *H. cossus*. Kühner and Romagnesi (1953) state that it is related to *H. flavodiscus*, but we regard it as closer to *H. laurae*. Smith No. 63312 represents a large collection in all stages of development.

153
Hygrophorus chrysaspis Métrod
Rev. Mycol. 3: 153. 1938

Illustrations:
  Fig. 75.
  Métrod, Rev. Mycol. 3, pl. 2.

Pileus 2–7(10) cm broad, convex, at times obtuse, glutinous or viscid, matted-fibrillose beneath the gluten, white over all, becoming "pale pinkish buff," drying "clay color" to "tawny," disc usually drying darker to blackish or at times blackish stains or streaks scattered over the pileus, margin incurved. Context watery yellowish white, unchanging or finally yellowish when bruised; odor mild or not distinctive, at times faintly fragrant, taste mild.

Lamellae adnate or broadly adnate, white then "ivory yellow," becoming "napthalene yellow" where bruised, drying to "blackish brown (1)" (dark reddish brown), subdistant to close, medium broad, edges even.

Stipe 4–6(15) cm long, 2–8 mm thick, dull white, becoming "pale pinkish buff" or yellow where bruised, drying dingy, glutinous, gla-

Fig. 75.
H. chrysaspis

brous, apex pruinose-punctate and beaded with pale-yellow drops, equal or tapering downward.

Spores 7–8(9) × 3.5–4.5 μ, ellipsoid, smooth, pale yellowish in Melzer's reagent. Basidia 40–54 × 6–8 μ, 4-spored. Pleurocystidia and cheilocystidia none. Gill trama divergent, hyphae 3–9(12) μ broad. Cuticle a zone of brownish, gelatinous hyphae, some free ends more or less erect. Pileus trama of radially disposed hyphae. Clamp connections present on the cuticular hyphae.

HABIT, HABITAT, AND DISTRIBUTION—On soil, under hardwoods, especially beech, Michigan and Tennessee, August–October; also Europe.

MATERIAL STUDIED—MICHIGAN: Smith 6060, 39697, 44056, 57873, 58115, 58119, 58120, 58121, 58122. TENNESSEE: Hesler 4450, 4452, 9648, 19438, 22212, 22704. ENGLAND: Reid, Aldburg, Sept. 5, 1954. FRANCE: Métrod 557; collection by Josserand; collection by Huijsman. NETHERLANDS: Bas 1098. AUSTRIA: Moser, Sept. 14, 1960 (Hesler 24118).

OBSERVATIONS—When fresh, this species resembles *H. eburneus.* On drying, the pileus and lamellae of *H. eburneus* assume a buff to yellow color, whereas in *H. chrysaspis* the lamellae become very dark red-brown (near "blackish brown [1]"), and the pileus becomes "clay color" to "tawny" or rusty brown, with dark to blackish disc. These changes in color, according to Kühner and Romagnesi (1953), may take place in one or two days if the carpophores are left in the laboratory. They also state that J. Schaeffer recognizes *H. chrysaspis* with the aid of KOH which immediately causes a brownish orange to chrome yellow coloration, whereas KOH does not noticeably react on *H. eburneus.*

Through the courtesy of Métrod and Josserand of France, and Bas of the Netherlands, we have received specimens of *H. chrysaspis.* Our collections agree well with the European material in both macroscopic and microscopic details.

It is interesting to note that the original description indicates that the species occurs in conifer forests and that the carpophores are odorless and tasteless. Kühner and Romagnesi (1953), on the contrary, state "Odeur spéciale, plutot désagréable,"—"sous hetres." Our material, mostly from under beeches, has no strongly distinctive odor.

It is probable that Peck's *H. laurae* var. *unicolor,* which he reported (1902c) from New York, is *H. chrysaspis.* Kauffman (1918) recognized Peck's variety, but he attached it to *H. eburneus.*

154
Hygrophorus glutinosus Pk.
N. Y. State Mus. Bull. 54: 950. 1902

Hygrophorus rubropunctus Pk. N. Y. State Mus. Bull. 116: 49. 1907.
Illustrations:
Fig. 76.
Coker, Elisha Mitchell Sci. Soc. Jour. 64, pls. 17 and 18; pl. 25, fig. 3.
Hesler, Tenn. Acad. Sci. Jour. 26, fig. 4.

Pileus 4–5(10) cm, convex-hemispheric then convex, obtusely umbonate, glabrous, glutinous, the gluten colorless, disc "cream buff," elsewhere "ivory yellow," dry bright "primuline yellow," margin at first involute, even. Context white, thick on disc, thin on margin; odor and taste none.

Lamellae adnate to rounded-adnate, scarcely emarginate, at first white, then "ivory yellow," broad behind, abruptly narrowed in front, close then subdistant, alternately long and short, lamellullae of four ranks, edges even.

Stipe 4–9 cm × 8–15 mm, white, rough (scabrous-ridged), floccose-tomentose and glutinous-viscid up to an apical collar, enlarged below

Fig. 76. *H. glutinosus*

the collar (subventricose), gluten leaving pale yellowish-brown stains or spots (simulating reticulations), apex when fresh dotted with watery-drops which on drying form reddish glandular dots, solid.

Spores 8–10(12) × 5–6(7) μ, ellipsoidal, smooth, white in deposits, yellowish in Melzer's reagent. Pleurocystidia and cheilocystidia none. Basidia (48)56–60 × 8–10 μ, 2- and 4-spored. Gill trama of divergent hyphae, 7–9 μ broad. Cuticle a gelatinous zone, 350–600 μ thick, hyphae loosely tangled, tending toward being erect (as in *H. gliocyclus*), narrow (2–5 μ), yellowish. Hypodermium distinct, composed of parallel, periclinally disposed, narrow hyphae. Pileus trama of radially disposed hyphae. Clamp connections present on the cuticular hyphae but rare.

HABIT, HABITAT, AND DISTRIBUTION—On soil, in deciduous woods, Michigan, New York, North Carolina, Tennessee, Oregon, September–December.

MATERIAL STUDIED—MICHIGAN: Smith 15439, 57873. NEW YORK:

Peck (type, from Bolton, Sept., as *H. glutinosus* Pk.). NORTH CAROLINA: Coker 932, 3771, 4993. OREGON: Syse 709. TENNESSEE: Hesler 19398.

OBSERVATIONS—The type (labeled *H. glutinosus*) has been studied, and observations have been recorded as follows: Spores 8–10(12.5) × 5–6 μ, ellipsoid, slightly inequilateral, smooth, pale yellowish in Melzer's reagent. Basidia 43–55 × 6–7 μ, 2- and 4-spored, the 4-spored type predominant. Pleurocystidia and cheilocystidia none. Gill trama divergent, the hyphae 3–6 μ broad. Cuticle of gelatinous hyphae (see above). Clamp connections present.

This species is near *H. flavodiscus* which lacks the pronounced reddish glandular dots on the stipe-apex, and has spores smaller than those of *H. glutinosus*. We have not found a transfer of *Agaricus glutinosus* Bul. to *Hygrophorus* and so recognize Peck's original binomial, as did Murrill.

155

Hygrophorus albiflavus, sp. nov.

Pileus 3 cm latus, convexus, albus, viscidus, glaber; caro alba; odore et gustu mitis; lamellae adnato-decurrentes, pallidae, subdistantes, modice latae; stipes 5 cm longus, 7 mm crassus, pallidus, viscidus; annulus fibrillosus; sporae (9)10–14 × 6.5–7.5 μ, ellipsoideae. Specimen typicum in Herb. Univ. Mich.; lectum in Mt. Hood, Ore., Sept. 29, 1946, A. H. Smith 23910.

Pileus 3 cm broad, convex, white over all, viscid, appearing glabrous, margin even. Context white; odor and taste not distinctive.

Lamellae adnate-decurrent, pallid, subdistant, medium broad, edges even.

Stipe 5 cm long, 7 mm thick, pallid, viscid, glabrous up to an apical, fibrillose annulus.

Spores (9)10–14 × 6.5–7.5 μ, ellipsoid, smooth. Basidia 4-spored. Pleurocystidia and cheilocystidia none. Gill trama divergent. Cuticle of a broad turf of gelatinous hyphae. Pileus trama of radially disposed hyphae. Clamp connections present.

HABIT, HABITAT, AND DISTRIBUTION—On soil, Oregon, September.

MATERIAL STUDIED—OREGON: Smith 23910 (type, from Mt. Hood, 3800 ft., Sept. 29, 1946).

OBSERVATIONS—This species is white when fresh but, on drying, becomes warm buff to ochraceous buff, the colors, both fresh and dried, being somewhat suggestive of *H. flavodiscus*. But the larger spores and fibrillose annulus distinguish it. The veil suggests *H. velatus*, but that species has much smaller spores, and also *H. pleurotoides* Favre which has a dark reddish-brown pileus and a strong farinaceous taste and odor (Favre 1960, p. 393, and Plate I, fig. 1). *Hygrophorus whiteii* (page 280) has smaller spores, and a warm buff pileus.

156
Hygrophorus ponderatus Britz.
Bot. Centralbl. 80: 117. 1899

Illustrations:
  Fig. 77.
  Smith and Hesler, Lloydia 2, pl. 2.

Pileus 5–14 cm broad, convex then plane, finally depressed, white, viscid or glutinous, glabrous, margin even and at first incurved and floccose. Context white, compact, thick; odor and taste mild.

Lamellae adnate to decurrent, white, subdistant, rather broad, narrow at either end, often subtriangular.

Stipe 2.5–6(9) cm long, 15–35 mm thick, white, equal or tapering either way, at times subbulbous, and tapering below the bulb, lubricous or viscid-glutinous when wet, silky-fibrillose, solid. Partial veil arachnoid in young specimens.

Spores 6.5–9(10) × 4–5.5 μ, ellipsoid, smooth, pale yellowish in Melzer's reagent. Basidia 45–66 × 7–9 μ, 2- and 4-spored. Pleurocystidia

Fig. 77. *H. ponderatus*

and cheilocystidia none. Gill trama of divergent hyphae, cells 4–10 μ broad. Cuticle a gelatinous zone 160–250 μ thick, hyphae colorless, interwoven, narrow (2–3 μ), the surface hyphae repent in a narrow brown-pigmented zone, an ixocutis. No hypodermium differentiated. Pileus trama of radial hyphae, interwoven. Clamp connections on the cuticular hyphae.

HABIT, HABITAT, AND DISTRIBUTION—On soil, often in moss-hummocks, in pine and mixed woods, Tennessee, Georgia, and Alabama, November–January; also Europe.

MATERIAL STUDIED—ALABAMA: Hesler 22263. GEORGIA: Hesler 22227. TENNESSEE: Hesler 6192, 6199, 8435, 10093, 10948, 11836, 13019, 13028, 14099, 14121, 16619, 22557.

OBSERVATIONS—Britzelmayer (1899) characterized his species as having cap and stipe viscid, spores 8–9 × 4–5 μ, and "der Pilz in allen seinen Theilen aussen u. innen weiss." He compared it to *H. gliocyclus*. Nüesch (1922) suggested that it was closer to *H. penarius* because of the attenuated base of its stipe along with such characters as the slightly viscid pileus and stipe. Nüesch, apparently, had never collected the species, so it seems logical to limit ourselves to Britzelmayer's description. The outstanding characters of Hesler's collections are the white color in all parts (this color is retained in drying), the viscid pileus and stipe, spore size, and a general resemblance in stature to *H. gliocyclus*. It can be readily seen that the American collections agree perfectly with Britzelmayer's description on all important characters. We are inclined to discount any apparent differences in the size and shape of the stipe as variations similar to those frequently encountered in such comomn species as *H. eburneus*. In North America *H. ponderatus* is most likely to be confused with *H. sordidus* Pk., another large white species. The latter, however, has a truly dry stipe in all stages of its development.

SERIES DISCOIDEI (Bataille) stat. nov.

Subsection Discoidei Bataille, Flore Monogr. Hygrophores, p. 36. 1910.

Characters as given in key to series, page 249.

Type species: *Hygrophorus discoideus* Fr.

KEY TO SPECIES

1. Pileus dingy yellow-brown; gluten copious on stipe and stipe apex scabrous, the projections becoming yellow to olive in age .172. *H. paludosus*
1. Not with above combination of characters 2

157

Hygrophorus vernalis Sm.
Univ. Mich. Herb. Contr. 5: 20. 1941

Illustrations:
    Fig. 78.
    Univ. Mich. Herb. Contr. 5, pl. 4.

Pileus 3–5 cm broad, obtuse when young and with an incurved white downy-pubescent margin, obtusely umbonate in age, margin "pale vinaceous fawn," the disc "vinaceous buff" and with watery spots when young, in age flushed over all with brighter pale vinaceous colors, glabrous, viscid. Context thick, concolorous with the surface or whitish vinaceous; odor and taste not distinctive.

Lamellae arcuate when young, long decurrent in age, whitish (paler than the margin of the pileus), close, 50–55 lamellae reach the stipe, narrow (3.5 mm more or less), edges even.

Stipe 4–6 cm long, 7–9 mm thick, equal or slightly enlarged at the base, stuffed or becoming hollow, lower part covered by a thin layer of gluten, which forms sordid yellowish patches of varnish over the basal area, appressed cottony fibrillose to the apex (not punctate above), sordid whitish or concolorous with the gills, darker in age.

Spores 11–15.5 × 5.5–7 μ, ellipsoid, at times oblong-ellipsoid, smooth, yellow in Melzer's reagent. Basidia 50–70 × 7–11 μ, 2- and 4-spored. Pleurocystidia and cheilocystidia none. Gill trama divergent, hyphae 3–6 μ broad. Cuticle a broad (250–350 μ), gelatinous zone with

Fig. 78. *H. vernalis*

loosely interwoven, narrow (2–3 μ), radially disposed hyphae, an ixocutis. No hypodermium differentiated. Pileus trama of radial hyphae. Clamp connections rare on the cuticular hyphae and more common on the gill trama hyphae.

HABIT, HABITAT, AND DISTRIBUTION—Scattered under conifers, near snow banks, Washington, May–July.

MATERIAL STUDIED—WASHINGTON: Smith 13333, 14304 (type, from below Deer Lake, Olympic National Park, June 13, 1939), 15636.

OBSERVATIONS—This species is nearest *H. variicolor* Murr., which, however, is darker, is without a vinaceous tint, and has smaller spores.

158
Hygrophorus subsalmonius Sm. & Hes.
Lloydia 2: 30. 1939

Illustrations:
  Fig. 79; also 9b.
  Smith and Hesler, Lloydia 2, pl. 11.

Pileus 4–12(15) cm broad, convex, becoming plane or in age depressed from an elevated margin, disc "madder brown," "ferruginous," "cadmium orange," to "rufous," margin paler ("salmon-buff"), in age "madder brown," "ferruginous," "salmon-buff," "zinc orange" or "apricot-buff" over all, glutinous, the gluten pale amber or colorless, viscid in age, glabrous except for a cottony fibrillose margin. Context thick, firm, white, or at times faintly tinged sordid incarnate; odor and taste none or mild.

Lamellae adnate to slightly adnexed, usually becoming decurrent, at first "cartridge buff" or "sea-shell pink" then "pale pinkish buff," darker incarnate-tan in age or when decaying, close to subdistant, moderately broad, alternately long and short, edges even.

Stipe 3–10 cm long, 5–20 mm thick, whitish or tinged incarnate-tan, the color often deeper in age, equal or with a flaring apex and a narrowed base, basal portion glutinous from the remains of the thick gelatinous universal veil, minutely squamulose above the viscid portion, solid.

Spores 6.5–8 × 3–4.5 μ, ellipsoid, smooth, yellow in Melzer's reagent, white in mass. Basidia 38–50 × 6–9 μ, 4-spored. Pleurocystidia and cheilocystidia none. Gill trama divergent, hyphae 4–9(15) μ broad,

Fig. 79. *H. subsalmonius*

with a mediostrate of narrow (3–5 μ), parallel hyphae. Cuticle a broad gelatinous zone, the upper portion (200 μ) of clear gelatinous substance, the lower portion a turf, or ixotrichodermial palisade, of slender, erect hyphae, 90–130 × 2–4 μ. No hypodermium differentiated. Pileus trama homogeneous, of loosely interwoven, radial hyphae. Clamp connections present on the hyphae of the pileus trama and gill trama.

HABIT, HABITAT, AND DISTRIBUTION—Gregarious under oak and hickory or in brush along roadsides, Iowa, Michigan, Ohio, Tennessee, and Georgia, September–November.

MATERIAL STUDIED—GEORGIA: Hesler 22229. IOWA: Oleson, Fort Dodge, Nov. 7, 1919. MICHIGAN: Smith 6045, 6143 (type, Five Mile Woods, oak, Ann Arbor, Oct. 23, 1936), 15389, 32052, 34232; Staebler, Ann Arbor, Oct. 12, 1936. OHIO: Walters 145. TENNESSEE: Hesler 4445, 8406, 22218, 23525.

OBSERVATIONS—This species is related to *H. pudorinus* but has brighter colors; the pileus is salmon-buff to cadmium orange, the lamellae are sea-shell pink; the spores are slightly narrower; and the glutinous veil is thick and persistent. Finally, the squamules on the stipe apex, when dried, are pale orange, never as reddish dots as in *H. pudorinus*. In *H. subsalmonius* the cuticle is a striking ixotrichodermial palisade.

159
Hygrophorus variicolor Murr.
Mycologia 4: 210. 1912

Illustrations:
    Fig. 80.
    Smith and Hesler, Lloydia 2, pl. 10.

Pileus 4–7 cm broad, obtuse, at maturity slightly umbonate, sometimes plane and with a decurved margin, "tawny" to "cinnamon brown" on the disc, paler tawny toward the whitish margin, glutinous, more or less fibrillose streaked beneath the gluten, margin cottony tomentose and often beaded with drops of moisture. Context white, thick on the disc, firm; taste mild, odor of almonds when cut or bruised.

Lamellae bluntly adnate but soon short decurrent, pure white, close to subdistant (58–70 reach the stipe), equal, narrow (3–4.5 mm).

Stipe 8–10 cm long (3–5 cm in alpine forms), 10–15 mm thick at the apex, pure white over all or the base discolored slightly, gradually tapered to a long pointed subradicating base, solid, lower portion glutinous from the remains of a gelatinous universal veil, appressed fibrillose beneath the gluten, the upper half dry and pruinose to minutely white fibrillose-furfuraceous, often beaded with drops of moisture near the apex.

Spores 7–9 × 4.5–5.5 μ, ellipsoid, smooth, yellow in Melzer's reagent. Basidia 42–54 × 5.5–7 μ, 2- and 4-spored. Pleurocystidia and cheilocystidia none. Gill trama divergent, hyphae 4–9 μ broad. Cuticle a well-defined gelatinous layer, 150–270 μ thick, hyphae more or less erect, 3–6 μ broad, an ixotrichodermium. No hypodermium evident. Pileus trama of radial, subparallel hyphae. Clamp connections on the cuticular and gill trama hyphae.

HABIT, HABITAT, AND DISTRIBUTION—On soil, in woods, California, Oregon, and Washington, October–November.

MATERIAL STUDIED—CALIFORNIA: Sipe 392; Smith 8087, 8088, 8154, 8856, 26778. OREGON: Murrill 802 (type, from near Mill City, Nov. 9,

Fig. 80. *H. variicolor*

1911); Smith 8087. WASHINGTON: Flett, Bremerton, Dec. 18, 1939; Smith 3253.

OBSERVATIONS—The collections by Smith listed above agree with the type. This species is related to *H. discoideus* but differs in its size and in the more yellowish-brown colors. It also resembles *H. laurae* in certain respects, but the color changes in drying separate the two at once. When properly dried the gills of *H. laurae* do not become reddish brown. *H. arbustivus* Fr. sensu Rea is apparently the nearest European species. Rea's (1922) description is very suggestive of Murrill's species. The outstanding character of *H. arbustivus* is said to be that the apex of the stipe is covered by white free mealy granules. Murrill described the stipe as pulverulent, and the veil as represented by a few short brownish fibrils at the center of the stipe. A study of Murrill's type, however, shows that it is the species we have described above in spite of any apparent discrepancies in the original description. The glutinous veil may be present only around the base of the stipe and under unfavorable conditions might be easily overlooked. The difference between the pruinose to furfuraceous particles on the stipe of one and the free mealy granules on the other might easily be a difference of interpretation. However, in the absence of specimens of *H. arbustivus* for comparison, and due to conflicting opinions as to its characters among European investigators, we prefer to use the name given to the American material.

Notes on the type: Spores 7–8.5 × 4.5–5.7 μ, ellipsoid, smooth, pale yellow in Melzer's reagent. Basidia 34–48 × 5–6 μ, 2- and 4-spored. Pleurocystidia and cheilocystidia none. Gill trama divergent. Cuticle fibrillose, hyphae loosely interwoven, gelatinous. Clamp connections on the hyphae of both gill trama and cuticle.

160
Hygrophorus virgatulus Pk.
N. Y. State Mus. Ann. Rept. 26: 64. 1874

Pileus 2.5–5 cm broad, convex or expanded, whitish with a brownish disc, minutely virgate with innate blackish fibrils, viscid when moist.

Lamellae arcuate-decurrent, distant, medium broad, white.

Stipe 6–10 cm long, 4–6 mm thick, solid, viscid, equal or tapering downwards, with a few small white floccose scales at the top.

Spores 7–9 × 3.5–5 μ, ellipsoid, smooth, pale yellow in Melzer's reagent. Basidia 32–54 × 5–7 μ, 4-spored. Pleurocystidia and cheilocystidia none. Gill trama divergent, hyphae 4–8 μ broad. Cuticle of gelatinous, fuscous, radial, repent to more or less erect, thick-walled hyphae which vary in breadth (3–15 μ). No hypodermium evident. Pileus trama of radial hyphae. Clamp connections rare on the cuticular hyphae. Lactifers at times abundant in the gill trama.

HABIT, HABITAT, AND DISTRIBUTION—Subcaespitose, on soil in open woods, New York.

MATERIAL STUDIED—NEW YORK: Peck (type, from North Greenbush).

OBSERVATIONS—The type specimens from North Greenbush, New York, are pale and sordid yellowish brown. They do not remind one of *H. occidentalis*, *H. pustulatus*, or any other grayish-brown species which we have studied. The description of microscopic characters given above is based on our study of the type.

161
Hygrophorus elegantulus Pk.
Torrey Bot. Club Bull. 22: 200. 1895

Pileus 2.5–5 cm broad, convex or nearly plane, grayish yellow or slightly tawny, glabrous, viscid. Context white.

Lamellae slightly decurrent, white, distant, rather narrow to medium broad.

Stipe 5–7.5 cm long, 6–8 mm thick, white or whitish, apex floccose-squamulose, elsewhere glabrous, glutinous, equal, sometimes abruptly pointed at the base, solid.

Spores 7–10 × 4.5–5.5(6.5) μ, ellipsoid, smooth, yellowish in Melzer's reagent. Basidia 38–45 × 6–7 μ, 4-spored. Pleurocystidia and cheilocystidia none. Gill trama divergent, hyphae 4–6 μ broad. Cuticle of the pileus a broad zone (175–400 μ thick) of slender (2–5 μ broad) gelatinous hyphae, the outer portion of the zone brownish, the inner portion colorless. No hypodermium evident. Pileus trama interwoven, hyphae radially disposed. Stipe cuticle similar to that of the pileus. Clamp connections present on the cuticular hyphae of the pileus and the stipe.

HABIT, HABITAT, AND DISTRIBUTION—In woods, Maryland, November.

MATERIAL STUDIED—MARYLAND: Peck (type, collected by T. Taylor, in November).

OBSERVATIONS—The description of the microscopic characters given above is based on our study of the type. The single carpophore of the type also resembles somewhat *H. paludosus* in general appearance. The pileus has been almost skeletonized by insects, so that the preparation of sections was tedious.

162

Hygrophorus laurae Morgan
Cincinnati Soc. Nat. Hist. Jour. 6: 180. 1883

Illustrations:
  Fig. 81.
  Murrill, Mycologia 2, pl. 27, f. 10.
  Peck, N. Y. State Mus. Bull. 54, pl. 77, figs. 6–14.
  Morgan, Cincinnati Soc. Nat. Hist. Jour. 6, pl. 9.

Pileus 2–10 cm broad, at times more or less umbonate, convex-expanded or sometimes depressed on the disc, viscid to glutinous, white or whitish, the disc washed with reddish brown, pinkish tan, "cinnamon-buff," or yellowish brown, the margin at times "cartridge buff," sometimes changing to "ochraceous tawny" on being dried, more or less silky shining beneath the gluten, margin even, undulate or sometimes crenate. Context white, firm, rather thick; odor and taste not distinctive.

Lamellae broadly adnate, decurrent by a tooth, at times arcuate, subdistant to close, white then flesh-tinged to "cartridge buff," narrowed at either end, broadest at the center, at times anastomosed, rarely forked, edges even.

Stipe 2.5–7 cm long, (5)10–27 mm thick, whitish to pale buff or dingy, fibrillose below, at first the apex floccose-squamulose, then fibrillose, tapering downward, sometimes curved at the base, viscid or glutinous over the lower portion, solid, at times becoming hollow.

Spores 5.5–7(8) × 3.5–4.5 μ, ellipsoid, smooth, pale yellowish in Melzer's reagent, white in mass. Basidia 38–53 × 5–7 μ, some 2-spored, mostly 4-spored. Pleurocystidia and cheilocystidia none. Gill trama divergent, hyphae 3–7 μ broad, with scattered lactifers. Cuticle a gelatinous zone, 125–180 μ broad, hyphae more or less erect, 2.5–4 μ broad, forming an ixotrichodermium. No hypodermium evident. Pileus trama of interwoven hyphae, chiefly radially disposed. Clamp connections present in the cuticular and the gill trama hyphae.

HABIT, HABITAT, AND DISTRIBUTION—Gregarious to subcaespitose, in deciduous and mixed coniferous-deciduous woods, Massachusetts, New York, Maryland, Tennessee, North Carolina, Michigan, and Canada (Ontario), June–December.

MATERIAL STUDIED—MARYLAND: Lyons 1455. MASSACHUSETTS: Davis, Stow, Sept. 23–30, 1911. MICHIGAN: Kauffman, Ann Arbor, Oct. 20, 1926, 814; Smith 5048, 15478, 20704, 34246; Thiers 4302. NEW YORK: Kauffman, Ithaca, Oct. 23, 1902. NORTH CAROLINA: Coker 13213; Couch 3883; Kauffman, Hot Springs, Aug. 21, 1924; Totten 1392. TEN-

Fig. 81. *H. laurae*

NESSEE: Hesler 19402; Jones 4459; Sharp 14050. CANADA: (Ontario) Kelly 1273; Smith 4881.

OBSERVATIONS—In most of our dried material the pileus is pale buff with a paler margin. In Tennessee collection No. 14050, the pileus is "warm buff" with a tinge of brown on the disc, suggesting *H. laurae* var. *decipiens* Pk. In another Tennessee collection (No. 19402) the pileus when dried is "cinnamon" to "cinnamon-buff." The squamules over the stipe-apex dry white or pale yellowish. *H. laurae* is distinguished from *H. flavodiscus* by the colors of both fresh and dried specimens.

163

Hygrophorus discoideus (Fr.) Fr.

Hymen. Eur., p. 408. 1874

> *Agaricus discoideus* Fr., Syst. Myc., p. 33. 1821.
> *Limacium discoideum* (Fr.) Kummer, Führ. in Pilzk., p. 119. 1871.

Illustrations:
> Fig. 82.
> Bresadola, Icon. Myc., tab. 310.
> Juillard-Hartmann, Icon. Champ., pl. 50, fig. 19.

Pileus 2–5 cm broad, convex or with a slight umbo at first, at maturity with a decurved margin and the disc flattened or umbonate, at times with an elevated margin in age, glutinous to viscid, glabrous or faintly downy near the margin at first, "hazel" to "chestnut" on the disc, "salmon-buff" to "ochraceous buff" near the margin, scarcely fading. Context thin, whitish or tinged testaceous, odor and taste not distinctive.

Lamellae whitish or tinged pinkish tan, close to subdistant, narrow, decurrent.

Stipe 4–9 cm long, 3–5 mm thick, equal, solid, becoming hollow, evenly white fibrillose above, slightly viscid below from the scant remains of a distinct gelatinous universal veil, upper portion covered with white fibrillose points, white over all, occasionally with gilvous stains at the base.

Spores 5.5–7 × 3.5–4.5 μ, ellipsoid, smooth, pale yellowish in Melzer's reagent. Basidia 40–56 × 6–7 μ, 4-spored. Pleurocystidia and cheilocystidia none. Gill trama divergent, hyphae 5–10 μ. Cuticle a gelatinous zone 70–180 μ thick, with loosely tangled imbedded hyphae

Fig. 82. *H. discoideus*

which are 2–4 μ broad. No hypodermium evident. Pileus trama interwoven, hyphae more or less radially disposed. Lactifers present in the pileus trama. Clamp connections present on the cuticular hyphae.

HABIT, HABITAT, AND DISTRIBUTION—Scattered to gregarious under conifers and in *Sphagnum* bogs, Michigan, Ontario, Colorado, California, Idaho, and Oregon, September to December; also Europe.

MATERIAL STUDIED—CALIFORNIA: Smith 9336. COLORADO: Smith 52637. IDAHO: Smith 47083, 53229, 53460, 53555. MICHIGAN: Bailey 92; McVaugh & Smith 31914; Smith 1109, 1247, 4718, 43701, 43977, 51021, 58240. OREGON: Smith 3419, 19165, 19505, 19645, 26661, 27291. AUSTRIA: Moser, Sept. 14, 1960 (Hesler 24134).

OBSERVATIONS—In the American collections the spores seldom measure more than 7 μ long. A specimen of this species collected in Sweden by Lundell has spores practically the same size but has a thicker stipe. Bresadola's (1928) description and illustration correspond with the American material in all respects except spore size (7–9 μ). Konrad (1929) describes *H. discoideus* as having spores 6–8 × 3.5–5 μ, but does not give the dimensions of the stipe in his description. Some European investigators agree that *H. discoideus* favors a coniferous habitat, a characteristic also constant of our specimens. Moser (1955) finds it in both conifer and deciduous forests. The collections reported for Michigan by Smith (1937a) did not show the gilvous stains on the stipe as described by Bresadola, but this character has been noted in subsequent collections.

Kühner and Romagnesi (1953, p. 57) give *H. discoideus* Fr. as a synonym of *H. leucophaeus* Fr. They give its spores 6.5–8.7 × 3.5–4.5 μ. We recognize both species; in *H. leucophaeus* the stipe is dry, and in *H. discoideus* it is viscid.

SERIES AUREI (Bataille) stat. nov.

Subsection Aurei Bataille, Flore Monogr. Hygrophores, p. 35. 1910. Characters as given in key to series, page 249.
Type species: *H. aureus* Arrh. in Fries.

KEY TO SPECIES

1. Pileus dark olive brown to olive blackish but changing to yellow and finally red ....164. *H. hypothejus*
1. Not with above pattern of color change 2
   2. Pileus scarlet fading to reddish orange and finally yellowish; growing under larch 3
   2. Pileus color-pattern not as above 4

164

Hygrophorus hypothejus (Fr.) Fr.

Epicr. Myc., p. 324. 1838

> *Agaricus hypothejus* Fr., Syst. Myc., p. 35. 1821.
> *Hydrocybe arenicola* Murr., Mycologia 4: 208. 1912.
> *Hygrophorus subpustulatus* (Murr.) Murr., Mycologia 4: 210. 1912.
> *Limacium hypothejum* (Fr. ex Fr.) Kummer, Führ. in Pilzk., p. 119. 1871.

Illustrations:
  Fig. 83.
  Böhme, Norsk Soppbok, pl. 8, fig. 79.
  Boudier, Icon. Myc., pl. 32.
  Bresadola, Icon. Myc., tab. 317.
  Cooke, Illus. Brit. Fungi, pl. 891.
  Gillet, Champ. Fr., pl. 126 (337).
  Juillard-Hartmann, Icon. Champ., pl. 48, fig. 1.
  Lange, Flora Agar. Dan., 5, pl. 162 D & D¹.
  Patouillard, Tab. Analyt., no. 510.
  Ricken, Die Blätterp., pl. 5, fig. 5.
  Smith and Hesler, Lloydia 2, pl. 5.
  Wakefield and Dennis, Common British Fungi, pl. 32, fig. 3.

Pileus 2–8 cm broad, slightly umbonate, then convex to plane or remaining slightly umbonate, sometimes with a depressed disc and an elevated margin at maturity, glutinous, glabrous or somewhat agglutinated-fibrillose near the margin, "bone brown" to "olive brown" on the disc, elsewhere "pale dull green-yellow," "yellow ocher," "buckthorn brown," or "Vandyke brown," colors becoming brighter in age ("straw yellow" to "ochraceous orange" or occasionally "scarlet" in extreme age near the margin), disc remaining more or less dark olive brown. Context thin, yellow near the pellicle, watery whitish above the lamellae; odor and taste not distinctive.

Lamellae decurrent, white at very first, soon pale yellow and finally more or less concolorous with the margin of the pileus, narrow to moderately broad, subdistant to distant.

Stipe (2.5)8–16 cm × (3)6–12(15) mm, tapering slightly downward, flesh whitish or yellowish near the exterior, the lower two-thirds glutinous, partial veil floccose and leaving a subapical, fibrillose, evanescent annular zone, apical region silky and yellowish, variously colored below, olive brown, olivaceous yellow, bright yellow, orange or scarlet, solid.

Spores (from deposit) 7–9 × 4–5 μ, ellipsoid, smooth, white in mass, bright yellow in Melzer's reagent. Basidia 42–60 × 6–7 μ, 4-spored. Pleurocystidia and cheilocystidia none. Gill trama divergent, hyphae 3–7(10) μ broad. Cuticle of gelatinous hyphae. Clamp connections present in the cuticle and gill trama. The minute anatomy of the stipe is as follows: In longitudinal section the component hyphae are subparallel to somewhat interwoven; in transverse section the hyphae are observed as more or less pseudoparenchymatous. In this species the hyphae are not as distinctly parallel as in *H. roseibrunneus* and therefore lack the distinct pseudoparenchymatous appearance as observed in the latter species. The cuticle is of gelatinous hyphae which form a distinct zone 150–350 μ thick, hyphae narrow (2.5–4 μ), colorless. Hypodermium none differentiated or only slightly developed. Pileus trama interwoven, hyphae radially arranged.

HABIT, HABITAT, AND DISTRIBUTION—Gregarious under conifers, Massachusetts, New York, District of Columbia, North Carolina, Tennessee, Alabama, Georgia, Florida, Michigan, Colorado, Idaho, California, Oregon, and Washington; also Europe, June–December.

MATERIAL STUDIED—ALABAMA: Burke 91a, 92, 2070; Earle (Auburn, Dec. 23, 1899, and Dec. 16, 1900). CALIFORNIA: Morse & Duran (Oakland, Feb. 3, 1933). COLORADO: Kauffman, Tolland, Aug. 24, 1920. DISTRICT OF COLUMBIA: J. N. Rose & G. M. Rose (Chevy Chase, Nov. 30, 1916). FLORIDA: Hesler 21044. GEORGIA: Hesler 20274. IDAHO: Smith 15919, 44314, 45462, 45995, 46078, 46086, 46380, 54834, 60040; Smith & Bigelow 46752, 46981. MASSACHUSETTS: Davis, Stow, Oct. 1909, Nov. 1910, 1920; Morris (Waltham, Nov. 11 and 12, 1907). MICHIGAN: Mains 34186; Smith 38486, 43730, 43820, 43892, 43926, 50781, 50831, 58191, 62048. NEW YORK: House (North Bay, Oct. 13, 1915, as *H. fuligineus*). NORTH CAROLINA: Coker 1493 (as *H. fuligineus*), 2015. OREGON: Gruber 1941; Kauffman & Brown, Takilma, Nov. 26, 1925; Murrill 861, 1049; Sipe 466, 790, 907; Smith 3477, 3486, 3566, 8162, 19187, 20051, 23761, 24122, 26774, 27070, 27071, 27609, 55577. TENNESSEE: Hesler 3772, 4421, 4422, 4468, 6193, 6200, 8450, 10133, 10143, 10145, 10946, 10954, 13030,

13039, 20763, 20771. WASHINGTON: Flett, Bremerton, Oct. 30, 1933; Grant, Langley, 1923; Smith 48827; Murrill (type of *H. subpustulatus,* Seattle, Oct. 20–Nov. 1, 1911). ENGLAND: Dennis, Surrey, Oct. 14, 1950; Reid, Kent, Oct. 30, 1960. GERMANY: Krieger 481, Fungi Saxonici. NETHERLANDS: Bas, Nov. 8, 1954. BELGIUM: Heinemann (Hesler 23980). SWEDEN: Romell (Femsjo, Aug. 1911).

OBSERVATIONS—Murrill (1916) reports it as occurring throughout temperate North America. In Oregon both the slender form and the robust form were collected. The species is quite variable but at the same time readily recognizable. The tendency of the fruiting bodies to become rather brightly colored has led us to place it in this subsection along with other bright yellow or reddish species. We have not collected *H. arenicola* Murr. nor *H. subpustulatus* Murr., which Murrill indicates as synonyms of *H. hypothejus.* Moreover, the types could

Fig. 83. *H. hypothejus*

not be located at New York. *H. fuligineus* is distinct from *hypothejus* and is generally recognized as such by American investigators. *H. hypothejus* is our most common *Hygrophorus* under two-needle pines during wet weather in the fall.

165
Hygrophorus speciosus Pk. var. **speciosus**
N. Y. State Mus. Ann. Rept. 29: 43. 1878

Illustrations:
    Fig. 84.
    Bresadola, Icon. Myc., tab. 312 (as *H. aureus*)

Pileus 2–5 cm broad, convex, expanding, at times umbonate, at first orange to orange-red, fading to bright golden yellow, golden-fulvous to reddish yellow, the disc often not fading, glutinous, margin even. Con-

Fig. 84. *H. speciosus* var. *speciosus*

text white to yellowish, soft; odor and taste mild.

Lamellae adnato-decurrent, white to yellowish, edges yellowish, rather narrow, distant or subdistant, edges even.

Stipe 4–10 cm long, 4–8 mm thick, white or whitish, at times becoming pale tawny or concolor with the pileus, the gluten staining the stipe dull orange at it dries, apex white-pruinose above the glutinous, fugacious tawny-reddish ring-like outer veil, at times the base enlarged-clavate, stuffed.

Spores 8–10 × 4.5–6 μ, ellipsoid, smooth, pale yellow in Melzer's reagent. Basidia 48–66 × 5–8 μ, mostly 2-spored, some 4-spored, rarely 1-spored. Pleurocystidia and cheilocystidia none. Gill trama divergent, hyphae 5–11 μ broad, at times with a brownish, narrow mediostrate. Cuticle a gelatinous zone, 100–280 μ broad, with narrow (2–5 μ), colorless, interwoven hyphae which tend to be erect (an ixotrichodermium). No hypodermium differentiated. Pileus trama of interwoven, radially disposed hyphae. Clamp connections present on the cuticular hyphae.

Habit, Habitat, and Distribution—Gregarious to subcaespitose on soil, in bogs and under larch, Washington, Oregon, Idaho, Arizona, Michigan, Alabama, Tennessee, Pennsylvania, New York, Massachusetts, Maine, and Canada (Quebec), August–October.

Material Studied—ALABAMA: Burke 91b. ARIZONA: Lowe 9265. IDAHO: Bigelow 47157; Cooke 18554; Gruber P55, P85; Slipp 574, 1275, 1474; Smith 23579, 53566, 52790, 53942. MAINE: Webster, Kennebunk, Oct. 20, 1901. MASSACHUSETTS: Bigelow 9370. MICHIGAN: Bailey 110; Smith 1077, 1086, 1237, 15480, 27611, 31953, 38758, 43976, 58294; Smith & Shaffer 53432. NEW YORK: Kauffman, North Elba; Peck (type, from Grieg, Lewis Co.); Smith 966; Snell, Newcomb 1934. OREGON: Smith, Ochocho National Forest, Nov. 13, 1941; 19515, 19806, 23732, 24117, 27358, 27389, 27438, 27880, 53523. PENNSYLVANIA: Rea 442. TENNESSEE: Hesler 4427. WASHINGTON: Copeland, Bumping River, Oct. 17, 1948; Smith 54118. CANADA: (Quebec) Smith 61489; (Ontario) Jackson 9630.

Observations—H. aureus was first described as growing under hardwoods. We have no species from such a habitat remotely resembling the description in Fries' Monographia. We do have two similarly colored Hygrophori growing under larch, one with a fibrillose inner veil and one without it. As near as we can determine, the one lacking the inner veil is what Peck described and illustrated as H. speciosus. The other taxon was best described by Kauffman as a robust H. speciosus, and we here describe it as a variety of H. speciosus naming it in his honor.

There seems little to be gained by our commenting on the various related species which have passed under the name *H. aureus* in Europe. Suffice it to say that Kühner and Romagnesi recognized *H. speciosus* in their flora, and their account is convincing enough for us. We cannot agree with Singer (1951) in considering *H. aureus* as a variety of *H. hypothejus*, because of the habitat difference; the latter forms mycorrhiza with pine, the former grows under hardwoods.

Observations in Peck's type: Spores 8–9 × 4.5–5.5 μ, ellipsoid, smooth, pale yellow in Melzer's reagent. Basidia 41–54 × 6–8 μ, 4-spored. Pleurocystidia and cheilocystidia none. Gill trama divergent, hyphae 4–8 μ broad. Cuticle of gelatinous hyphae. Clamp connections present.

166
Hygrophorus speciosus var. *kauffmanii*, var. nov.

Hygrophorus coloratus Pk., N. Y. State Mus. Bull. 122: 21. 1908.

Illustrations:
Fig. 85.
Bresadola, Icon. Myc., tab. 313.
Farlow, Icon. Farlow., pl. 28.

Pileus 2–8 cm latus, campanulatus deinde extenso-umbonatus, coccinus vel rubro-luteus, deinde flavus, umbo semper ruber, glutinosus, glaber; lamellae decurrentes, albae demum pallido-citrinae, distantes, medio-latae, extremis acutae; stipes 3–10 cm longus, 8–15(20) mm crassus, albidus, gelatinae universales reliquiae infra, peronatus usque ad evanidam annularem zonam; sporae 8–10 × 5–6 μ, ellipsoideae. Specimen typicum in Herb. Univ. Mich.; lectum Mud Lake Bog, Cheboygan Co., Mich., Oct. 9, 1955, Smith 50929.

Pileus 2–8 cm broad, campanulate at first, then expanded-umbonate or umbo obsolete in age, bright scarlet red or rosy reddish orange when young, fading near the margin to yellow but remaining orange-red on the umbo, glutinous, pellicle separable, glabrous, margin at first incurved, soon spreading. Context white, yellow or orange tinted under the pellicle, moderately thick, soft; odor and taste not distinctive.

Lamellae decurrent, white to pale citrine, distant, rather broad, acute at the ends, intervenose.

Stipe 3–10 cm long, 8–15(20) mm thick, whitish, equal or subcompressed, coated over the lower half with gelatinous universal veil remnants, peronate from a thin white-fibrillose partial veil up to the evanescent annular zone, becoming white floccose-fibrillose, variegated with glistening spots from the drying of the gluten, upper portion subglabrous, spongy within, rarely hollow.

Fig. 85. *H. speciosus* var. *kauffmanii*

Spores 8–10 × 5–6 μ, ellipsoid, smooth, pale yellow in Melzer's reagent. Basidia 38–55 × 6–8 μ, 4-spored. Pleurocystidia and cheilocystidia none. Gill trama divergent, hyphae 4–15 μ. Cuticle of repent to more or less erect, gelatinous hyphae, 2–4 μ broad. No hypodermium differentiated. Pileus trama of radial hyphae. Clamp connections on the cuticular and gill trama hyphae.

HABIT, HABITAT, AND DISTRIBUTION—Scattered to gregarious, under pine, cedar, tamarack, and spruce, and in *Sphagnum* bogs, Maine, Massachusetts, and Michigan, October.

MATERIAL STUDIED—MICHIGAN: Smith 43891, 50929 (type, Mud Lake Bog, Cheboygan Co., Oct. 9, 1955).

OBSERVATIONS—Farlow (1929) reports it from Maine and Massachusetts, on swampy ground, usually under or near tamarack trees. For further discussion, see under the account of *H. speciosus* var. *speciosus*.

167
Hygrophorus whiteii, sp. nov.

Pileus 2.5–5 cm latus, convexus, "warm buff," viscidus, glaber; caro alba, tenuis, odore et gustu mitis; lamellae decurrentes, modice arcuatae, "warm buff," subdistantes, modice latae; stipes 4–7 cm longus, 5–8 mm crassus, pallidus, viscidus; sporae 9–11 × 5–6(7) μ, ellipsoideae. Specimen typicum in Herb. Univ. Mich. conservatum; lectum Patrick Point, Calif., Dec. 15, 1956, A. H. Smith 56693.

Pileus 2.5–5 cm broad, convex, expanding somewhat convex, "warm buff," viscid, glabrous, margin even. Context white, thin; odor and taste not distinctive.

Lamellae decurrent, more or less arcuate, "warm buff," subdistant, medium broad, lamellulae numerous, at times anastomosing, edges even.

Stipe 4–7 cm long, 5–8 mm thick, pallid, viscid, somewhat silky-appressed, equal or slightly enlarged below.

Spores 9–11 × 5–6(7) μ, ellipsoid, smooth, pale yellow in Melzer's reagent. Basidia 44–60 × 6–9 μ, 4-spored. Pleurocystidia and cheilocystidia none. Gill trama divergent, hyphae 6–12 μ broad. Cuticle a gelatinous zone, an ixocutis, colorless, hyphae mostly repent. No hypodermium differentiated. Clamp connections present. Pileus trama of radially disposed hyphae.

HABIT, HABITAT, AND DISTRIBUTION—On soil, under spruce, California, December.

MATERIAL STUDIED—CALIFORNIA: Smith 56693 (type, from Patrick Point, Dec. 15, 1956).

OBSERVATIONS—This species is related to *H. eburneus*, but differs in its pale-yellow pileus and lamellae, and in its larger spores. It is perhaps closest to *H. flavodiscus* which has smaller spores and becomes more orange-colored on drying.

168
Hygrophorus flavodiscus Frost apud Pk.
N. Y. State Mus. Ann. Rept. 35: 134. 1884

Illustration:
  Fig. 10d.

Pileus 2–7 cm broad, convex or plane, smooth, glutinous, the gluten drying in radial streaks, white, with a pale-yellow or reddish-yellow disc, becoming ochraceous orange to orange-buff on drying, margin white-fibrillose. Context firm, white; odor and taste mild.

Lamellae adnate or short-decurrent, becoming rather long-decurrent, subdistant, medium broad, at first pinkish, fading to whitish, the interspaces sometimes veiny.

Stipe 3–7.5 cm long, 6–14 mm thick, subequal, sheathed nearly to the apex with a glutinous universal veil, white, sometimes slightly stained with yellow, fibrillose to scabrous punctate at the apex.

Spores 6–8 × 3.5–5 μ, ellipsoid, smooth, yellowish in Melzer's reagent. Basidia 34–48 × 5–8 μ, 4-spored. Pleurocystidia and cheilocystidia none. Gill trama of divergent hyphae, 3–8 μ broad. Cuticle a gelatinous zone 180–350 μ thick, with tangled, imbedded, narrow (3–5 μ) hyphae with a conspicuous, yellow pigment-deposit. No hypodermium differentiated. Pileus trama interwoven, hyphae radially disposed. Clamp connections present on the cuticular hyphae.

Habit, Habitat, and Distribution—Gregarious to subcaespitose, in pine woods, Massachusetts, Pennsylvania, Maine, New York, Idaho, and Oregon, October–November.

Material Studied—idaho: Smith 54067, 54792. maine: Parlin 15373, 15374a. massachusetts: Bigelow 7957, 7958, 9397. new york: Peck (type). oregon: Smith 19794, 26993, 27067, 27333, 55825. pennsylvania: Overholts 16593.

Observations—The color-change of the pileus on drying, the color of the lamellae, and the size of the spores distinguish this species from its relative *H. gliocyclus*. In *H. gliocyclus* the lamellae are yellowish, and the spores are 8–10(11) × 4.5–6 μ. The pileus of *H. flavodiscus* is white with a pale-yellow or reddish-yellow disc; on drying, however, the pileus becomes ochraceous orange or ochraceous buff (decidedly yellow). In *H. gliocyclus* there is only slight change in the color of the pileus on drying. See also remarks under *H. gliocyclus*.

Notes on Peck's type: Spores 6–8 × 3.5–5 μ, ellipsoid, yellowish in Melzer's reagent. Basidia 34–52 × 6–7 μ, 4-spored. Pleurocystidia and cheilocystidia none. Gill trama divergent, hyphae 3–8 μ broad. Cuticle a gelatinous zone 180–350 μ thick, with tangled, imbedded, narrow (3–5 μ) hyphae, with a conspicuous, yellow pigment-deposit. No hypodermium differentiated. Pileus trama interwoven, hyphae disposed both radially and periclinally. Clamps present in cuticle.

169
Hygrophorus gliocyclus Fr.
Monogr. Hymen. Suec. 2: 311. 1863

Illustration:
   Bresadola, Icon. Myc., tab. 302.

Pileus (2)4–9 cm broad, convex, obtuse or expanded, subumbonate, "chamois" to "cream buff," whitish on margin, glutinous, with a separable pellicle, glabrous, margin even, at first involute. Context compact and thick on the disc, abruptly thin on the margin, white, unchanging; odor and taste mild.

Lamellae broadly adnate to decurrent, subdistant, broad behind, narrow in front, "ivory yellow" to more dingy-yellowish in age, edges even.

Stipe (2)3–6 cm long, (6)8–12(20) mm thick, equal to slightly ventricose, abruptly attenuated below, whitish to "chamois," sheathed by a hyaline, glutinous veil which terminates in a narrow sometimes obsolete, glutinous annulus, the apical region at first white floccose but becoming silky-fibrillose, solid.

Spores 8–10(11) × 4.5–6 μ, ellipsoid, smooth, pale yellowish in Melzer's reagent. Basidia 46–57 × 6–8 μ, 2- and 4-spored. Pleurocystidia and cheilocystidia none. Gill trama divergent, hyphae 3–7 μ broad. Cuticle a gelatinous zone 200–900 μ thick, hyphae repent on the surface but more or less erect below but not a palisade, narrow (3–5 μ). No hypodermium evident. Pileus trama of hyphae which are radial and parallel to only slightly interwoven. Clamp connections present in the cuticular hyphae.

HABIT, HABITAT, AND DISTRIBUTION—Gregarious or subcaespitose under spruce and pine, Tennessee, Georgia, Idaho, Wyoming, Oregon, and California; also Europe, September–January.

MATERIAL STUDIED—CALIFORNIA: Pusateri, Sequoia National Park, Fall 1941. GEORGIA: Hesler 22234. IDAHO: Smith 46284, 46467, 59707. OREGON: Gruber, Takilma, Nov. 28, 1942; Smith 24956, 24999, 27960, 28136. TENNESSEE: Hesler 17252, 17270, 19560, 20241, 20774, 22224, 22234, 22564. WYOMING: Kanouse, Medicine Bow Mts., Sept. 7, 1923; Kauffman, same. BELGIUM: Heinemann 1520.

OBSERVATIONS—*Hygrophorus gliocyclus* is distinguished from its close relative *H. flavodiscus* on the character of the lamellae and spores. The lamellae of *H. flavodiscus* are at first pinkish, then fading to whitish, and its spores are 6–8 × 3.5–5 μ. Moreover, in *H. flavodiscus,* when fresh, the pileus is white with a pale-yellow or reddish-yellow disc. In general, the stipe of *H. flavodiscus* is more slender than in *H. gliocyclus.*

As we interpret this species, following American usage of the name, it is a robust *Hygrophorus* very readily attacked by insect larvae and occurring principally with pine. This we realize is not entirely consistent with treatments by European authors. The problem needs further study.

SERIES OLIVACEOUMBRINI (Fr.) stat. nov.

Subsection Olivaceoumbrini Fries, Hymen. Eur., p. 409. 1879.
Characters as given in key to series, page 249.
Type species: *H. olivaceoalbus* Fr.

KEY TO SPECIES

1. Lamellae crowded and sinuate; spores 4–5 × 3.5–5 μ . . . .
. . . . .170. *H. subpratensis*
1. Lamellae and spores not as above 2
  2. Odor amygdaline; pleurocystidia and cheilocystidia 46–60 × 4–6 μ
. . . . .171. *H. amygdalinus*
  2. Not as above 3

3. Stipe showing a thin to conspicuous inner fibrillose veil beneath the glutinous outer veil 4
3. Stipe lacking a fibrillose inner veil 9
   4. Inner veil white 5
   4. Inner veil colored 6
5. Context and lamellae soon tinged or colored yellow; under pines ....164. *H. hypothejus*
5. Growing under hardwoods; lamellae and stipe apex (squamules at least) finally stained olive ....172. *H. paludosus*
5. Stipe white and unchanging; pileus fuscous ....
   ....173. *H. fuscoalbus* var. *fuscoalbus*
   6. Hyphae of the epicutis of the pileus with dark yellow-brown granules as observed in Melzer's reagent ..177. *H. olivaceoalbus* var. *gracilis*
   6. Not as above 7
7. Spores 10–16 × 6–9 μ; inner veil rudimentary .....174. *H. limacinus*
7. Spores 8–12 μ long; inner veil well-developed 8
   8. Inner veil thin ....176. *H. olivaceoalbus* var. *intermedius*
   8. Inner veil copious ....175. *H. olivaceoalbus* var. *olivaceoalbus*
9. Clamp connections absent on hyphae of fruiting body; spores 9–12 × 5–6.5 μ ....178. *H. adiaphorus*
9. Clamp connections present 10
   10. Spores 12–18(20) × 7–9 μ ....179. *H. megasporus*
   10. Spores smaller 11
11. Ornamentation over upper portion of stipe white, and unchanging in age or when bruised 12
11. Ornamentation colored or becoming so 15
   12. Pileus whitish with a brownish disc, and minutely virgate with innate black fibrils ....160. *H. virgatulus*
   12. Pileus not as above 13
13. Pileus uniformly olive-black to blackish ....182. *H. fuligineus*
13. Pileus disc and margin colors not uniform 14
   14. Pileus margin whitish, disc gray to brownish gray ....
   ....180. *H. occidentalis*
   14. Pileus margin cinereous to "tilleul buff," disc pale drab to avellaneous ....181. *H. mesotephrus*
15. Squamules at apex of stipe golden yellow, finally cinereous ....
   ....184. *H. tephroleucus* var. *aureofloccosus*
15. Not as above 16
   16. Stipe 2–3(4) mm thick, white at first, surface fibrils and punctae cinerescent ....183. *H. tephroleucus* var. *tephroleucus*
   16. Stipe thicker 17
17. Stipe 5–8 mm thick; with dark gray, conspicuous punctae near the apex ....185. *H. pustulatus*
17. Stipe 11–20 mm thick; apex silky-floccose, becoming orange-brown punctate when dried, in KOH becoming instantly orange; no inner fibrillose veil ....186. *H. paludosoides*

170
Hygrophorus subpratensis Murr.
Mycologia 3: 199. 1911

Pileus 3–4 cm broad, convex, obtuse, pale fuscous when young, becoming pallid or whitish with a darker disc, slimy-viscid, pellicle separable, margin even. Context white, unchanging; odor and taste mild.

Lamellae deeply sinuate, white, broad, crowded.

Stipe 3–4 cm long, 3–4 mm thick, white, slimy-viscid, cylindric, equal, spongy-solid. Partial veil slimy-viscid, scarcely leaving an annulus.

Spores 4–5 × 3.5–5 μ, globose to subglobose, smooth, colorless in Melzer's reagent, at times adhering together in fours. Basidia 26–33 × 5–6 μ, 4-spored. Pleurocystidia and cheilocystidia none. Gill trama divergent. Epicutis of loosely arranged, gelatinous hyphae. Clamps present on epicuticular hyphae. Stipe exhibiting a gelatinous sheath.

HABIT, HABITAT, AND DISTRIBUTION—On lawns and on banana trash, Cuba, June.

MATERIAL STUDIED—CUBA: Earle 68, 373 (type, Santiago de las Vegas, June 1, 1905).

OBSERVATIONS—The description of microscopic characters given above is based on our study of the type.

The pileus of the type (dried) is "ochraceous tawny," and superficially resembles *H. pratensis*, but differs in its divergent hyphae of the gill trama, its globose to subglobose spores, and slimy-viscid stipe.

Dennis (1953) says the spores in deposit are white, becoming yellowish with age.

171
Hygrophorus amygdalinus Pk.
Torrey Bot. Club Bull. 25: 322. 1898

Illustrations:
   Figs. 2k, 2l, 9c.
   Coker, Elisha Mitchell Sci. Soc. Jour. 64, pl. 16.

Pileus 2.5–3.5 cm broad, at first nearly hemispheric, finally plane with a drooping margin, gray-drab or grayish brown, at all ages, viscid, fibrous, margin incurved and felted-spongy, the marginal fibrils representing an ephemeral veil. Context pure white, firm, about 5–6 mm thick near the stipe, rapidly thinning toward the margin; odor strong of bitter almonds, taste mild.

Lamellae adnate or more commonly slightly decurrent, rounded in front, narrowed behind, white, rather distant, about 2.5 mm wide, alternately long and short or nearly so.

Stipe 5–15 cm long, 4–6 mm broad, concolorous, surface viscid, felted, minutely scurfy-squamulose, crooked, terete or somewhat grooved or flattened, base pointed and yellowish or equal and whitish or grayish brown, stuffed.

Spores 8–12 × 4.5–6 μ, ellipsoid to subellipsoid, smooth, yellowish in Melzer's reagent. Basidia 42–74 × 7–11 μ, 2- and 4-spored. Pleurocystidia 46–78 × 4–9 μ, subcylindric to more or less clavate, often irregular, appendiculate; cheilocystidia 40–62 × 3–7 μ, subcylindric, ventricose, tapering or appendiculate. Gill trama divergent, hyphae 4–8 μ broad. Cuticle an ixotrichodermium, the hyphae fuscous, at times branched. Hypodermium present, similar to that of *H. fuligineus.* Clamp connections present. Pileus trama loosely interwoven.

HABIT, HABITAT, AND DISTRIBUTION—Gregarious on soil, in pine woods, District of Columbia and North Carolina.

MATERIAL STUDIED—DISTRICT OF COLUMBIA: Peck (type, collected by Mrs. E. M. Williams, Nov. 20, 1897). NORTH CAROLINA: Coker 10698, 10700.

OBSERVATIONS—Our notes on the type are recorded as follows: Spores 8–12 × 4.5–6.5 μ, ellipsoid or subellipsoid, smooth, yellowish in Melzer's reagent. Basidia 42–74 × 7–11 μ, 2- and 4-spored. Pleurocystidia 46–58 × 4–6 μ, subcylindric, slightly constricted, not projecting; cheilocystidia 42–57 × 4–6 μ, similar. Gill trama divergent, hyphae 5–7.5 μ broad. Cuticle of fuscous, septate, branched, gelatinous hyphae forming a turf, or ixotrichodermial palisade, with free hyphal ends extending beyond the general level of the epicutis. Hypodermium present, similar to that of *H. fuligineus.* Pileus trama loosely interwoven. Clamp connections present on the cuticular hyphae.

Coker's two collections resemble the type closely in all respects. Murrill (1916) placed it in synonymy with *H. hypothejus,* but in this latter species the colors are different and the spores are smaller than in *H. amygdalinus.* Moreover, the odor in *H. hypothejus* is not distinctive.

172

Hygrophorus paludosus Pk.
Torrey Bot. Club Bull. 29: 70. 1902

Illustrations:
> Fig. 86; also 9e.
> Smith and Hesler, Lloydia 2, pl. 7.

Pileus 4–10 cm broad, convex or obtusely conic, then plane or broadly depressed in age, "pale ochraceous buff" to "pinkish-vinaceous,"

Fig. 86. *H. paludosus*

very glutinous, gluten colorless becoming smoky, in age appearing zoned, streaked or netted beneath the gluten, margin even, involute, fibrillose. Context thick, rather firm, white, not changing color when cut or bruised; odor and taste not distinctive.

Lamellae adnate, becoming decurrent, white, often becoming sordid greenish-spotted in age, moderately broad, close to subdistant, edges even.

Stipe 5–12 cm long, 10–20 mm thick, equal above a narrowed base, subradicating, solid, thick-glutinous over the lower two-thirds, gluten pale smoky to nearly hyaline at first and leaving sordid bands over the lower portion when dry, and a thin white-fibrillose sheath present beneath the gluten, white and scabrous-punctate above, in age the scales or points staining sordid yellowish to greenish, white beneath the gluten, in age sometimes sordid greenish at the base.

Spores 8–11 × 5–7 μ, ellipsoid, smooth, white in mass, pale yellow in Melzer's reagent. Basidia 42–60 × 7–9 μ, 2- and 4-spored. Pleurocystidia and cheilocystidia none. Gill trama divergent, hyphae 4–12 μ broad. Cuticle an ixotrichodermium, about 350–550 μ thick, hyphae slender (2–5 μ), septate, more or less erect, the zone similar to that of *H. fuligineus* but in *H. paludosus* the epicuticular hyphae are pale fuscous. Hypodermium well-developed, similar to that in *H. fuligineus*.

Pileus trama interwoven, homogeneous, hyphae radially disposed. Clamp connections present on the hyphae of the gill trama and the cuticle.

HABIT, HABITAT, AND DISTRIBUTION—Scattered to gregarious, in humus, in deciduous and conifer woods, Michigan, Tennessee, and Florida, August–January.

MATERIAL STUDIED—FLORIDA: Hesler 16170, 20255. MICHIGAN: Smith 5005, 5026, 6144, 11127, 15454, 20655, 20935, 32436, 32574, 38842, 38852, 43422, 51161, 58114. TENNESSEE: Hesler 7851, 9709, 14066, 14774, 15214, 18284.

OBSERVATIONS—We have been unable to locate the type of this species, but representative material has been collected and redescribed from Michigan by Smith (1934a). Continued collecting in the woods from which the first specimens were obtained has brought out certain interesting facts. The greenish spots on the gills and sordid yellowish-green stains on the upper part of the stipe do not always develop— particularly in dry weather. As a result of this observation, and many collections of a species from the West Coast which seemed to be *H. olivaceoalbus* Fr., we were led to study Kauffman's specimens of the latter. All of his specimens labeled *H. olivaceoalbus* are similar and do not show any signs of the fuscous fibrillose sheath which is the distinguishing character of that species. Upon comparing specimens of *H. paludosus* with those Kauffman named *H. olivaceoalbus*, it was at once apparent that they were the same. Hence we believe that Kauffman's (1918) description of *H. olivaceoalbus* actually applies to material of *H. paludosus* which did not develop the characteristic stains. In searching the literature for a European species which is closely related to Peck's, one is at once impressed with the similarity of *H. fuscoalbus* sensu Ricken. The latter is said to grow in coniferous woods, however, and, except for spore size, might be regarded as closer to *H. fuligineus*.

173
Hygrophorus fuscoalbus (Lasch) Fr. var. fuscoalbus
Epicr. Myc., p. 324. 1838

> *Agaricus fuscoalbus* Lasch, Linnaea 4: 520. 1829.
> *Limacium fuscoalbum* (Lasch) Kummer, Führ. in Pilzk., p. 119. 1871.

Illustrations:
Juillard-Hartmann, Icon. Champ., pl. 49, fig. 9.
Ricken, Die Blätterp., pl. 5, fig. 1 (as *Limacium*).

Pileus 2–5 cm broad, convex, expanding more or less, plane, fuscous, then cinereous, viscid, glabrous, margin pale, incurved, white-floccose. Context grayish white; odor and taste none.

Lamellae adnate to decurrent, white with a pale pinkish-buff reflection, rather thick, close, broad.

Stipe 3–6 cm long, 8–15 mm thick (broader when compressed), white, with a layer of white-floccose fibrils beneath the glutinous veil, peronate-slimy up to a superior line, when dry white floccose at the apex, often enlarged downward, solid.

Spores 9–13 × 5.5–7 μ, ellipsoid, smooth, pale yellow in Melzer's reagent. Basidia 52–77 × 7–9 μ, 4-spored. Pleurocystidia and cheilocystidia none. Gill trama divergent, hyphae 6–12 μ broad. Cuticle a gelatinous zone 90–250 μ thick, hyphae tangled, pale fuscous, narrow (3–4 μ) broad. No hypodermium differentiated. Pileus trama interwoven, hyphae radially disposed. Clamp connections present on the cuticular hyphae.

HABIT, HABITAT, AND DISTRIBUTION—On soil, New York, Michigan, Colorado, Idaho, Washington, Oregon, and Canada; Europe, August–November.

MATERIAL STUDIED—COLORADO: Kauffman, Tolland, Aug. 20, 1920. IDAHO: Smith 47140. MICHIGAN: Kauffman, Ann Arbor, Oct. 23, 1926; Smith 1124, 15475. NEW YORK: Kauffman, North Elba, Sept. 1914; Ithaca, Sept. 1903. OREGON: Kauffman & Brown, Takilma, Nov. 29, 1925. WASHINGTON: Flett 181. CANADA: Cain, Ontario, Oct. 2, 1951. AUSTRIA: Moser 1948 (Hesler 24132). BELGIUM: Heinemann 1918.

OBSERVATIONS—In Europe, apparently, the pileus is olive-gray to blackish, Moser (1955). Peck's collection from North Elba, N. Y., which he identified as *H. fuscoalbus*, has spores 7.5–9 μ long; it should be called *H. pustulatus*. Bataille (1910, p. 189) lists *anguinaceus* Jungh. as a synonym.

174
Hygrophorus limacinus Fr.
Epicr. Myc., p. 324. 1838

Limacium limacinum (Fr.) Kummer, Führ. in Pilzk., p. 118. 1871.
Illustrations:
Fig. 87.
Bresadola, Icon. Myc., tab. 315.

Pileus 3–7 cm broad, convex with an incurved margin, becoming nearly plane, obtusely umbonate with an inrolled margin, "sepia" or darker on the disc, paler (near "snuff brown") toward the pallid margin, glutinous, the gluten hyaline, appearing streaked to appressed-squamulose beneath the gluten; odor and taste mild, no color changes, but in KOH slowly yellow and then dull orange (on pileus); on stipe apex lemon-chrome changing to orange.

Lamellae broadly adnate to decurrent, 2–3 tiers of lamellulae, white to whitish, in age watery-grayish, distant or subdistant, broad, edges even.

Stipe (2.5)6–8 cm long, (4)8–12 mm thick, apex white, elsewhere slightly grayish from a thin coating of fibrils, or no fibrils evident, equal

Fig. 87.
  H. limacinus

to enlarged downward, with a thick layer of hyaline gluten to near apex, solid; no inner veil.

Spores 10–15(17) × 6–9 μ, ellipsoid, smooth, pale yellow in Melzer's reagent. Basidia 58–92 × 9–14 μ, 2- and 4-spored. Pleurocystidia and cheilocystidia none. Gill trama divergent, hyphae 6–14(22) μ broad. Cuticle a zone (120)300–450 μ thick, with fuscous, gelatinous hyphae. Clamp connections present on the cuticular hyphae.

HABIT, HABITAT, AND DISTRIBUTION—On soil, under hardwoods and conifers, Michigan and California, October and December.

MATERIAL STUDIED—CALIFORNIA: Smith 56311, 56347, 56350, 56476.

OBSERVATIONS—Moser (1955) gives the spores 10–14 × 7–9 μ, and Kühner and Romagnesi (1953) 9–13 × 5.5–7.5 μ. We have examined Peck's North Greenbush collection labeled *H. limacinus*, and find that the pilei are shining, "warm buff" to "antimony yellow," and the spores are 9–10.5 × 5–6 μ. Undoubtedly Peck's collection is *H. paludosus*.

Hygrophorus limacinus differs from *H. paludosus* in lacking an inner veil, and in its hyaline gluten. The dried specimens are almost as dark as those of *H. fuligineus*, but in *H. paludosoides* the spores are smaller and the fruiting bodies are larger.

175

Hygrophorus olivaceoalbus (Fr.) Fr. var. **olivaceoalbus**
Epicr. Myc., p. 324. 1838

> *Agaricus olivaceoalbus* Fr., Syst. Myc., p. 35. 1821.
> *Limacium olivaceoalbum* (Fr. ex Fr.) Kummer, Führ. in Pilzk., p. 119.
>   1871.

Illustrations:
>   Fig. 88.
>   Bresadola, Icon. Myc., tab. 316.
>   Bresadola, Fungi Trident., tab. 92 (obese form).
>   Juillard-Hartmann, Icon. Champ., pl. 47, fig. 45.
>   Kauffman, Agar. Mich., pl. 25.
>   Lange, Flora Agar. Dan. 5, pl. 162A.
>   Smith and Hesler, Lloydia 2, pl. 8.

Pileus 3–8(12) cm broad, convex or with a somewhat pronounced umbo, often nearly flat when expanded, glutinous to viscid, conspicu-

Fig. 88. *H. olivaceoalbus* var. *olivaceoalbus*

ously virgate beneath the gelatinous layer with smoke-gray to black fibrils, disc umber to black, the margin paler and dark to light ash-gray. Context thick on the disc, soft, white; odor and taste not distinctive.

Lamellae adnate to subdecurrent, pure white or somewhat ashy at the base, close to subdistant, moderately broad, thickish.

Stipe 8–12(15) cm long, 10–30 mm thick, peronate to near the apex with a double sheath, the outer layer glutinous, the inner layer of appressed blackish fibrils similar to those on the pileus and forming a subfloccose, evanescent, apical, annular zone or submembranous annulus, in age the sheath often breaks up into dark concentric ragged bands over the lower portion, white and glabrous to pruinose above the annulus, clavate to equal, solid, white within.

Spores 9–12 × 5–6 μ, ellipsoid, smooth, yellowish in Melzer's reagent. Basidia 46–62 × 7–10 μ, 4-spored, sterigmata stout. Pleurocystidia and cheilocystidia none. Gill trama divergent, hyphae 3–8 μ broad. Cuticle a broad (250–450 μ) zone of gelatinous, repent, fuscous hyphae, 2–3 μ broad, an ixocutis. No hypodermium evident. Pileus trama of radial hyphae. Clamp connections on the cuticular hyphae.

HABIT, HABITAT, AND DISTRIBUTION—Caespitose, gregarious, or scattered under redwood and spruce, California, Oregon, Idaho, Colorado, Michigan, New York, and Canada; July–December; also Europe.

MATERIAL STUDIED—CALIFORNIA: Smith 3635, 3698, 8785, 9061, 9141, 9588, 56414, 56547, 56897, 56955, 57018. COLORADO: Hesler 12691; Mains 5203; Smith 52187. IDAHO: Smith 23519, 23577, 53295, 53501, 54815, 54759, 60100, 60207. MICHIGAN: Bailey 34; Kauffman 2478. NEW YORK: Kauffman, Ithaca, Oct. 31, 1903. OREGON: Smith 3603. CANADA: (Quebec) Hoare 24703, 27013. DENMARK: J. P. Jensen (Hesler 23957).

OBSERVATIONS—The outstanding character of this species is the double sheath over the greater portion of the stipe. The outer layer is glutinous, and the thin inner layer is composed of floccose fibrils similar in color with and at first connected to the fibrillose coating under the gluten of the pileus. As the stipe elongates the inner sheath breaks up into irregular fuscous bands. The American specimens have been compared with specimens from Dr. Rolf Singer, collections from Leningrad, U.S.S.R., and Mr. Marcel Josserand, Lyon, France. Kauffman's (1922) collections of *H. fuscoalbus* from Colorado belong in *H. olivaceoalbus*. For comments on the species Kauffman referred to *H. olivaceoalbus*, see *H. paludosus*.

176

Hygrophorus olivaceoalbus var. *intermedius,* var. nov.

Pileus 3–10 cm latus, convexus demum planus, modice umbonatus, glutinosus, cinereis fibrillis striatus; caro crassa, alba, odore et gustu mitis; lamellae decurrentes, albae deinde pallidae ("tilleul buff"), distantes demum subdistantes, latae; stipes 3–9 cm longus, 10–25 mm crassus, aequalis vel anguste clavatus, viscidus, cinereo-fibrillosus; sporae 9–12 × 5.5–7 μ, ellipsoideae demum oblongae. Specimen typicum in Herb. Univ. Mich.; lectum Trout Lake, San Juan Mts., Colo., Aug. 17, 1956, A. H. Smith 52370.

Pileus 3–10 cm broad, convex to plane with an inrolled margin, expanding to slightly umbonate to plane, margin finally uplifted in some, surface glutinous when fresh and streaked beneath the gluten with gray fibrils (paler than "light drab"), in age either streaked or if dried out often slightly squamulose; flesh thick, white, odor none, taste mild.

Lamellae decurrent, white becoming pallid ("tilleul buff"), thick, forked and anastomosing, distant to subdistant, broad, edges even.

Stipe 3–9 cm long, 10–25 mm thick, equal, ventricose or narrowly clavate downwards lower two-thirds viscid and with a layer of gray fibrils like those on cap terminating in a superior annular zone, white and silky above the zone.

Spores 9–12 × 5.5–7 μ, ellipsoid to oblong, hyaline in KOH, and yellowish-hyaline in Melzer's reagent, smooth; when revived often with refractive material variously distributed just beneath the thin wall. Basidia 4-spored, 50–60 × 8–9 μ, with a long flexuous pedicel. Pleurocystidia and cheilocystidia none. Gill trama divergent. Pileus with a gelatinous cuticle of appressed hyphae 4–6 μ broad, their content yellowish gray in KOH, beneath this the flesh hyaline and floccose. Clamp connections present.

HABIT, HABITAT, AND DISTRIBUTION—Caespitose-scattered under *Picea engelmanii,* Trout Lake, San Juan Mts., Colorado, August.

MATERIAL STUDIED—COLORADO: Smith 52370 (type, from Trout Lake, San Juan Mts., Aug. 17, 1956).

OBSERVATIONS—This is essentially a large *Hygrophorus* of the stature of *H. fuligineus* but differs in larger spores and a very thin layer of pale-gray fibrils beneath the viscid coating of the stipe. In the dried specimens the lower part of the stipe is pale gray (usually paler than the cap) because of this layer. Because of the colored inner veil and the large spores, it would seem to be *H. olivaceoalbus.* However, a species answering well to the description of *H. olivaceoalbus* is well known to us from the conifer forests of the north coast of California. It has an equal (or nearly so) elongated stipe with conspicuous sheath of dark-colored fibrils which break up into zones or patches. These two are readily distinguished at sight in both the fresh and dried condition.

J. Lange (1935–40) comments on a paler form of *H. olivaceoalbus* which grades into *H. limacinus*.

177

Hygrophorus olivaceoalbus var. **gracilis** Maire

Treballs del Museu de Ciencies Naturals de Barcelona 15 (Bot. Ser.), p. 53. 1933

Pileus 1.5–3 cm broad, conic, campanulate or plane, glutinous, virgate with dark-cinereous fibrils beneath the gluten, disc blackish, margin sordid olivaceous-cinereous. Context whitish or tinged cinereous, odor and taste not distinctive.

Lamellae white, broad, distant, decurrent, edges even.

Stipe 6–8 cm long, 5–7 mm thick, surface covered by a thin glutinous sheath over the lower portion, smoky olive beneath the gluten and appressed fibrillose with smoky-olive fibrils, apical annular zone white above and ashy gray beneath, white and silky at the apex.

Spores 10–14 × 5.5–7.5 μ, ellipsoid, at times slightly inequilateral, smooth, pale yellowish in Melzer's reagent. Basidia 42–57 × 7–9 μ, 2-, 3-, and 4-spored. Pleurocystidia and cheilocystidia none. Gill trama divergent, hyphae 3–6 μ broad. Cuticle a broad (175–250 μ) gelatinous zone with fuscous, loosely tangled, narrow (2–3.5 μ) hyphae having dark-brown granules in them as seen in Melzer's reagent. No hypodermium differentiated. Pileus trama of radial hyphae. Clamp connections present on the hyphae of the cuticle, gill trama, and subhymenium.

HABIT, HABITAT, AND DISTRIBUTION—Scattered under fir, Washington, Oregon, and Michigan, October–November.

MATERIAL STUDIED—OREGON: Smith 9211, 8211 (as form *minor*). WASHINGTON: Smith 18080. MICHIGAN: Smith 62065.

OBSERVATIONS—This is an apparently constant slender form in which, at least in our material, the number of spores borne on a basidium varies greatly in a single pileus. This condition is correlated with an increase in spore size. The dark granules as seen in Melzer's reagent in the hyphae of the gelatinous epicutis are the most distinguishing feature of the variety.

178

Hygrophorus adiaphorus, sp. nov.

Pileus 1.5–3 cm latus, obtusus deinde ferme planus, plerumque umbonatus, fibrillosus, glutinosus, medio fuscus demum subniger, margine cineraceus; lamellae distantes, medio-latae, adnatae demum decurrentes, albae; stipes 3.5–6 cm longus, 4–7 mm crassus, albus et sericus superne, cinereus demum fumeus infra; sporae 9–12 × 5–6.5 μ, subellipsoideae demum oblongae. Specimen typicum in Herb. Univ. Mich.; lectum Wilderness State Park, Oct. 15, 1960, Smith 63359.

Pileus 1.5–3 cm broad, obtuse becoming nearly plane but usually retaining a slight umbo, surface streaked with fine dark fibrils beneath a coating of slime, disc fuscous to blackish, gray to cinereous at margin; context white, fragile, odor not distinctive.

Lamellae distant, moderately broad, broadly adnate to short decurrent, waxy white, drying creamy-pallid or the edges yellowish.

Stipe 3.5–6 cm long, 4–7 mm thick, equal, solid, white and silky over apical fourth, lower three-fourths covered by a slime coating giving a gray to umber tone to that part, and this tone mostly preserved in drying, no inner fibrillose veil present.

Spores 9–12 × 5–6.5 μ, subelliptic to oblong or one end slightly broader than the other, smooth, hyaline in KOH and merely yellowish in Melzer's solution. Basidia 2-spored, 38–52 × 5–7 μ, in KOH seen to contain many oil drops, reddish in Melzer's reagent. Pleurocystidia and cheilocystidia none. Gill trama of divergent hyphae. Pileus epicutis of appressed but interwoven narrow (2–4 μ) gelatinous hyphae hyaline to dingy yellowish in KOH. Clamp connections absent (but bumps on hyphae near the cross walls often occur on epicuticular hyphae).

HABIT, HABITAT, AND DISTRIBUTION—Solitary under spruce and fir, Wilderness State Park, Emmet County, Mich., Oct. 15, 1960.

MATERIAL STUDIED—MICHIGAN: Smith 63359, type.

OBSERVATIONS—This species is easily mistaken in the field for *H. megasporus,* and closely resembles the slender form of *H. olivaceoalbus* though a fibrillose inner veil is not present beneath the gluten of the stipe. It is this nondescript appearance which we have chosen to emphasize in our choice of a species epithet. Its claim to distinction is based on the lack of clamp connections on the hyphae of the carpophore and the relatively small spores (for this group) on 2-spored basidia. The lack of clamps in a species in this series is a matter of considerable theoretical interest in view of the situation which has been found in other sections of this subgenus.

179
Hygrophorus megasporus Sm. & Hes.
Lloydia 2: 25. 1939

Illustration:
    Fig. 89.

Pileus 2–5 cm broad, fleshy, at first broadly campanulate, with a mammillate umbo, at length expanded plane, surface beneath "buffy olive" with the umbo "clove brown," margin slightly paler, glutinous from the hyaline veil, glabrous, the surface often uneven from the drying gluten, margin incurved and membranous. Context thin, white, unchanging; odor and taste mild.

Lamellae adnate with a tooth, becoming subdecurrent, pure white, close to subdistant, 3–4 mm broad, thickish, waxy, a few forked.

Fig. 89. *H. megasporus*

Stipe (4)5–10 cm long, 3–6(8) mm thick, slender, whitish, in age tinted like the pileus from the drying veil, white within, equal or slightly ventricose and attenuated at the base, solid, covered at first by a hyaline glutinous sheath.

Spores (10)12–18(20) × 7–9 μ, ellipsoid, smooth, yellowish in Melzer's reagent. Basidia 55–71 × 7–12 μ, 4-spored. Pleurocystidia and cheilocystidia none. Gill trama divergent, hyphae 4–7 μ broad. Cuticle a well-defined gelatinous zone, 260–350 μ thick, of brownish hyphae (3–6 μ broad) which are interwoven, and both radially and periclinally disposed. No hypodermium evident. Pileus trama of interwoven, radial hyphae. Clamp connections present on the cuticular hyphae.

HABIT, HABITAT, AND DISTRIBUTION—Scattered or solitary, rarely subcaespitose on humus or mossy areas, in dense coniferous forests, California, Oregon, and Washington, October–December.

MATERIAL STUDIED—CALIFORNIA: Smith 56476. OREGON: Smith 20210, 24976, 28399, 28400. WASHINGTON: Brown, Lake Quinault, Nov. 3, 1925; Kauffman, Lake Quinault, Nov. 5, 1925, and type, from Lake Quinault, Nov. 2, 1925.

OBSERVATIONS—In his notes Kauffman points out that this species belongs in the subgenus *Limacium* (section *Hygrophorus*) and is close to *H. olivaceoalbus*. It has the same stature as the slender variety of the latter, but lacks the peronate sheath of fuscous fibrils beneath the gluten on the stipe, possesses a glabrous pileus, and much larger spores borne on 4-spored basidia.

180
Hygrophorus occidentalis Sm. & Hes.
Lloydia 2: 18. 1939

Illustrations:
Fig. 90.
Smith and Hesler, Lloydia 2, pl. 6.

Pileus 2–8(10) cm broad, convex, soon plane, at maturity the disc slightly depressed and the margin decurved, in age the disc deeply and broadly depressed and the margin elevated, glutinous, somewhat appressed-fibrillose streaked, color variable, disc "hair brown" to "fuscous," at times yellowish or smoky, the margin white to pale cinereous. Context thin, white; odor and taste not distinctive.

Lamellae adnate, becoming subdecurrent or decurrent, white, then tinged cream, close to subdistant, narrow to moderately broad, thin, edges even.

Fig. 90. *H. occidentalis*

Stipe 2–7 cm long, 3–10(15) mm thick, pallid or concolorous with the pileus, equal above a tapered base, glutinous below, with appressed white fibrils beneath the gluten, apex minutely white punctate or pruinose-punctate, white within, solid.

Spores 6–8 × 3.5–5 μ, ellipsoid, smooth, yellow in Melzer's reagent, white in mass. Basidia 29–43 × 6–8 μ, 4-spored. Pleurocystidia and cheilocystidia none. Gill trama of divergent hyphae, 4–7 μ broad. Cuticle a well-defined, brownish zone of more or less erect, gelatinous hyphae, an ixotrichodermium; hyphae 2.5–4 μ broad. No hypodermium evident. Pileus trama interwoven, more or less radially disposed. Clamp connections present on the cuticular hyphae.

HABIT, HABITAT, AND DISTRIBUTION—Gregarious to scattered, on soil in mixed oak-pine and in deciduous woods, Tennessee, Michigan, Oregon, and California, April–December.

MATERIAL STUDIED—CALIFORNIA: Collett, Butte Co., April 5, 1948. MICHIGAN: Smith 4957, 5088 (type, from Saginaw Forest, Ann Arbor, Oct. 8, 1936), 6054, 15321, 15412. OREGON: Smith 9099, 9188, 9275.

TENNESSEE: Hesler 4444, 13161, 17222, 19360, 22721, 23538; Hesler & Sharp 4465.

OBSERVATIONS—This species can be briefly characterized as a gray to fuscous *H. eburneus*. In Oregon both were collected in the same oak-pine woods and were scarcely distinguishable when young. The fuscous color is usually present at least on the disc at maturity, however, and soon spreads throughout the fruiting body as the specimens begin to dry. In Michigan and Tennessee it has been found in oak-pine woods and in stands of oak and hickory. When dried the specimens are often tinged with tawny brown and small ones somewhat resemble specimens of *H. discoideus*. The small spores should separate it readily from *H. limacinus, H. lividoalbus*, and *H. fuscoalbus*. It is possible that reports of *H. limacinus* for North America are based on this species. Nüesch's (1922) description of *L. mesotephrum* fits our species in most important characters, but again the spore size is not the same (10–12 × 5–8 μ). Rea (1922) gives the spores of the latter as 9 × 6 μ, and emphasizes yellowish stains on the stipe in addition to the small size (2–3 cm broad). All of these are characters which our specimens did not show.

181
Hygrophorus mesotephrus Berk. & Br.
Ann. Mag. Nat. Hist. 13 (2nd Series): 402. 1854
Illustration:
  Fig. 91.

Pileus 1.5–4 cm broad, convex becoming plane or slightly depressed, surface glabrous and glutinous, pale drab on disc and cinereous near the margin, in age the margin "tilleul buff" and center pale avellaneous. Context thin, soft, white, odor and taste not distinctive; KOH orange-yellow on pileus, fading to dingy yellow, no reaction with $FeSO_4$.

Lamellae distant, broad, broadly adnate, rarely slightly decurrent, waxy, white and unchanging, edges even.

Stipe 4–7 cm long, 4–8 mm thick, equal, solid, white, white-punctate at apex and punctae staining orange-yellow in KOH, appressed fibrillose below and with a very thin gelatinous coating from remains of an outer gelatinous veil; slime layer leaving yellowish stains in age at times, stipe soon dry and not otherwise discolored. No fibrillose inner veil present.

Spores 8–11 × 5–6 μ, smooth, ellipsoid, non-amyloid; basidia 4-spored, 45–60 × 8–10 μ, narrowly clavate. Pleurocystidia and cheilocystidia none. Gill trama divergent. Epicutis of pileus a trichodermium of gelatinous tangled hyphae 3–5 μ broad, and hyaline in KOH. Clamp connections present.

HABIT, HABITAT, AND DISTRIBUTION—Gregarious to scattered under oak, Stinchfield Forest, Dexter, Mich., Oct. 30, 1961.

MATERIAL STUDIED—MICHIGAN: Smith 64785.

OBSERVATIONS—The lamellae remain white to pallid in drying, a character at once distinguishing the species from *H. occidentalis.* In the latter the gills are at first white then tinged cream, and the pileus and stipe are more glutinous than in *H. mesotephrus.*

The original description characterizes the pileus as white with a brown disc, viscid and striate. At maturity the pilei in Smith's No. 64785 were whitish on the margin and avellaneous on the disc. The striations mentioned in the original description were not described in more detail, and thus we do not know whether they were slight sulcations (which is probable) or translucent striations. The illustration covers our material rather well, and the English authors mentioned the stains lower down on the stipe. If mature specimens are compared, our material is too close to *H. mesotephrus* as originally described to be placed anywhere else.

Fig. 91. *H. mesotephrus*

182

Hygrophorus fuligineus Frost apud Pk.

N. Y. State Mus. Ann. Rept. 35: 134. 1884

Illustrations:
Fig. 92; also 3, 9a.
Farlow, Icones Farlowianae, pl. 29.

Pileus 4–12 cm broad, convex, then obtuse or plane, with a layer of hyaline gluten beneath which the surface is at first blackish or "clove brown" to "brownish olive," slightly paler toward the margin, becoming grayish brown or olive-gray and subvirgate after the gluten dries, glabrous, margin at first involute, even. Context thick, white, slightly tinted under the separable colored cuticle; odor and taste not distinctive.

Lamellae adnate or subdecurrent, whitish to creamy white ("ivory yellow"), attenuated at either end, narrow to moderately broad, close to subdistant, rather thin, rarely forked.

Stipe 4–10(12) cm long, 10–25 mm thick, equal or tapering below, sometimes incrassate at the base, covered by the hyaline glutinous veil, annulus obsolete, whitish, sometimes fuscous dotted after drying, slightly silky or naked above, but at times scabrous, white, solid and white within.

Spores 7–9 × 4.5–5.5 μ, ellipsoid, smooth, pale yellow in Melzer's reagent, white in mass. Basidia 38–58 × 5–9 μ, 4-spored. Pleurocystidia and cheilocystidia none. Gill trama of divergent hyphae, 6–14 μ broad. Cuticle an ixotrichodermium, the zone 350–500 μ thick, the erect hyphae narrow (2–5 μ), scarcely a palisade. Hypodermium well-defined, of brownish, interwoven hyphae. Pileus trama interwoven. Clamp connections present.

HABIT, HABITAT, AND DISTRIBUTION—On soil, in conifer and mixed woods, Maine, Rhode Island, New York, Maryland, Tennessee, Florida, Michigan, Idaho, and Canada, August–January.

MATERIAL STUDIED—FLORIDA: Hesler 20275, 21061. IDAHO: Smith 46602. MAINE: Parlin 15338, 15418. MARYLAND: Shear 1403. MICHIGAN: Smith 33952, 43728, 43935, 50780, 62125. NEW YORK: Peck (type, from West Albany, November). RHODE ISLAND: Farlin, East Providence, Oct. 1902. TENNESSEE: Hesler 4446, 4447, 8454, 12952, 18326, 21565, 22929. CANADA: Groves et al F8192.

OBSERVATIONS—Bresadola (1928) considered *H. fuligineus* to be synonymous with *H. limacinus*, but his illustration of the latter certainly does not represent the American species. His description, however,

Fig. 92. *H. fuligineus*

might apply to either *H. fuligineus* or *H. paludosus*. We have not noted
a tendency of the gills to become grayish in *H. fuligineus*, and since
H. limacinus is usually described as having spores 10 μ or more long,
we do not believe that *H. fuligineus* should be reduced to synonymy
with it. Bresadola (1928) mentions having studied dried specimens of
the American species, and states that its spores measure 8–10 × 5–6 μ.
The possibility that he actually examined a specimen of *H. paludosus*
in which the greenish and yellowish stains did not develop is by no
means excluded, since the two are very similar in many respects. In
spore deposits, however, the spores of *H. paludosus* are consistently
larger than those of *H. fuligineus*, the apex of the stipe of the latter is
not as scabrous, and there are differences in color in addition which
are sufficient to establish them as distinct. Murrill (1916) lists
H. fuligineus as a synonym of *H. hypothejus*, but the former does not
develop yellow colors as found in the latter.

183

Hygrophorus tephroleucus (Fr.) Fr. var. **tephroleucus**
Epicr. Myc., p. 328. 1838

> *Agaricus tephroleucus* Fr., Syst. Myc., p. 34. 1821.
> *Limacium tephroleucum* (Fr.) Kummer, Führ. in Pilzk., p. 119. 1871.
> Illustrations:
> Fig. 93.
> Lange, Flora Agar. Dan. 5, pl. 163A.
> Smith and Hesler, Lloydia 2, pl. 9.

Pileus 1–3 cm broad, convex to plane, occasionally slightly depressed, not umbonate, pallid-cinereous near the margin, dark ashy gray over the disc, fading to pale ashy gray over all in age, viscid, appearing appressed fibrillose under the gluten, in age appressed-scaly. Context whitish, soft, thin; odor and taste not distinctive.

Lamellae adnate, becoming decurrent, white, becoming creamy in age, subdistant, broad.

Stipe 4–6 cm long, 2–3(4) mm thick, white over all at first, equal, solid, white within, white fibrous-punctate near the apex, more or less fibrillose below, base in young specimens coated with a thin layer of gluten, soon dry, the fibrils over the upper part cinerescent and dark gray in age.

Spores (7)8–10 × 4–5 μ, ellipsoid, smooth, pale yellow in Melzer's reagent. Basidia 40–58 × 6–8 μ, 4-spored. Pleurocystidia and cheilocystidia none. Gill trama divergent, hyphae 4–9 μ broad. Cuticle of gelatinous, more or less erect or somewhat repent, fuscous, narrow

Fig. 93. *H. tephroleucus* var. *tephroleucus*

(3–4 μ) hyphae, usually forming somewhat of an ixotrichodermium, more rarely an ixocutis. No hypodermium evident. Pileus trama of radial, more or less parallel hyphae. Clamp connections present on the cuticular and gill trama hyphae.

HABIT, HABITAT, AND DISTRIBUTION—Gregarious under conifers and in *Sphagnum* bogs, Florida, Michigan, Idaho, California, and Oregon; also in Canada, Argentina, and Europe; September–February.

MATERIAL STUDIED—CALIFORNIA: Smith 56486, 56822, 56888, 56953. FLORIDA: Hesler & Meyer 20245. IDAHO: Smith 53233. MICHIGAN: Bailey 143; Smith 999, 1108, 1135, 1235, 31929, 43973, 50957, 51035. OREGON: Smith 4844, 26660; Smith & Gruber 19247. CANADA: Groves 11881. ARGENTINA: Singer M413.

OBSERVATIONS—Our material corresponds well to the descriptions of most European investigators. Nüesch (1922) describes the stipe as dry. The thin layer of gluten disappears very soon, and, depending on weather conditions, one might describe the stipe as viscid on one occasion and as dry on the next. Consequently the above-mentioned discrepancy is not serious. The outstanding characters are the ash-colored pilei, and the fibrils on the stipe which are typically white but soon change to gray. Konrad (1936) apparently believes that *H. olivaceoalbus* var. *gracilis* is the fungus Fries described under the name *H. tephroleucus*. It remains to be seen whether or not this concept will be generally accepted by European investigators. Konrad would probably have placed the species here described as *H. tephroleucus* under *H. pustulatus*. The pilei of the California collection of the latter, however, were not as fibrillose as those of *H. tephroleucus*, and the stems were punctate above as in *H. pudorinus* rather than furnished with fine fibrillose points as in *H. tephroleucus*.

184
Hygrophorus tephroleucus var. aureofloccosus Sm. & Hes.
Lloydia 2: 26. 1939

Illustration:
    Fig. 94.

Pileus 2–5.5 cm broad, convex, finally expanding-convex-depressed or plane, at times umbonate, "deep mouse gray," "drab" to "hair brown," or near "fuscous," paler when covered by leaves, viscid, innately squamulose to glabrous, often pustulate, margin incurved often floccose, even or crenulate. Context white, medium thick; odor and taste not distinctive.

Lamellae adnate-decurrent, white, finally pale, creamy in age,

Fig. 94. *H. tephroleucus* var. *aureofloccosus*

subdistant to nearly close, medium broad, lamellulae numerous and alternating, edges even.

Stipe 2.5–7(12) cm long, 3–8(10) mm thick, at times compressed, apex and base whitish or base yellowish, elsewhere tinged brownish or concolorous with the pileus, floccose-squamulose or scabrous, tips of scales golden-yellowish at first, then ashy to brownish or darker, viscid, equal or tapering downward, solid, becoming hollow.

Spores 8–15 × 4.5–6(6.5) μ (mostly 8–10 × 4.5–5 μ, several 10–15 × 5–6 μ), ellipsoid to sublanceolate, smooth, pale yellow in Melzer's reagent. Basidia 44–58 × 6–8 μ, 2- and 4-spored, sterigmata at times long (10–38 μ). Pleurocystidia and cheilocystidia none. Gill trama divergent, hyphae 7–15 μ broad. Cuticle of fuscous, more or less erect, loosely tangled, gelatinous, narrow (3–4.5 μ) hyphae, an ixotrichodermium. No hypodermium differentiated. Pileus trama of radial, more or less parallel hyphae. Clamp connections present on the hyphae of the cuticle and the gill trama.

HABIT, HABITAT, AND DISTRIBUTION—Gregarious in pine, spruce, and cedar-pine (mixed), and oak woods, Alabama, Florida, Georgia, Kentucky, and Tennessee, October–January.

MATERIAL STUDIED—ALABAMA: Hesler 22261. FLORIDA: Hesler 20245, 21051. GEORGIA: Hesler 21082, 21605. TENNESSEE: Hesler 3144, 4466 (type, under pine, Knox County, Dec. 2, 1934), 4467, 8444, 8453, 10102, 10949, 13026, 13035, 13047, 23556.

OBSERVATIONS—The golden-yellow tips of the scales over the upper portion of the stipe distinguish it at once. The change in color which they undergo indicates a relationship of the variety to *H. tephroleucus* rather than to *H. pustulatus,* although the pileus surface has the characters of both.

185
Hygrophorus pustulatus (Fr.) Fr.
Hymen. Eur., p. 411. 1874

> *Agaricus pustulatus* Fr., Syst. Myc., p. 34. 1821.
> *Limacium pustulatum* (Fr.) Kummer, Führ. in Pilzk., p. 119. 1871.

Illustrations:
> Bresadola, Icon. Myc., tab. 321, fig. 2 (as f. *minor*).
> Juillard-Hartmann, Icon. Champ., pl. 49, fig. 2.
> Lange, Flora Agar. Dan. 5, pl. 162C.

Pileus 2–4.5 cm broad, convex, at times papillate, margin inrolled and cottony when young, becoming plane, arched at maturity, ashy with a darker brownish disc (near "buffy brown"), viscid, glutinous when wet, somewhat virgate with radiating fibrils, opaque. Context soft and white, rather thin, tapering slightly to the margin; odor and taste not distinctive.

Lamellae somewhat decurrent, bluntly adnate, close to subdistant, pure white, becoming narrow (4–5 mm).

Stipe 6–9 cm long, 5–8 mm thick, whitish, equal or slightly enlarged below, solid or stuffed at the apex, lower portion subviscid to viscid from the remains of a thin gelatinous universal veil, dry and covered by dark-gray punctate points above.

Spores 7–9 × 4–5 μ, ellipsoid, smooth, yellowish in Melzer's reagent. Basidia 46–61 × 6–8 μ, 2- and 4-spored. Pleurocystidia and cheilocystidia none. Gill trama divergent, hyphae 4–9 μ broad. Cuticle of gelatinous, fuscous hyphae, which are narrow (3–4 μ), erect to semi-erect, at times repent, usually forming an ixotrichodermium, more rarely an ixocutis. No hypodermium differentiated. Pileus trama of radial hyphae, more or less parallel. Clamp connections present on the cuticular hyphae.

HABIT, HABITAT, AND DISTRIBUTION—Gregarious under fir and

redwood, Michigan, Colorado, Wyoming, Idaho, California, and Washington, August–December; also Europe.

MATERIAL STUDIED—CALIFORNIA: Smith 3937, 56352. COLORADO: Smith 52704. IDAHO: Smith 23542, 23585, 46905, 53324, 54161; Smith & Bigelow 46181, 47016; Smith & Shaffer 53283; Shaffer 53507; Westerdale 60685. MICHIGAN: Smith 43527, 43627, 44053. WASHINGTON: Smith 49189. WYOMING: Smith 35721. DENMARK: J. P. Jensen (Hesler 23959).

OBSERVATIONS—The lower portion of the stipe is viscid to subviscid, whereas the upper portion is dry. Thus, this species is keyed out in both the subsections *Hygrophorus* and *Clitocyboides*. For additional comments on this species, see *H. tephroleucus.*

186
Hygrophorus paludosoides, sp. nov.

Illustration:
    Fig. 95.

Pileus 4–8 cm latus, obtusus demum convexus, glutinosus, olivaceo-brunneus demum pallido-fuligineus, deinde luteo-olivaceus vel pallidior; odore et gustu mitis; lamellae late adnate demum subdecurrentes, cremeo-albus vel paulum rubicundae, immaculatae, latae, subdistantes; stipes 4–8 cm longus, 11–20 mm crassus, possidens copiosum gluten inferiorem stipitis partem olivaceo-fuligineis lineis et panniculis tingens, fusco-olivaceus, siccus, apice albo-serico-floccosus sine scabie, saepe possidens guttas pellucidas quae siccatae aureo-brunneae fiunt; velum interius nullum; spores 7–9 × 5–5.5 µ, ellipsoideae. Specimen typicum in Herb. Univ. Mich.; lectum in Highlands, Mich., Sept. 16, 1961, A. H. Smith 64303.

Pileus 4–8 cm broad, obtuse to convex, the margin incurved, broadly convex or with an obtuse umbo when mature, surface glutinous, olive brown to pale fuliginous, drying tawny olive or paler, margin thinly cottony at first. Context white, firm, odor and taste mild.

Lamellae broadly adnate to subdecurrent, broad, subdistant, creamy white or with a faint pinkish reflection, not spotted, edges even.

Stipe 4–8 cm long, 11–20 mm thick, equal to a narrowed base, solid, white within, with a copious gluten which stains the lower half of the stipe with olive-fuliginous streaks and patches and dries to a tawny olive, as does the gluten on the pileus, apex white silky-floccose and lacking scabrosity, but often beaded with droplets of a hyaline liquid, in drying this layer pulling apart into patches, becoming orange-brown and giving a punctate appearance to dried specimens; no inner dry

Fig. 95. *H. paludosoides*

fibrillose veil present. KOH on apex of stipe instantly orange, also orange on gluten.

Spores 7–9 × 5–5.5 μ, smooth, ellipsoid, non-amyloid. Basidia 4-spored. Pleurocystidia and cheilocystidia none. Gill trama divergent. Epicutis of pileus a thick layer of gelatinous hyphae yellowish in KOH, and with considerable amorphous debris in the layer, the hyphae 3–4.5 μ in diameter and most crooked to coiled. Clamp connections present.

HABIT, HABITAT, AND DISTRIBUTION—Gregarious or subcaespitose, under beech, Michigan, September–October. Type collected by A. H. Smith 64303, Haven Hill, Highlands, Mich., Sept. 16, 1961.

MATERIAL STUDIED—MICHIGAN: Smith 64303, the type, and Smith 64762.

OBSERVATIONS—This species was collected along with *H. paludosus*, and a critical comparison of the fresh material was made. The KOH reaction separated the two at once. In *H. paludosus* the punctae over the stipe apex stain lemon yellow at first, and slowly darken to orange, whereas in *H. paludosoides* the change is instantaneous to orange. In the latter, the gills have not been observed to stain olive, as in *H. paludosus*, and the pilei of *H. paludosoides* are paler and grayer when fresh than are those of *H. paludosus*. In *H. paludosoides* the slime on the stipe becomes almost cinnabar in KOH.

SUBSECTION CAMAROPHYLLI Sm. & Hes.

Lloydia 2: 32. 1939.

Gelatinous outer veil absent, fibrillose "inner" veil present or absent; stipe dry.

Type species: *H. camarophyllus* Fr.

KEY TO SERIES

1. Pileus white to whitish at first, or only the disc tinged with other colors and then only so at or past maturity . . . . Series *Clitocyboides,* below
1. Pileus distinctly colored when young 2
   2. Stipe thick and soft, ornamentation at apex of scabrous points quickly yellow in KOH, and drying reddish brown; pileus buff to salmon color . . . . .Series *Pudorini*, p. 332
   2. Stipe not with red-brown points as dried 3
3. Lamellae soon spotted vinaceous or becoming vinaceous red over all. . . . . .Series *Rubentes*, p. 340
3. Not staining as in above choice 4
   4. Pileus pink, yellow, brown, or rusty to vinaceous brown . . . . .Series *Fulventes*, p. 353
   4. Pileus in gray to black or blackish brown . . . . .Series *Camarophylli*, p. 379

SERIES CLITOCYBOIDES ser. nov.

Pileus albidus; stipes siccus.

Type species: *H. sordidus* Pk.

KEY TO SPECIES

1. Spores typically 3 μ or less broad 2
1. Spores 3.5–6 μ broad 3
   2. Stipe typically 1–2 cm thick, 3–5 cm long . . . . .187. *H. subsordidus*
   2. Stipe 5–8 cm long, 5–9 mm thick . . . . .188. *H. diaphanes*
3. Stipe furnished with a fibrillose veil which sometimes leaves a fibrillose zone 4
3. Veil absent, examine unexpanded specimens .6

187
Hygrophorus subsordidus Murr.
Elisha Mitchell Sci. Soc. Jour. 55: 371. 1939

Illustration:
Fig. 96.

Pileus 4–10 cm broad, convex, finally expanding, often somewhat depressed, entirely white or the disc at times straw yellow, minutely rivulose-silky or appearing glabrous, viscid, margin even, undulate or lobed. Context white, unchanging, thick, abruptly thin on the margin; odor and taste mild.

Lamellae adnexed or adnate-subdecurrent, white, unchanging, narrow, subdistant, some forking midway, lamellulae numerous, edges even.

Stipe 3–8 cm long, 10–20 mm thick, white, moist and usually somewhat lubricous, not viscid, equal or often tapering downward, apex pruinose, elsewhere fibrillose, subrimose, solid.

Fig. 96. *H. subsordidus*

Spores (5.5)6–8 × 3–4 µ, oblong-cylindric, smooth, white in mass, yellow in Melzer's reagent. Basidia 35–44 × 5–6 µ, 4-spored. Pleurocystidia and cheilocystidia none. Gill trama divergent, hyphae 6–12 µ broad. Cuticle a distinct gelatinous zone 125–180 µ thick, the hyphae (2.5–4 µ broad) forming an ixotrichodermium (not a palisade). No distinct hypodermium differentiated. Pileus trama of loosely interwoven radial hyphae which are rather broad (5–20 µ). Clamp connections present on the cuticular hyphae.

HABIT, HABITAT, AND DISTRIBUTION—Gregarious in oak-pine woods, Florida, Alabama, and Texas, November–December.

MATERIAL STUDIED—ALABAMA: Burke 90. FLORIDA: Murrill F18403 (type, from Newman's Lake, near Gainesville, Nov. 15, 1938), unnumbered (Jan. 18, 1940, and Dec. 22, 1941); Hesler 20244, 21039, 21042, 21049. TEXAS: Thiers 1428.

OBSERVATIONS—This species is distinguished from *H. sordidus* by the narrower lamellae and more slender spores. One collection (Hesler 20244) was found growing in an arc of a fairy ring, about ten feet in diameter.

Notes on the type: Spores 6–8 × 3–3.5 µ, oblong-cylindric, smooth, non-amyloid, white in mass, or on white paper tinged cream. Basidia 36–42 × 5–6 µ, 4-spored. Pleurocystidia and cheilocystidia none. Gill trama of divergent hyphae, 7–13 µ broad. Cuticle of interwoven, gelatinous hyphae, with numerous free ends; clamp connections present.

188
Hygrophorus diaphanes, sp. nov.

Pileus 3–5 cm latus, se extendens depressum, glaber, viscidus, albus, demum rubicundo-ochraceus, deinde albus siccatus; lamellae angustae, adnatae demum aliquantum decurrentes, distantes demum subdistantes, colore flos-lacteae; stipes 5–8 cm longus, 5–9 mm crassus, mox cavus, fragilis, siccus, apice pruinosus, glaber infra, albus, rubicundo-flavus; sporae 5.5–7 × 3 µ, oblongae. Specimen typicum in Herb. Univ. Mich.; lectum Sharron Hollow, Washtenaw County, Mich., Aug. 13, 1960, A. H. Smith 62895.

Pileus 3–5 cm broad, broadly convex, expanding to shallowly depressed with an arched margin, surface glabrous, viscid, white, pellicle darkening to pinkish buff but fading to white in drying, very thin, translucent when wet. Context thin, white, fragile, odor and taste not distinctive, KOH and $FeSO_4$ no reaction.

Lamellae narrow, broadly adnate to somewhat decurrent, distant to subdistant, creamy white when fresh, unchanging on drying, edges even.

Stipe 5–8 cm long, 5–9 mm thick, equal to tapered downward, soon hollow, *very fragile*, surface dry, naked except for the pruinose apex, white, slowly flushed yellow in places but drying white or whitish.

Spores 5.5–7 × 3 μ, oblong, hyaline in KOH, hyaline to yellowish in Melzer's solution. Basidia 4-spored, 32–38 × 5–6 μ. Pleurocystidia and cheilocystidia none. Gill trama of hyaline hyphae diverging from a thin central strand. Epicutis of pileus of narrow hyaline gelatinous hyphae, very easily separated from context and usually lost in sectioning. Clamp connections present.

Habit, Habitat and Distribution—Scattered under beech on low ground, Sharron Hollow, Washtenaw County, Mich., Aug. 13, 1960.

Material Studied—michigan: Smith 62895, type.

Observations—The specimens remind one of an *Hygrocybe*, but the divergent gill trama is very distinct. The specimens are so delicate that most of those making up the type collection were ruined before they could be dried. The dry stipe, minute spores, and diaphanous character of the fruiting body make this an easily recognized species. *H. subsordidus* Murrill is the most closely related species, but it is firm and fleshy like *H. sordidus*. The stature of *H. diaphanes* is most like that of *H. flavescens*. It is species of this stature which lead one to think that the sections *Hygrocybe* and *Hygrophorus* could have originated one from the other with only a minor genetic adjustment.

189
Hygrophorus subalpinus Sm.
Univ. Mich. Herb. Contr. 5: 19. 1941

Illustrations:
    Fig. 97.
    Smith, Univ. Mich. Herb. Contr. 5, pl. 3.

Pileus 4–6 cm broad, broadly convex when young, becoming obtuse or plane, sometimes with a slight umbo and the margin spreading or decurved, opaque, snow white over all and with a distinct luster, viscid, pellicle thin and scarcely separable from the flesh, merely subviscid in age, not discoloring appreciably, often having patches of the broken veil adhering along the margin. Context thick (1 cm more or less near the stipe), white, soft; odor and taste perfectly mild.

Lamellae decurrent from the first, close (68–113 reach the stipe, many very narrow individuals extend to the stipe making the count difficult), narrow (3–4 mm), one row of short individuals, concolorous with the pileus or a duller white, edges even.

Stipe short, 3–4 cm long, 1–2 cm thick at the apex, base bulbous when young, nearly equal in age, somewhat rounded beneath the bulb, solid, white within, peronate to the apex of the bulb by a white membranous sheath which terminates in a flaring submembranous to fibrillose inferior annulus, white and silky above, annulus sometimes evanescent, no gelatinous universal veil evident.

Spores 8–10 × 4.5–5(6) μ, ellipsoid, smooth, pale yellow in Melzer's reagent. Basidia 48–62 × 7–9 μ, 2- and 4-spored. Pleurocystidia and cheilocystidia none. Gill trama divergent, hyphae 4–7 μ broad. Cuticle of repent, more or less radial, gelatinous hyphae, at times appearing a distinct gelatinous zone 125–300 μ thick, the hyphae 3–5 μ broad, an ixocutis. Pileus trama of radially disposed hyphae. Clamp connections present on the pileus trama hyphae.

Habit, Habitat, and Distribution—Gregarious under conifers, Washington, Oregon, Idaho, Colorado, Wyoming, and Michigan, June–October.

Material Studied—colorado: Davidson, June 1956. idaho: Smith 44557, 44810, 55040; Smith & Bigelow 44684; Trueblood 58608. michigan: Smith 38581, 43890. oregon: Smith 19655, 20041, 20125, 25032, 25033, 26689, 26992, 27639, 28125. washington: Smith 14397, (type, from Deer Park, Olympic Mts., June 16, 1939), 14418. wyo-

Fig. 97. *H. subalpinus*

MING: Hittle 30; Thiers, Medicine Bow Mts., July 5, 1950; Wilson, Medicine Bow Mts., July 12, 1950.

OBSERVATIONS—*Hygrophorus ponderatus* Britz. closely resembles *H. subalpinus* in color and stature, but differs in possessing a gelatinous outer veil. It differs from *H. sordidus* Pk. in having a dry membranous sheath and a more or less membranous annulus, as well as a thick, equal or somewhat bulbous stipe. The close, narrow, waxy gills are also distinctive. If it were not for the decidedly waxy appearance of the lamellae and the typical divergent gill trama, *H. subalpinus* could be placed in *Armillaria* next to *Armillaria arenicola*, with which it has a superficial resemblance.

190
Hygrophorus saxatilis Sm. & Hes.
Lloydia 5: 89. 1942

Illustrations:
    Fig. 98; also 7b.
    Smith and Hesler, Lloydia 5, pl. 18.

Pileus 3–8(10) cm broad, obtuse with an inrolled margin when young, becoming plane or with a low obtuse umbo and decurved finely pubescent margin, color whitish to very pale buff with a developing cinnamon tinge ("pale pinkish buff" to "light pinkish cinnamon") and occasionally spotted or zoned with "pinkish-cinnamon" spots or zones, slightly viscid when young and moist but soon merely moist or dry, glabrous or when dry appearing appressed-fibrillose under a lens. Context thick, soft, watery-punctate and "pinkish buff" to "light pinkish cinnamon"; taste mild, odor lacking or faintly fragrant and reminding one of dried peaches.

Lamellae short-decurrent, "light ochraceous salmon" to "light pinkish cinnamon" (more or less pinkish cinnamon-tan) and very beautiful, evenly colored, bright when young and becoming duller in age, subdistant (30–36 reach the stipe), 1–2 tiers of lamellulae, frequently more or less wrinkled or crisped, very soft and fragile, narrow to moderately broad (3–6 mm and tapered both ways), rather thick, edges even.

Stipe 6–8(12) cm long, 10–15(20) mm thick at apex, surface whitish or concolorous with the pileus, equal or narrowed slightly toward the base, solid, flesh concolorous with that of the pileus, unchanging, dry, thinly appressed-fibrillose to the fibrillose-pruinose apex, often appearing more or less longitudinally striate, glabrescent in age and then concolorous with the gills.

Fig. 98. *H. saxatilis*

Spores 7–9.5 × 4–5(6) μ, subellipsoid, smooth, pale yellowish in Melzer's reagent. Basidia 46–60(70) × 6–9 μ, 2- and 4-spored. Pleurocystidia and cheilocystidia none. Gill trama divergent, hyphae 4–8 μ broad. Cuticle undifferentiated; surface hyphae of the pileus repent, narrow (2–3 μ), colorless, more or less parallel, only slightly gelatinous, a cutis. No hypodermium differentiated. Pileus trama of loosely interwoven, more or less radial hyphae. Clamp connections present on the hyphae of the cuticle, gill trama, and subhymenium.

HABIT, HABITAT, AND DISTRIBUTION—Scattered under conifers on steep hillsides or very rocky dry soil, Washington, Oregon, and Idaho, August–October.

MATERIAL STUDIED—IDAHO: Smith 53746, 54144, 54365. OREGON: Smith 18156 (type, from Lost Creek, Oct. 30, 1941), 19254, 19991,

24438, 24962, 26654, 27543, 28390. WASHINGTON: Bigelow 48905; Smith 17665, 17769, 17896, 17979, 31213, 31719, 48592, 48931; Smith & Bigelow 47821, 49078.

OBSERVATIONS—This is a very striking and easily recognized species because of the beautiful gills. The odor is very easily missed in collections of only a few fruiting bodies, but when several baskets full are brought into a room the odor becomes very noticeable. At Lost Creek, Oregon, where the fungus was found most abundantly, it was noticed that spore-prints made on the top of one cap by an over-hanging pileus were more or less dark ochraceous salmon in color, darker than the color of the pileus on which the deposit was made. All spore-prints made in the laboratory from these and other pilei were white. We still have no explanation for these observations. At least a dozen colored spore-prints were observed in the field at Lost Creek, and it was apparent that the age of the cap had no bearing on spore-color. The habitat of this fungus is distinctive insofar as our data go, but data based on a single season's collections must not be given too much emphasis. The character of the stipe is also peculiar for a species of this section in that it is evenly fibrillose at first and pruinose at the apex instead of scabrous. No evidences of a partial veil were visible even in the smallest buttons. It appears to be related to *H. karstenii* Sacc. & Cub., but differs in its more or less salmon-colored rather than yellow gills.

191
Hygrophorus karstenii f. minor Bres.
Icon. Myc., tab. 331. 1928

Illustrations:
  Fig. 99.
  Bresadola, Icon. Myc., tab. 331.

Pileus 3–5 cm broad, broadly convex to nearly plane with an in-rolled margin, expanding to broadly convex or with an arched margin, color a dull creamy white and unchanging, surface glabrous, subviscid to touch when wet but soon dry and then with an unpolished appearance or shining in places along the margin. Context white thickish, soft; odor and taste not distinctive.

Lamellae decurrent, creamy yellowish, waxy, close, becoming sub-distant, narrow to moderately broad, some forking, edges even.

Stipe 3–5 cm long, 6–12 mm thick, solid, equal or nearly so, white within, surface dry and matted-fibrillose causing it to appear un-polished, the fibrillose silky coating extending to apex, no veil present.

Spores 7–9 × 4.5–5 μ, ellipsoid to somewhat ventricose-ovate, hyaline, pale yellowish in Melzer's solution; as revived in Melzer's they are seen to have a slightly thickened wall. Basidia 46–55 × 8–9 μ, 4-spored, clavate, and with long often flexuous pedicels. Pleurocystidia and cheilocystidia not differentiated. Gill trama with a subparallel central strand of narrow hyaline hyphae which on either side diverge toward the subhymenium. Cuticle an undifferentiated cutis, hyphae repent, similar to those of the pileus, non-gelatinous. No hypodermium differentiated. Pileus trama intricately interwoven, neither strikingly radial nor periclinal. Clamp connections present on the surface hyphae of the pileus.

HABIT, HABITAT, AND DISTRIBUTION—Gregarious under *Populus trichocarpa, Thuja plicatilis, Tsuga heterophylla,* and *Pseudotsuga taxifolia;* Nisqually River, Mt. Rainier National Park, Wash., August; also Europe.

MATERIAL STUDIED—WASHINGTON: Smith 30480.

OBSERVATIONS—The slight stickiness of the pileus is similar to that of wet specimens of *Inocybe geophylla* and is not caused by gelatinous hyphae. Hence the statement of Kühner and Romagnesi (1953, p. 58) applies to our collection. *H. saxatilis* and *H. karstenii* f. *minor* are closely related but distinct. The former has a truly gelatinous pellicle as well as differently colored gills. *H. karstenii* f. *karstenii* is a much

Fig. 99. *H. karstenii* f. *minor*

more highly colored agaric, almost exactly like *H. saxatilis* in appearance, but apparently the latter has more of a salmon tint to the gills and definitely has a thin gelatinous pellicle. The two are very closely related, however, and would merit a critical comparative study. Also, it may very well be true that *H. karstenii* f. *minor* is a distinct species, but as yet we do not know its range of variation; it could easily be merely a stage in the development of color and size which has become arrested when small and weakly colored. It is evident from the account of Favre and C. Poluzzi (1947) that a change in color occurs as the carpophores enlarge and age.

192

Hygrophorus tenax, sp. nov.

Pileus 2–4 cm latus, convexus, deinde planus vel depressus, albidus, discus subluteus, interdum luteus laesus, primum viscidus, cito siccus, glabrosus deinde fibrillosus vel squamulosus; odore et gustu blandus; lamellae sub-decurrentes, pallidae demum "pinkish buff," subdistantes, angustae; stipes 3–5 cm longus, 4–6 mm crassus, albidus, tarde subluteus laesus, siccus, apice fibroso-punctatus, satis fibrosus, tenax, nullum velum; sporae 6–8 × 3.5–4.5 μ, ellipsoideae. Specimen typicum in Herb. Univ. Mich. conservatum; lectum prope Warren Dunes State Park, Mich., Oct. 1, 1955, A. H. Smith 50625.

Pileus 2–4 cm broad, convex, expanding to plane or slightly depressed, dull white with a tendency toward yellow on the disc, at times showing yellowish stains where injured, surface thinly viscid when young but soon dry and merely with a slight resinous feel, glabrous but soon more or less appressed-fibrillose to squamulose, margin ribbed in age. Context thin but tough (for this genus); odor and taste not distinctive.

Lamellae slightly decurrent, near "pinkish buff" (not as white as the pileus), unchanging when injured, subdistant, narrow, edges even.

Stipe 3–5 cm long, 4–6 mm thick, whitish, slowly discoloring to yellowish on bruising, equal or narrowed downward, dry, apex fibrous-punctate, rather fibrous-tough, veil none.

Spores 6–8 × 3.5–4.5 μ, ellipsoid with a curved apiculus, smooth, hyaline in KOH, yellowish-hyaline in Melzer's reagent. Basidia 30–40 × 6–7 μ, 4-spored, pale yellowish in Melzer's. Pleurocystidia and cheilocystidia none. Gill trama divergent, hyphae 6–14 μ broad. Cuticle of subgelatinous hyphae 3–5 μ broad, some with enlarged end-cells but these not truly cystidioid, the hyphae more refractive in KOH than is usual for the genus. Clamp connections present.

HABIT, HABITAT, AND DISTRIBUTION—Scattered in an upland beech woods, Michigan, October.

MATERIAL STUDIED—MICHIGAN: Smith 50625 (type, from near Warren Dunes State Park, Oct. 1, 1955).

OBSERVATIONS—The rather tough consistency, small spores, lack of any veil, and refractive hyphae of the pellicle distinguish it from any other *Hygrophorus* known to us. The gills become dark brown in drying as do those of *H. bakerensis* and a few other species in the section *Hygrophorus*. The stature is that of *H. eburneus*.

193
Hygrophorus pseudochrysaspis, sp. nov.

Illustration:
Fig. 100.

Pileus 3–6 cm latus, albus deinde obscuro-coriaceus vel subflavus, paulum glutinosus, mox siccus, aquoso-pellucidus contusus; carne albus, odore paulum amygdalino; lamellae decurrentes, cremeo-albae demum obscuriores, deinde atro-rufo-brunneae siccae, subdistantes, latae; stipes 4–11 cm longus, 4–10 mm crassus, deorsum angustior vel subaequalis, mollo-floccosus cum hyalino aut subflavo humore, velum gelatinosum nullum, apice scabiosus, punctae prompte atro-brunneae in KOH; sporae 6.5–8(9) × 4–5 μ, ellipsoideae. Specimen typicum in Herb. Univ. Mich.; lectum in Mich., Sharron Hollow, Sept. 15, 1961, A. H. Smith 64266.

Pileus 3–6 cm broad, obtuse with an inrolled margin, expanding to plane or nearly so, sometimes convex, at other times with a low broad umbo, snow white at first slowly becoming dull white and gradually dingy buff or more yellowish, injured areas soon watery-translucent, surface thinly glutinous but soon dry, margin at times faintly sulcate. Context white, thin; odor like that of *H. agathosmus* but weaker, taste mild. KOH soon dark yellow-brown; $FeSO_4$, no reaction.

Lamellae decurrent, subdistant, broad, creamy white becoming dingy cream color, not spotting when bruised but becoming dark reddish brown in drying, edges perfectly even and concolor with the gill-faces.

Stipe 4–11 cm long, 4–10 mm thick at apex, narrowed downward or nearly equal solid, firm, surface at first covered by a soft flocculence which exudes droplets of a hyaline to yellowish liquid, no gelatinous veil present in the youngest buttons, but stipe feeling slimy when the droplets are present, appearing yellowish and water-soaked where handled, apex minutely scurfy, and points quickly dark brown in KOH.

Spores 6.5–8(9) × 4–5 μ, ellipsoid, smooth, not revived, amyloid. Basidia 4-spored, dingy yellowish in KOH. Pleurocystidia and cheilocystidia none. Gill trama divergent. Epicutis of pileus a tangled mass of hyphae 3–5 μ in diameter, refractive in KOH (but not gelatinous in the usual sense), originating as a trichodermium but the structure soon collapsing. Clamp connections present.

Habit, Habitat, and Distribution—Gregarious under hardwoods, beech, oak, etc., summer and fall, Michigan.

Material Studied—michigan: Smith 64389, 64266, 64245.

Observations—We doubt that this species is *H. chrysaspis* as originally described by Métrod. The hyphae forming the epicutis of the pileus are broader (1.5 as compared to 3–5 μ), and Métrod, although mentioning yellow drops on the stipe, stated clearly that the stipe was viscid, which means to us that it must have had a glutinous

Fig. 100. *H. pseudochrysaspis*

veil. It is significant that he clearly aligned it to *H. eburneus* "Ce Limacium est certainement voisin de *Hygrophorus eburneus. . . ."* Kühner and Romagnesi say of the droplets on the stipe "non glutineuses" but report it under beech.

With the discovery of *H. tenax* and previous knowledge of the color changes that take place on the gills of *H. variicolor* and *H. bakerensis* on drying, it must now be admitted that there are a number of species known with the color change of *H. chrysaspis*. We limit our recognition of *H. chrysaspis* to a fungus of the conifer forests, odorless, and with a gelatinous veil and the epicutis of the pileus as given above.

The account of Kühner and Romagnesi (1953, p. 58) might apply to *H. pseudochrysaspis*. This question needs to be investigated.

194
Hygrophorus subpungens Sm. & Hes.
Sydowia 8: 312. 1954

Pileus 1.5–3(4) cm broad, obtuse when young, the margin incurved, soon nearly plane or with just a trace of an obtuse umbo, in age the disc depressed as a result of the uplifting of the margin, viscid, dull white ("tilleul buff") at first, gradually darkening on the disc in age to near pale avellaneous, the margin remaining dingy whitish. Context thin, soft, dull white, unchanging or gradually becoming vinaceous buff to avellaneous; odor faint but spicy-fragrant, taste mild.

Lamellae broadly adnate and becoming short-decurrent, subdistant to nearly close, one tier of lamellulae, moderately broad, dark "tilleul buff" young (pallid), becoming "cinnamon-buff" and in age nearly clay color, edges even.

Stipe 2.5–4 cm long, 3–7 mm thick, equal, sometimes hollow in age, dry, whitish and pruinose over all at first, glabrescent, becoming dingy where handled but never as dark as the old gills.

Spores 7–8 × 4.5–5 μ, elliptic in face view, in side view slightly bean-shaped, smooth, yellowish in Melzer's reagent. Basidia 4-spored, 44–56 × 7–8 μ, basidia in sections of hymenium revived in KOH dull pale cinnamon in color. Pleurocystidia and cheilocystidia none. Gill trama divergent, hyaline, hyphae 4–7 μ broad. Cuticle a gelatinous zone 70–120 μ thick, hyphae repent, radial, 2–3 μ broad, an ixocutis. No hypodermium differentiated. Pileus trama of radial hyphae, 4–10 μ broad. Clamp connections present.

HABIT, HABITAT, AND DISTRIBUTION—Densely gregarious on wet soil near a beaver pond, Oregon, October.

MATERIAL STUDIED—OREGON: Smith 22027 (type, from East Fork, Salmon River, Mt. Hood, Oct. 20, 1944).

OBSERVATIONS—This species is related to *H. discoideus* which, however, has a gelatinous veil. Excellent material was studied, and the lack of a glutinous veil in *H. subpungens* was definitely established. The colors of *H. subpungens* are paler and the spores smaller than in *H. discoideus*. It is only remotely related to *H. russocoriaceus* which, according to material from Bas, in the Netherlands, is a *Camarophyllopsis*.

195
Hygrophorus pusillus Pk.
Torrey Bot. Club Bull. 29: 69. 1902

Hydrocybe pusilla (Pk.) Murr., North Amer. Flora 9: 377. 1916.

Illustrations:
Fig. 101.
Smith and Hesler, Lloydia 2, pl. 13.

Pileus 1–4(5) cm broad, convex, soon flattened, white, or disc tinged creamy yellow to pale incarnate-tan, viscid, glabrous, margin often elevated in age and plicate-crenate. Context soft, white, thin; odor faintly but distinctly aromatic, or of anise; taste mild.

Lamellae adnate becoming short-decurrent, white, subdistant (24–30 reach the stipe), two rows of short gills present near the margin, some forking, thickish.

Stipe 2–7 cm long, 1–8 mm thick, white, dry, glabrous or the apex very faintly fibrillose-pruinose, flesh white, solid.

Spores 7–9 × 4–5 μ, or at times smaller, ellipsoid, smooth, yellowish in Melzer's reagent. Basidia 46–61 × 6–7 μ, 2- and 4-spored. Pleurocystidia and cheilocystidia none. Gill trama divergent, hyphae 4–9 μ broad. Cuticle of gelatinous hyphae which form an ixotrichodermium. Clamp connections present on the cuticular hyphae and gill trama hyphae. Pileus trama of interwoven, somewhat radial hyphae.

HABIT, HABITAT, AND DISTRIBUTION—Scattered or in troops, under conifers, Idaho, California, Oregon, Washington, and New York, September–December.

MATERIAL STUDIED—CALIFORNIA: Smith 8631, 8737, 56750. IDAHO: Henderson (Peck's type, from Moscow Mts., Nov.); Slipp 1311. NEW YORK: Kauffman, Adirondack Mts., Sept. 7, 1921. OREGON: Smith 8737, 8942, 9210, 18204, 20207, 27772, 28335. WASHINGTON: Kauffman, Lake Quinault, Oct. 27, 1925; Smith 17849, 17957, 17969, 48898, 49192.

OBSERVATIONS—Notes on the type have been prepared as follows: Spores 5–7 × 3.5–4 μ, ellipsoid, smooth, pale yellowish in Melzer's reagent. Basidia 30–37 × 4.5–6 μ, 4-spored. Pleurocystidia and cheilo-cystidia none. Gill trama of hyphae only slightly divergent, appearing subparallel in some lamellae, 4–8 μ broad. Cuticle of appressed, somewhat gelatinous hyphae. Clamps present in gill trama.

Specimens larger than the type have been found by Smith. In these specimens the spores are slightly larger than in the type, and the gill trama of dried material shows divergent hyphae which tend to be subparallel.

In Europe *H. russocoriaceus* seems to be very similar. Bataille (1910) and Nüesch (1922) place it in the subgenus *Camarophyllus*. Peck's species without question belongs in section *Hygrophorus* and differs from descriptions of the European species in its slightly colored disc of the pileus. Kauffman collected it in New York and Washington, and Smith found it growing in great quantities in southern Oregon and northern California. The odor and slightly colored pileus distinguish *H. pusillus* from *H. piceae*. Moreover, the carpophores of the latter are usually larger than in the former.

Fig. 101. *H. pusillus*

196

Hygrophorus piceae Kühn. & Romagn.

Illustrations:
Fig. 102; also 10e.
Karsten, Myc. Fenn., tab. 32.

Pileus 1–4(6) cm broad, convex, becoming plane or with an up-lifted margin, snow white over all, viscid, glabrous to innately ap-pressed fibrillose under the viscidity, context soft, white; odor and taste not distinctive.

Lamellae adnate, decurrent in age, snow white, becoming pale pinkish buff, subdistant (25–30 reach the stipe), broad, some forked near the margin of the pileus, rather thin, edges even.

Stipe (1.5)3–5 cm long, 3–5(8–12) mm thick, tapering downward, moist to dry (no gelatinous veil present in button stage), glabrous over lower half, upper half covered by a white cottony fibrillose coat-ing, apex not scabrous, hollow.

Fig. 102. *H. piceae*

Spores 6–8(10) × 4–5(6) μ, ellipsoid, smooth, white in deposit, yellowish in Melzer's reagent. Basidia 48–62 × 6–8 μ, 4-spored. Pleurocystidia and cheilocystidia none. Gill trama divergent, with an opaque mediostrate of parallel hyphae, the divergent hyphae 4–8 μ broad. Cuticle a zone (200–300 μ thick), of gelatinous, tangled, narrow (2–4 μ), colorless, branched, more or less erect hyphae, some free ends extending above the gelatinous zone, an ixotrichodermium similar to that in *H. paludosus*. No hypodermium differentiated. Pileus trama of more or less parallel, periclinally arranged hyphae. Clamp connections rare on the cuticular hyphae.

HABIT, HABITAT, AND DISTRIBUTION—In spruce woods and in swampy areas, Maine, Massachusetts, New York, Michigan, California, Oregon, Washington, and Idaho, August–December.

MATERIAL STUDIED—CALIFORNIA: Epling 526; Smith 9335, 56333. IDAHO: Smith 23526, 53748, 54140. MAINE: Bigelow 4165, 4364, 4376, 4446. MASSACHUSETTS: Bigelow 9392. MICHIGAN: Smith 33535, 36028, 38146, 38537, 43423, 43780, 43868, 43979, 51033, 62055, 60193, 60625. NEW YORK: Singer 136. OREGON: Smith 19244, 19688, 24656, 26857, 27636. WASHINGTON: Smith 17527, 17652, 17692, 17714, 17892; Smith & Bigelow 48515, 48976.

OBSERVATIONS—This species has been found repeatedly in the Pacific Northwest and in northern Michigan late in the season. The divergent hyphae of the gill trama at once separates it from various white species of *Camarophyllopsis*. We (1939, p. 34) at first identified the American collections as *H. albidus* Karsten, but specimens identified by Karsten have been examined and have gills that darken as in *H. albicastaneus*. Karsten's species is, however, a *"Limacium."* Since the description of Kühner & Romagnesi covers our specimens almost perfectly, we do not hesitate to assign our collections there.

197
Hygrophorus marianae, sp. nov.

Pileus 2.5–4 cm latus, late convexus, subviscidus, albidus demum pallide roseus vel rubro-virgatus; lamellae albidae, decurrentes, immaculatae; stipes 7–11 cm longus, 6–10 mm crassus, radicatus, siccus; sporae 6–8.4 × 3.6–5.4 μ; hyphae fibulatae. Specimen typicum lectum Santa Barbara, Calif., Feb. 21, and 28, 1939, Paul and Marian Rea 114.

Pileus 2.5–4 cm broad, nearly plane, the margin becoming turned up, slightly viscid when moist, white at first becoming coral pink and virgate with darker red fibrils, or ground color near ochraceous buff and streaks vinaceous red. Context white, not colored under the cuticle, unchanging, thin, taste mild, odor not recorded (apparently none present).

Lamellae white, broad (5 mm), distant, arcuate, decurrent, unequal, usually only one tier of lamellulae, not forking, somewhat interveined or occasionally anastomosing, edges thin.

Stipe 7–11 cm long, 6–10 mm thick, deeply rooting to possessing a distinct pseudorhiza from which up to 6 carpophores may develop, pure white where exposed, pruinose above, fibrillose striate, dry, tending to split longitudinally; pseudorhiza covered with a false "volva" which can be peeled off and consists of a tough gray-brown layer lined on the inside by white fibrous-tomentose layer and covered over the exterior by dirt.

Spore deposit white; spores 6–8.4 × 3.6–5.4 μ, ellipsoid, smooth. Basidia 2- and 4-spored, hyaline in KOH, 30–36 × 5–7 μ, rather short. Pleurocystidia and cheilocystidia none; gill trama clearly of divergent hyphae; epicutis of pileus a thin layer of interwoven hyaline narrow (2–4 μ) subgelatinous hyphae. Clamp connections present.

HABIT, HABITAT, AND DISTRIBUTION—On ground in oak woods, solitary to caespitose (a number of carpophores from a single pseudorhiza), Rocky Nook Park, Santa Barbara, Calif. Type collected by Paul and Marian Rea 114 and 114a, Feb. 21, 28, 1939.

OBSERVATIONS—The pseudorhiza is a unique feature in *Hygrophorus*, but the color change of the pileus is perhaps equally as distinctive, and relates the species to those of series *Rubentes*. In series *Clitocyboides* it is closest to *H. ellenae* on spore characters, but, though both can occur caespitosely, *H. el'enae* lacks the pseudorhiza. We suspect the 4-spored basidia produce spores about 3.5 μ broad. The "volva" described by the Reas is, as they realized, not the remains of a veil but rather a "cortex" composed of mycelium and soil.

198

Hygrophorus albicastaneus (Murr.), comb. nov.

Clitocybe albicastanea Murr., Mycologia 5: 206. 1913.

Pileus 3–7 cm broad, hemispheric to broadly convex, at length slightly depressed in the center, glabrous, viscid when moist, white, becoming yellowish and finally dull rusty brown on drying. Context fleshy, thick (10 mm), white, compact, firm.

Lamellae white, becoming yellowish and on drying dingy brown to dark reddish brown (as in *H. variicolor*), adnate but finally decurrent, narrow (3–5 mm), subdistant, attenuated at both ends finally, 1–2 tiers of lamellulae.

Stipe 4–8.5 cm long, 12–14 mm thick (or as thin as 4–7 mm) solid to stuffed, tapered toward the base, often flexuous "perhaps subviscid" (Rea), white, apex dotted with white dots or squamules, appressed fibrillose and nearly glabrous below.

Spores 7–9.5 × 4–5.5 μ, ellipsoid, smooth, hyaline, non-amyloid. Basidia 4-spored, 34–42 × 6–8 μ, hyaline in KOH. Pleurocystidia and cheilocystidia none. Gill trama of divergent hyphae (but in revived material the picture is often obscured by incomplete reviving of the hyphae). Pileus epicutis of hyaline gelatinous narrow hyphae more or less interwoven. Clamp connections present.

HABIT, HABITAT, AND DISTRIBUTION—Sainta Ynez Valley near Paradise Camp, Santa Barbara County, Calif. On the ground in oak woods, Feb. 9, 1940, Paul Marshall Rea H361. The type was growing under oak near Searsville Lake, Calif., Dec. 28, 1902, McMurphy 61.

OBSERVATIONS—We were at first inclined to the opinion that Clitocybe albicastanea Murr. was the same as H. chrysaspis, partly because Murrill reduced his species to synonymy under H. eburneus. However, there is no indication from anyone that C. albicastanea ever had a glutinous veil, and Rea's notes support McMurphy's observations indicating none was present. Rea's description of the stipe as "perhaps subviscid" can mean only one thing, that the stipe was soft and slightly tacky to the touch, as is the cap of Inocybe geophylla when it is wet. Hence, it is legitimate to regard H. albicastaneus as belonging in section Clitocyboides where it is closely related to H. variicolor, but distinct because it is white at first.

199
Hygrophorus marzuolus (Fr.) Bres.
Atti. Accad. Agiati Rovereto II: 3. 1893

> Agaricus marzuolus Fr., Syst. Myc. 1: 84. 1821.
> Illustration:
> Dumée, Granjean, et Maire, Bull. Soc. Mycol. France, tab. 28, pl. 15.

Pileus 4–7 cm broad, convex, expanding, disc whitish, marginal portion gray, radiately streaked, viscid, margin even. Context watery-pallid and gray-punctate; odor and taste none.

Lamellae adnate to adnexed, gray, unchanging, distant, broad.

Stipe 5–7 cm long, 8–12 mm thick, gray above, pallid below, moist, not viscid.

Spores 7–8.5 × 4.5–5 μ, ellipsoid, smooth, yellowish in Melzer's reagent. Basidia 48–69 × (6)7–9 μ, mostly 4-spored, a few 2-spored. Pleurocystidia and cheilocystidia none. Gill trama divergent, hyphae 5–9 μ broad. Cuticle a narrow (60–85 μ) gelatinous zone of repent hyphae, an ixocutis. Pileus trama of radially disposed hyphae. Clamp connections present on the cuticular hyphae.

HABIT, HABITAT, AND DISTRIBUTION—On soil, under bear-grass near snow bank, Idaho, June; also Europe.

MATERIAL STUDIED—IDAHO: Smith 58365. FRANCE: Heinemann 2666. SWITZERLAND: Huijsman, May 3, 1958. AUSTRIA: Moser, April 15, 1951 (Hesler 24131).

OBSERVATIONS—The Idaho collection (Smith 58365) agrees well with the collections from France and Switzerland. In each collection the pileus, under a lens, is virgate. Gill color and microscopic characters are similar. In the American material the pileus cuticle in section shows a narrow gelatinous zone; in the French specimen the pileus cuticle shows either no gelatinous hyphae or only a very narrow layer; in the material from Switzerland there is a narrow but definite gelatinous zone. Bresadola (1928) says the pileus is subviscid, soon dry. It is interesting to note that Smith found his collection in June, near snow; and in Austria, Moser (1955) reports it in the early spring after melting snow.

Hygrophorus marzuolus is related to *H. camarophyllus* in which the pileus is also virgate, but darker from the beginning, the lamellae closer (close to sometimes subdistant), and the spores somewhat longer. *H. agathosmus* has the pileus glutinous to viscid, the context has a distinctive amygdaline odor, and the spores are slightly longer.

200

Hygrophorus ellenae, sp. nov.

Pileus 2.5–6 cm latus, convexo-depressus, margo involutus deinde parum similis infundibulo, albus deinde tinctus luteo colore, parum viscidus, mox siccus; odore et gustu mitis; lamellae arcuatae demum decurrentes, angustae vel medio-latae, subdistantes, albae deinde tinctae luteo colore; stipes 5–9 cm longus, (2)4–12(15) mm crassus, siccus, albus, apice sericus vel pruinosus; sporae 7–9.5(10) × 4–4.5(5) μ, imagine obliqua non aequilaterales, in fronte subovatae. Specimen typicum in Herb. Univ. Mich.; lectum prope Summit, Boise National Forest, Idaho, June 15, 1958, Ellen Trueblood 307.

Pileus 2.5–6 cm broad, broadly convex-depressed with an inrolled margin, shallowly infundibuliform in age, margin often becoming undulating or wavy, surface smooth and shining, white, slowly developing a tinge of apricot, slightly viscid when moist but soon dry. Context white, soft; odor and taste not distinctive.

Lamellae arcuate to decurrent, narrow to only moderately broad, subdistant, white at first, slowly becoming tinged apricot, 1–2 tiers of lamellulae, edges even; when dried pallid to dingy ochraceous buff.

Stipe 5–9 cm long, (2)4–12(15) mm thick, equal or nearly so, surface dry, twisted fibrillose-striate, white-tomentose at base, white, when dried dingy pallid to grayish, apex silky to slightly pruinose but not scabrous.

Spore deposit white. Spores 7–9.5(10) × 4–4.5(5) μ, obscurely inequilateral in profile, subovate in face view, hyaline in KOH and yellowish in Melzer's solution, smooth, thin-walled. Basidia 48–60 × 7–8 μ, 4-spored, hyaline in KOH, sections of hymenium yellowish in Melzer's. Gill trama divergent. Epicutis of pileus a thin layer of gelatinous narrow (1.5–3 μ) hyphae yellowish to hyaline in KOH. Clamp connections present.

HABIT, HABITAT, AND DISTRIBUTION—Caespitose under pine and fir, gravelly soil. Cottonwood Creek near Summit, Boise National Forest, Idaho. June 15, 1958, Ellen Trueblood 307.

OBSERVATIONS—This species appears to be closely related to H. saxatilis and H. karstenii but differs in gill color. In both these species the gills are yellow at first. The clusters of fruiting bodies of H. ellenae remind one of Clitocybe, but the bilateral gill trama excludes that genus. H. subsordidus has a stockier fruiting body with slightly narrower spores. There is the possibility that Wyoming collections tentatively identified as H. subsordidus actually represent H. ellenae, but we have made our decision on the spore characters. The fruiting bodies of the various western collections all compare better with each other than they do with Florida specimens of H. subsordidus.

201
Hygrophorus sordidus Pk.
Torrey Bot. Club Bull. 25: 322. 1898

Illustrations:
    Fig. 103.
    Hard, Mushrooms, fig. 176.
    Kauffman, Agar. Mich., pl. 27.
    Smith and Hesler, Lloydia 2, pl. 12.

Pileus 8–20 cm broad, convex then expanded plane, pure white or rarely tinged yellowish buff on the disc, viscid, glabrous, margin at first involute and subfloccose, even. Context moderately compact, thick, white; odor and taste mild.

Lamellae adnate to decurrent, white, slightly yellowish in age, subdistant, rather broad, acuminate at the ends, subintervenose.

Fig. 103. *H. sordidus*

Stipe 6–10 cm long, 15–30 mm thick, white, dry, equal, often attenuated toward the base, glabrous, even, upper portion obscurely floccose, solid.

Spores 6–8 × (3.5)4–5.5 μ, ellipsoid, smooth, yellowish in Melzer's reagent. Basidia 38–50 × 5–7 μ, 4-spored (rarely 2-spored). Pleurocystidia and cheilocystidia none. Gill trama divergent, hyphae 4–8 μ broad. Cuticle a gelatinous zone 200–280 μ thick, of two distinct zones: (1) an outer zone 50 μ thick of brownish hyphae; (2) an inner, subjacent zone 150–230 μ thick, of colorless, loosely interwoven hyphae; all cuticular hyphae 2–4 μ broad (from type). No hypodermium differentiated. Pileus trama of radial hyphae. Clamp connections present on the cuticular hyphae.

HABIT, HABITAT, AND DISTRIBUTION—Gregarious on soil in open oak-hickory woods, District of Columbia, Maryland, Massachusetts,

New York, North Carolina, Michigan, and Illinois, July–November.

MATERIAL STUDIED—DISTRICT OF COLUMBIA: Williams (Peck's type, Takoma Park, Nov. 1897). ILLINOIS: Leathers, Coles Co., Sept. 24, 1949. MARYLAND: Charles, near Cabin John, Nov. 9, 1911. MASSACHUSETTS: Bigelow 9411. MICHIGAN: Kauffman 604 (1362); Smith 6071, 6113, 7093, 7295, 15322, 18487, 18775, 18915, 21165, 32012, 34212, 36320, 62291. NEW YORK: Kauffman, Ithaca, Aug. 14, 1903. NORTH CAROLINA: Coker 2004; Totten & Holland, Chapel Hill, Nov. 16, 1919.

OBSERVATIONS—Notes on the type: Spores 6–8 × 4–5.5 μ, ellipsoid, smooth, pale yellow in Melzer's reagent. Basidia 40–52 × 5–7 μ, 4-spored. Pleurocystidia and cheilocystidia none. Gill trama divergent, hyphae 2–4 μ broad. Cuticle of gelatinous hyphae (see above). Clamp connections present in the cuticle.

Peck recognized the close similarity of this species to *H. penarius* Fr. It differs from the latter in the absence of a gelatinous universal veil, the typically white gills and pileus, and obscurely floccose apical region of the stipe. *H. penarius* may occur in the United States. Forms which apparently were *H. penarius* have been found in Michigan but not in good enough condition to permit a critical study.

In Tennessee, Georgia, and Alabama, there is a common white species, *H. ponderatus*, which resembles *H. sordidus*, but the former has a viscid stipe.

SERIES PUDORINI (Bataille) stat. nov.

Subsection Pudorini Bataille, Flore Monogr. Hygrophores, p. 32. 1910.

Characters as given in key to series, page 309.

Type species: *H. pudorinus* Fr.

KEY TO VARIETIES AND FORMS

1. Stipe viscid, odor of jasmine ....
............(see *H. pudorinus* sensu Kühner & Romagnesi, 1953: 57)
1. Stipe not viscid, odor slight to pronounced 2
   2. Pileus pallid to whitish, or the disc merely with yellowish tint ....
   ....204. *H. pudorinus* var. *fragrans* f. *pallidus*
   2. Not colored as above 3
3. Pileus tinged grayish on disc ....205. *H. pudorinus* var. *subcinereus*
3. Pileus pallid pinkish to salmon color 4
   4. Pileus up to 20 cm broad; stipe becoming zinc orange in base ......
   ....203. *H. pudorinus* var. *fragrans*
   4. Pileus 3–12 cm broad; stipe merely yellowish in base or base not colored ....202. *H. pudorinus* var. *pudorinus* f. *pudorinus*

202

Hygrophorus pudorinus (Fr.) Fr. var. pudorinus f. pudorinus
Epicr. Myc., p. 322. 1838

Agaricus pudorinus Fr., Syst. Myc., p. 33. 1821.
Limacium pudorinum (Fr.) Wünsche, Die Pilze, p. 117. 1877.

Illustrations:
Fig. 104.
Bresadola, Icon. Myc., tab. 308.
Gillet, Champ. Fr., pl. 123 (347).
Juillard-Hartmann, Icon. Champ., pl. 47, fig. 6.
Lange, Flora Agar. Dan. 5, pl. 163D.
Peck, N. Y. State Mus. Bull. 67, pl. 83, figs. 1–6.
Pomerleau, Mushrooms of Eastern Canada and the U. S., fig. 17B.
Ricken, Die Blätterp., pl. 4, fig. 3.

Pileus 5–10(12) cm broad, firm, convex to campanulate, obtuse, or subexpanded, pale tan to pinkish buff or pale flesh color, glabrous, viscid, margin at first involute and minutely white downy, even. Context compact, thick, white or tinged incarnate; odor and taste not distinctive, or odor slightly fragrant.

Fig. 104. *H. pudorinus* var. *pudorinus* f. *pudorinus*

Lamellae subdecurrent, acuminate, white to pallid or sometimes tinged pale incarnate but never reddish-spotted, narrow, subdistant, thickish, sometimes forked, intervenose.

Stipe 4–9 cm long, 10–20 mm thick, white to buff or incarnate tinged, equal or tapering downward, stout, dry, solid, compact, upper portion white floccose-punctate, the scales or points becoming reddish in age or as the fruiting body dries, more or less appressed-fibrillose toward the base, typically dry but sometimes subviscid to the touch when the basal portion becomes water-soaked.

Spores 6.5–9.5 × 4–5.5 μ, ellipsoid, smooth, pale yellowish in Melzer's reagent. Basidia 41–62 × 5.5–7 μ, 2- and 4-spored. Pleurocystidia and cheilocystidia none. Gill trama divergent, 4–10 μ broad. Cuticle an ixotrichodermium, the hyphae 2–3 μ broad, mostly more or less erect, others repent and then radial, pale fuscous. No hypodermium differentiated. Pileus trama of interwoven, radially disposed hyphae. Clamp connections on the hyphae of the cuticle, the pileus trama, and the gill trama.

HABIT, HABITAT, AND DISTRIBUTION—Scattered to gregarious in bogs or in mixed coniferous forests, Maine, New York, Michigan, Colorado, Idaho, New Mexico, California, Oregon, and Ontario, August–October; also Europe and U.S.S.R.

MATERIAL STUDIED—CALIFORNIA: Smith 55925. COLORADO: Baxter, Tolland, Aug. 26, 1920; Kauffman, Tolland, Sept. 4, 1920; Smith 51624, 52643, 52810. IDAHO: Gruber P43; Smith 23516, 23535, 46477, 46824, 47115, 59795, 59840, 59983, 60295; Westerdale & Smith 59572, 59872, 60218. MAINE: Bigelow 4674, 4753, 4754. MICHIGAN: Bailey 48; Smith 1103, 1123, 35935, 36100, 43658, 43834, 43878, 50888; Thiers 4174. NEW MEXICO: Barrows, Santa Fe, Sept. 1955. NEW YORK: House, Newcomb, Sept. 30, 1922; Kauffman & Mains, North Elba, Sept. 12, 1914; Smith 965. OREGON: Brown, Corvallis, Nov. 20, 1925. CANADA: (Quebec) Drayton F8724; Groves & Conners F8676; (Ontario) Hoark 34620; Smith 4843, 4892. DENMARK: M. Lange (Hesler 23956).

OBSERVATIONS—We are basing our concept of this species on that of Kauffman (1918). Most investigators, including Peck (1907) in the United States, have described the stipe as viscid. In our collections from the areas cited above we were unable to demonstrate the presence of a gelatinous sheath at any stage of development. At times, however, the fibrillose covering at the base of the stipe may become quite moist or water-soaked, and under such conditions the hyphae gelatinize slightly producing a slight stickiness. A similar condition has been noted in species of *Cortinarius* of the subgenus *Inoloma*. This should not be regarded as true viscidity. Since dried specimens of both

Kauffman's and our collections compare very well with those in Peck's herbarium as well as with material from Dr. Rolf Singer from the U.S.S.R., we have designated them *H. pudorinus*.

It is possible that the viscidity described for the stipe of this species by Kühner and Romagnesi (1953) is the kind referred to above, but even so, North American specimens do not have the odor they describe.

203
Hygrophorus pudorinus var. *fragrans* (Murr.), comb. nov.
Mycologia 4: 210. 1912

> *Hygrophorus fragrans* Murr., Mycologia 4: 210. 1912.

Illustrations:
> Fig. 105.
> Smith and Hesler, Lloydia 2, pl. 14.

Pileus 7–20 cm broad, convex, becoming plane or with a slightly uplifted margin, margin remaining inrolled and downy pubescent until maturity, surface glutinous, becoming viscid, somewhat felty fibrillose under the gelatinous pellicle, color "apricot orange" to "salmon color" on the disc, "sea-shell pink" or paler near the margin, not fading appreciably. Context pale "salmon color" in the pileus, white in the stipe, staining yellow and finally orange when bruised; odor faintly fragrant, taste mild.

Lamellae adnate, "pale pinkish buff" to "pale pinkish cinnamon," never truly white, thin, close, becoming subdistant (60–80 reach the stipe), moderately broad (1–1.5 cm).

Stipe 10–20 cm long, 1.5–3.5 cm thick, narrowed to a point at the base, solid, surface dry, fibrillose over lower half, scabrous-punctate and often beaded with drops over the upper half, color white or flushed with pink, staining yellow, finally orange when bruised, base "ochraceous buff" to "zinc orange" inside and out.

Spores 7–9.5 × 4.5–5.5 μ, ellipsoid, smooth, hyaline, non-amyloid. Basidia 44–52 × 6–8 μ, 4-spored. Pleurocystidia and cheilocystidia none. Gill trama of divergent hyphae, 3–6 μ broad. Cuticle a gelatinous zone 300–400 μ thick, hyphae tangled, those on surface brownish in KOH, those below colorless, narrow (2–4.5 μ). No hypodermium differentiated. Pileus trama interwoven to somewhat subparallel, radially disposed. Clamp connections present on the hyphae of the cuticle and the gill trama.

HABIT, HABITAT, AND DISTRIBUTION—Gregarious under spruce, hemlock, and redwood, California, Colorado, and Oregon, November–December.

Fig. 105. *H. pudorinus* var. *fragrans*

MATERIAL STUDIED—CALIFORNIA: Smith 3858, 8703, 9029, 9564. COL-
ORADO: Shope 383. OREGON: Kauffman, Franklin, Sept. 19, 1915; Murrill
1009 (type, from Corvallis, Nov. 1911); Smith 27493, 27590, 27591,
27914, 28097.

OBSERVATIONS—Smith has studied this species in great detail both
in favorable and unfavorable seasons along the Pacific Coast. It is usually found growing gregariously under spruce. It differs from the form
of *H. pudorinus* found in the eastern United States, apparently, in the
bright ochraceous base of the stipe, the pronounced tendency to stain
yellow and finally orange when bruised, and the pinkish-buff to
pinkish-cinnamon gills. Fruiting bodies in all stages of development
have been studied, and no indications of a gelatinous universal
veil were present. It is interesting to note that in many respects
this western variety corresponds to Fries' description of *H. pudorinus*
better than does the *H. pudorinus* of eastern United States or of most
European authors. Fries (1821) described the stipe as "glaber," obviously referring to the lack of a veil. Later (1838) he stated "Proximus
H. eburneo, sed firmior, stipite sicco glabro et colore uniformi I. lute-
scenti-maculoso distinctus. Cortina nulla." In 1874 he stated of the stipe
"vellum nullum. Pileus non pelliculosus, interdum (ut caro alba) luteo-
maculatus." It is difficult to understand why a species with a distinct
gelatinous universal veil has been referred to *H. pudorinus* by certain
European investigators. The colors as Fries described them, the tendency to stain yellow, and the stipe characters of both *H. pudorinus* Fr.
and *H. fragrans* Murr. are practically identical. The color of the gills in
the latter might serve to separate it. However, studying the situation at
every opportunity since our first publication (1939), we have come to
the conclusion that *H. fragrans* can only be justified as a variety of the
Friesian species.

204
Hygrophorus pudorinus var. *fragrans* f. *pallidus*
(Sm. & Hes.), comb. nov.
Lloydia 2: 38. 1939

Hygrophorus fragrans f. *pallidus* Sm. & Hes., Lloydia 2: 38. 1939.

Pileus 5–9 cm broad, convex with an inrolled margin, at first "warm
buff" on the disc and nearly white on the margin, fading in age to
"pinkish buff" on the disc and becoming "cartridge buff" or more sordid
on the margin, gluten sometimes forming yellowish sordid patches over
the surface, surface viscid, glabrous or faintly fibrillose-streaked beneath the gluten, margin cottony tomentose. Context thick, white,

changing to delicate pink under the cuticle or around the edges of injuries, fragile, taste mild, odor faintly fragrant.

Lamellae bluntly adnate, becoming subdecurrent, close to subdistant, white, broad (1–1.3 cm).

Stipe 10–18 cm long, 10–25 mm thick, white over all, base staining rusty yellow, solid, equal to subventricose, whitish within, surface densely white floccose-squamulose above, appressed-fibrillose below, slightly viscid (tacky) at the base when wet.

Spores 8–10 × 5–6 μ, ellipsoid smooth. Basidia 4-spored. Pleurocystidia and cheilocystidia none. Gill trama divergent, hyphae 4–7 μ broad. Cuticle a gelatinous zone, 275–400 μ thick, with a narrow zone of brown (in KOH), surface hyphae, beneath which is a tangled zone of colorless hyphae, an ixocutis. No hypodermium differentiated. Pileus trama of interwoven, radial hyphae. Clamp connections present on the hyphae of the cuticle, the pileus trama, and the cuticle.

Habit, Habitat, and Distribution—On soil, under hemlock and redwood, California, December.

Material Studied—california: Smith 3685 (type, Trinidad, Dec. 1, 1935).

Observations—Since first collecting this form under spruce in northern California, *H. fragrans* has been found in great abundance, and the context was never observed to change to the colors described above. It thus seems advisable to consider this variant as representing a distinct color form of the species.

205
Hygrophorus pudorinus var. *subcinereus* (Sm. & Hes.), stat. nov.
Sydowia 8: 308. 1954

> *Hygrophorus pudorinus* f. *subcinereus* Sm. & Hes., Sydowia 8: 308. 1954.

Illustration:
Fig. 106.

Pileus 3–7 cm broad, obtuse becoming obtusely umbonate with a decurved and inrolled margin, finally plano-umbonate, color pallid or with a cinereous shade over the disc (this retained in dried specimens), gradually becoming pallid over all and then the disc finally more or less pale pinkish buff to pinkish buff, glabrous viscid. Context white, taste pleasant; odor faintly fragrant.

Lamellae arcuate, subdecurrent, distant, moderately broad, white.

Stipe 4–7 cm long, 8–12 mm thick at apex, staining yellow where handled, the punctae near the apex becoming orange-yellow in drying, white otherwise, equal, solid, white-fibrillose punctate above, veil none, surface typically dry but base often moist (not truly viscid anywhere).

Spores 8–11 × 5–6 μ, ellipsoid, smooth, yellowish in Melzer's solution. Basidia 50–62 × 7–8 μ, 4-spored. Pleurocystidia and cheilocystidia none. Gill trama strongly divergent from a central strand. Pileus a gelatinous cuticle (100–150 μ thick), of narrow (3–5 μ) interwoven hyphae, an ixotrichodermium. No hypodermium differentiated. Pileus trama of interwoven hyphae which are radially disposed. Clamp connections present.

HABIT, HABITAT, AND DISTRIBUTION—Gregarious under balsam and spruce, Wilderness State Park, Mich., October.

MATERIAL STUDIED—MICHIGAN: Smith 43858 (type, Oct. 7, 1953).

OBSERVATIONS—Wilderness State Park, Michigan, is the one place in the United States where Smith has found *H. pudorinus* fruiting abundantly every autumn when rainfall has been adequate. During the season of 1953 which was relatively dry, there were numerous groups of carpophores, but the individuals averaged smaller than those collected during the wet year of 1951. During 1953 var. *subcinereus* was encountered on several occasions and regarded merely as faded normal

Fig. 106. *H. pudorinus* var. *subcinereus*

fruiting bodies. However, when a good collection of young freshly developing specimens was finally located, it was evident at once that we were dealing with a distinct color form. The cinereous tone in perfectly developing material is of significance since there generally has been a strong tendency to regard color as a primary character in this genus. Singer (1951) has placed considerable emphasis upon it, and all investigators have tended to regard the *H. pudorinus* group as quite distinct from the *H. pustulatus* group. The discovery of *H. pudorinus* f. *subcinereus* points to a possible, heretofore unsuspected, bridge between these groups.

It would be interesting to culture var. *subcinereus* and get it to produce fruiting bodies. On two occasions, groups of carpophores of f. *pudorinus* were found in which there was a sector of the gray-capped carpophores of var. *subcinereus*. Both types appeared to be coming from the same mycelium. Such circumstantial evidence as this, of course, is anything but conclusive, but when one meets such a situation twice in a few days, it is very suggestive.

SERIES RUBENTES (Fr.) stat. nov.

Subsection Rubentes Fries, Hymen. Eur., p. 407. 1874.
Characters as given in key to series, page 309.
Type species: *Hygrophorus erubescens* Fr.

KEY TO SPECIES

1. Taste of pellicle bitter and persistent; lamellae "ivory yellow" (pale greenish yellow) at first . . . . .206. *H. amarus*
1. Not with above combination of characters 2
  2. Lamellae crowded, markedly decurrent and narrow . . . .
  . . . . .207. *H. proximus*
  2. Lamellae broader and more distant 3
3. Fibrillose veil present (check expanded caps) . . . .208. *H. purpurascens*
3. Veil absent 4
  4. Spores 8–12 × 2–3.2 μ .209. *H. russuliformis*
  4. Spores broader 5
5. Lamellae close to crowded; growing in deciduous woods . . . .
  . . . . .210. *H. russula*
5. Lamellae distant to subdistant, rarely close 6
  6. When mature the pileus, gills, and stipe evenly dark vinaceous red
  . . . . .211. *H. capreolarius*
  6. Not evenly colored at maturity 7
7. Pileus 5–8 cm broad; stipe 4–7 cm long, 6–12 mm thick . . . .
  . . . . .212. *H. erubescens* var. *erubescens*
7. Pileus 2–3 cm broad; stipe 6–10 long, 4–8 mm thick . . . .
  . . . . .213. *H. erubescens* var. *gracilis*

206

Hygrophorus amarus Sm. & Hes.

Lloydia 2: 50. 1939

Pileus 3–8 cm broad, subhemispheric at first, then convex, expanded plane, obtuse or subdiscoid, color varying from "warm buff" to "flesh color" at first, sometimes "antimony yellow" or tinged "salmon color" to "ochraceous orange" on the disc, paler on the margin, glutinous, not streaked, glabrous and even, margin at first incurved and white floccose. Context white, unchanging, 5–10 mm thick on the disc, rather compact; odor slight, taste very bitter to nauseous and persistent.

Lamellae adnate, at length arcuate with a decurrent tooth, "ivory yellow," becoming incarnate-spotted, waxy, close to subdistant, rather broad (6–10 mm).

Stipe long or short, 5–7 cm or 8–13 cm long, 10–15(20) mm thick at the apex, white or tinged incarnate, covered throughout by an innate dense white floccose-fibrillose sheath, tapering downward or attenuated at the base, dry or slightly viscid at first, solid.

Spores 7–8.5 × 4.5–6 μ, ellipsoid, smooth, colorless to very pale yellow in Melzer's reagent. Basidia 46–60 × 5–8 μ, 2- and 4-spored. Pleurocystidia and cheilocystidia none. Gill trama divergent, hyphae 4–6 μ broad. Cuticle a conspicuous, gelatinous zone, 200–350 μ thick, with tangled, narrow (2–5 μ broad) hyphae, some more or less erect, forming an ixotrichodermium. Cuticular hyphae with a few small, rather inconspicuous clamp connections. No hypodermium differentiated. A few lactifers present. Pileus trama of more or less radial hyphae.

HABIT, HABITAT, AND DISTRIBUTION—Gregarious to subcaespitose under spruce and Douglas fir, Washington, Wyoming, and Idaho, July–November.

MATERIAL STUDIED—IDAHO: Wehmeyer (Copeland, Sept. 11, 1922). WASHINGTON: Kauffman (type, from Lake Quinault, Nov. 2, 1925). WYOMING: Wehmeyer, Hoback Forest Camp and Camp Davis, July 22, 1940.

OBSERVATIONS—All of the collections, except one by Dr. Wehmeyer, were made by Professor C. H. Kauffman, and our description is taken from his notes. *H. erubescens* is sometimes described as being bitter. However, in *H. erubescens* the taste is indistinctive, and the pileus is dark reddish brown in contrast to the bitter taste and the buff to yellow colors in *H. amarus*. Moreover, the gills of *H. amarus* are ivory yellow, and in *H. erubescens* they are pinkish, becoming spotted or stained reddish. The stature of *H. amarus* is somewhat similar to that of *H. pudorinus*, but the fibrillose sheath of the stipe should distinguish *H. amarus*.

207

Hygrophorus proximus Krieger
Mycologia 19: 310. 1927

Illustration:
Krieger, Mycologia 19, pl. 34, fig. 3.

Pileus 5.5 cm broad, slightly repand, pinkish-creamy, and with a fine purplish-red scattered tomentum that forms darker spots of purple-red on the moderately elevated disc. Context very thin toward the margin, white or very faintly pinkish. While drying, the plant emitted an odor of rancid lard.

Lamellae markedly decurrent, creamy white, very narrow, crowded, unequal.

Stipe 5 cm long, 12 mm thick, white, with a pinkish-lavender tinge, tapering a little below, slightly fibrillose with a few purplish fibrils, punctate above with pale tomentose dots.

Spores 5.5–7.5 × 3.5–4.5 μ, ellipsoid, smooth, pale yellow in Melzer's reagent. Basidia 36–42 × 5–7 μ. Pleurocystidia and cheilocystidia none. Gill trama of divergent hyphae. Cuticle an ixocutis, 60–200 μ thick, hyphae loosely interwoven. No hypodermium differentiated. Clamp connections few.

HABIT, HABITAT, AND DISTRIBUTION—On soil, Maryland, October.

MATERIAL STUDIED—MARYLAND: Kelly 287 (type, collected by Olga Kelly, Belair, Oct. 7, 1919).

OBSERVATIONS—A portion of the type is deposited in the University of Michigan Herbarium. The dried gills of it are very difficult to section.

Krieger (1927) reports the following observations: "It seems near *H. erubescens* Fries, hence the specific name. The gills of my plant are much closer and narrower, and the spores considerably smaller than in the Friesian species."

The above account of microscopic characters is based on our study of the type. The macroscopic characters given above are from Krieger (1927).

A note accompanying the specimen states that half of a carpophore is deposited in the National Herbarium.

208

Hygrophorus purpurascens (Fr.) Fr.
Epicr. Myc., p. 322. 1838

Agaricus purpurascens Fr., Syst. Myc., p. 34. 1821.
Limacium purpurascens (Fr.) Kummer, Führ. in Pilzk., p. 118. 1871.

Illustrations:
    Fig. 107.
    Smith and Hesler, Lloydia 2, pl. 21. 1939.

Pileus (3)6–12(15) cm broad, convex, becoming plane, margin remaining decurved until late maturity, color of fibrillose layer "neutral red," "mineral red," or "deep livid brown" on the disc, paler and near "rhodonite pink" on the margin, flesh beneath the fibrils whitish, often splashed and streaked purplish red, viscid, pellicle separable to disc, nearly dry in age, appressed-fibrillose, margin cottony-fibrillose, sometimes becoming appressed-scaly. Context white, thick on disc, thin on margin, firm; odor and taste mild.

Lamellae adnate to decurrent, white then "shell pink" to purplish red, or spotted purplish red, close to subdistant, narrow, edges even.

Fig. 107. *H. purpurascens*

Stipe 3–10 cm long, 10–24 mm thick, more or less concolorous with the pileus below and often spotted with dark purplish red, attenuated below, dry, silky at the apex, solid. Partial veil white, fibrillose, leaving an apical, fugacious ring which becomes purplish red.

Spores 5.5–7(8) × 3–4.5 μ, ellipsoid, smooth, yellowish in Melzer's reagent. Basidia 40–56 × (5)6–8 μ, sterigmata long, 2- and 4-spored. Gill trama of divergent hyphae, 4–10 μ broad. Cuticle a broad (180–330 μ), gelatinous zone of more or less repent, slender (2–4 μ) hyphae, an ixocutis. No hypodermium differentiated. Pileus trama of interwoven, more or less radial hyphae 5–9 μ broad. Clamp connections on the cuticular hyphae.

HABIT, HABITAT, AND DISTRIBUTION—Gregarious to caespitose on soil, under spruce and pine, California, Oregon, Washington, Idaho, Colorado, New Mexico, Maine, and Tennessee, May–December; also Europe.

MATERIAL STUDIED—CALIFORNIA: Smith 8601, 8704, 9005, 9333. COLORADO: Kauffman, Leal, Aug. 20, 1917; Smith 52283, 52685. IDAHO: Gruber P21, 30; Smith 15872, 45671, 46476, 53205, 59116, 59980, 60015, 60212; Smith & Bigelow 46283; Stuntz 45945; Westerdale 59165. WASHINGTON: Bigelow 48512; Smith 17719, 18014, 31266, 48147. OREGON: Smith 19183, 19249, 23741, 26775, 26861, 27140, 28145, 55872. TENNESSEE: Hesler 17275. MAINE: Bigelow 4746. NEW MEXICO: Barrows, Santa Fe, 1955.

OBSERVATIONS—This species is closely related to *H. capreolarius* which lacks a partial veil, and has scaly-dotted areas on the disc. The colors of the two species when dried are similar. Nüesch (1922) lists *H. subpurpurascens* Allesch. as a synonym.

209

Hygrophorus russuliformis Murr.
Elisha Mitchell Sci. Soc. Jour. 55: 371. 1939

Pileus 5–8 cm broad, convex, finally more or less depressed, at times wavy, dull vinaceous ("brownish-vinaceous" to "deep brownish-vinaceous," with "vinaceous brown" streaks), margin paler, viscid, fibrillose-squamulose, margin at first incurved, even. Context white, unchanging, thick on the disc, thin on the margin; odor and taste mild.

Lamellae adnexed, rounded behind, white, becoming purplish where bruised, narrow, crowded, inserted, edges even.

Stipe 1–4 cm long, 14–20 mm thick, apex whitish, elsewhere streaked vinaceous, equal above the slightly enlarged base, striate, moist, not viscid, solid.

Spores 8–10(12) × 2–3.2 μ, oblong, often obliquely apiculate, smooth, colorless or very faintly yellowish in Melzer's reagent. Basidia 38–57 × 5–7 μ, 4-spored. Pleurocystidia and cheilocystidia none. Gill trama divergent, hyphae 2–7 μ broad. Cuticle a gelatinous zone 100–400 μ thick, hyphae pale brownish, narrow (1.5–4 μ), with scattered lactifers. Hypodermium none or indistinct. Pileus trama of loosely interwoven, radially disposed hyphae, with lactifers. The entire cuticular structure is similar to that of *H. russula*. Clamp connections present on the cuticular and gill trama hyphae.

HABIT, HABITAT, AND DISTRIBUTION—On soil, under oak, Florida, November–December.

MATERIAL STUDIED—FLORIDA: Murrill F18404 (type, from Gainesville, Nov. 16, 1938); Hesler 21062.

OBSERVATIONS—We have studied the type, and have collected and studied fresh material taken in Florida. The following notes were recorded on the type: Spores 8–12 × 2.5–3.5 μ, oblong, obliquely apiculate, smooth, colorless. Pleurocystidia and cheilocystidia none. Basidia 38–57 × 5–7 μ, 4-spored. Gill trama of divergent hyphae; sections of dried material show slightly interwoven to subparallel hyphae, but in sections allowed to stand a few hours in chloral hydrate the trama assumed the divergent form. Clamp connections present on the hyphae of the cuticle and gill trama.

The gill trama is divergent, but in sections of dried material it appears to be somewhat interwoven. The spores are indeed distinctive for an *Hygrophorus*. The species is related to *H. russula*. Murrill (1939a) says that dried specimens have an odor of coconut candy, an odor we have not detected.

210
Hygrophorus russula (Fr.) Quél.
Ench. Fung., p. 49. 1886

> *Agaricus russula* Fr., Hymen. Eur., p. 52. 1874.
> *Tricholoma russula* (Fr.) Gill., Champ., Fr., p. 91. 1874.
> *Melanoleuca russula* (Gill.) Murr., North Amer. Flora 10: 22. 1914.

Illustrations:
> Fig. 108.
> Bresadola, Fung. Mang., pl. 22 (as *Tricholoma russula*).
> Bresadola, Icon. Myc. 2, pl. 67 (as *T. russula*).
> Cooke, Illus., No. 1116, t. 926 (as *T. russula*).
> Hard, Mushrooms, fig. 51 (as *T. russula*).
> Kauffman, Agar. Mich., pl. 26.
> Krieger, Mushroom Handbook, pl. 20.
> Michael, Führer f. Pilzfreunde, 2 (as *T. russula*).
> Peck, N. Y. State Mus. Bull. 54, pl. 77, figs. 1–5 (as *T. russula*).
> Pomerleau, Mushrooms of Eastern Canada and the U. S., fig. 17A.
> Ricken, Die Blätterp., pl. 4, fig. 1.
> Smith and Hesler, Lloydia 2, pl. 18.

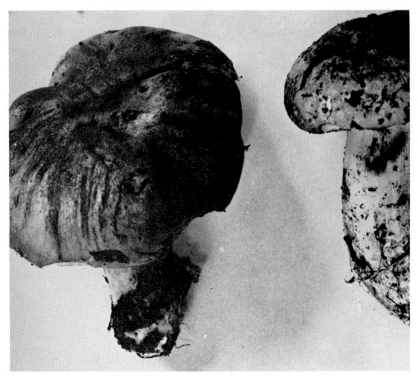

Fig. 108. *H. russula*

Pileus 5–12 cm broad, hemispheric or convex, sometimes broadly umbonate, expanding in age and often with an elevated margin, margin long remaining inrolled and finely cottony pubescent, color variable: "shrimp pink," "cameo pink," "coral pink," "vinaceous pink" or "deep vinaceous," the margin whitish to "Chatenay pink," disc purplish red or pinkish red, viscid, soon dry, usually streaked with purplish-red fibrils, surface smooth at first but breaking up into minute appressed-fibrillose patches giving the disc a granulose to subscaly appearance, sometimes staining yellowish when rubbed. Context thick, white or tinged pinkish, firm; odor and taste mild.

Lamellae bluntly adnate, becoming decurrent, white when young, soon flushed with pale pink and later spotted with sordid purplish-red spots, sometimes sordid purplish red over all in age, rather close, narrow to moderately broad, acuminate at the ends.

Stipe 3–7 cm long, 15–35 mm thick, white at first, becoming stained, streaked, or laved with pinkish, finally more or less concolorous with the pileus, equal or slightly tapering downward, at times subventricose, dry, apex pruinose to glabrous, glabrous below, solid.

Spores 6–8 × 3–4.5(5) μ, ellipsoid, smooth, white in deposits, yellowish in Melzer's reagent. Basidia 40–53 × 5–6 μ, 4-spored. Pleurocystidia and cheilocystidia none. Gill trama divergent with a mediostrate composed of large hyphae, 5–16 μ broad. Cuticle a well-defined gelatinous zone, 50–180 μ thick, with slender hyphae, 2–4 μ broad, loosely interwoven, imbedded (an ixotrichodermium, not a palisade). Fibril-aggregations on the pileus consist of mounds of brownish hyphae together with a brown pigment in the gluten. Hypodermium none differentiated. Pileus trama homogeneous, interwoven, radially disposed. Clamp connections present on the gill trama and cuticular hyphae.

HABIT, HABITAT, AND DISTRIBUTION—Gregarious, at times in arcs or fairy rings, in oak and mixed oak-pine woods, Canada, Massachusetts, New York, Michigan, Illinois, Tennessee, North Carolina, Alabama, Texas, and Washington; also Europe; August–December.

MATERIAL STUDIED—ALABAMA: Burke 2090, Robinson Springs, Nov. 29, 1942. ILLINOIS: Leathers, Charleston, Sept. 28, 1949. MASSACHUSETTS: Bigelow 8709; Seymour, Boston, Sept. 20, 1911. MICHIGAN: Kauffman 1359 (99), Marquette, Sept. 3, 1906; Smith 14938, 15285, 20725, 20773, 38383, 58151, 62124. NEW YORK: Kauffman, Ithaca, Oct. 4, 16, and 17, 1902. TENNESSEE: Hesler 4442, 4457, 4458, 9642, 13021, 14765, 16577, 19441, 19468. TEXAS: Thiers 1918, 4725. WASHINGTON: Kauffman, Olympic Mts., Oct. 16, 1915. CANADA: Bell 3764; Groves 8783, 21900; Smith 835, 14644. BELGIUM: Heinemann 2037.

OBSERVATIONS—*Hygrophorus erubescens* is most closely related to *H. russula*, but in the latter the lamellae are close to crowded (120–130 reach the stipe), and it usually grows in deciduous woods. In *H. erubescens* the lamellae are subdistant to close (75–95 reach the stipe); it grows in coniferous woods; the pilei are usually smaller and less compact; the stipes more slender; and the color-change to yellow when bruised is more pronounced.

211
Hygrophorus capreolarius (Kalchbr.) Sacc.
Fl. Ital. Crypt., Hymen., p. 342. 1915

Illustrations:
    Fig. 109.
    Bresadola, Icon. Myc., tab. 307.

Pileus 3–6(7) cm broad, convex-expanded, obtuse or subumbonate, "Vandyke red" and unicolorous, delicately streaked with purplish fibrils, viscid, soon dry, appressed scaly-dotted on the disc in age, the thick margin at first incurved and white silky. Context rather thick, whitish, reddish or concolorous; odor and taste not distinctive.

Lamellae adnate, becoming decurrent, at first pallid, becoming flesh color or dull pink, finally concolorous with the pileus, rather distant, broadest in the middle, narrowed at the ends, rigid, thickish, intervenose.

Stipe 3–6 cm or 5–10 cm long, 6–10(12) mm thick, whitish with a reddish tinge at first, becoming concolorous with the pileus, the apex usually remaining paler, dry, equal or subventricose, innately pruinose-fibrillose, substriate, apex floccose-punctate, veil lacking.

Spores 6.5–8 × 4.5–5 μ, ellipsoid, smooth, pale yellowish in Melzer's reagent. Basidia 44–58 × 6–7 μ, 4-spored. Pleurocystidia and cheilocystidia none. Gill trama divergent, hyphae 4–9 μ broad, with an opaque mediostrate. Cuticle an ixocutis, 100–180 μ thick, the hyphae colorless, 3–7 μ broad, septate, branched. No hypodermium differentiated. Pileus trama of interwoven hyphae which are chiefly disposed radially. The appressed scaly-dotted areas on the disc are composed of slightly convex concentrations of brownish hyphae. Clamp connections present on the hyphae of the pileus trama, gill trama, and cuticle.

HABIT, HABITAT, AND DISTRIBUTION—Scattered under spruce and in *Sphagnum* bogs, Maine, New York, Idaho, California, Oregon, and Washington, September–December; also Europe, and Japan (Hongo 1958a).

Fig. 109. *H. capreolarius*

MATERIAL STUDIED—CALIFORNIA: Pusateri 8; Smith 9333, 55924, 56301. IDAHO: Smith 55070, 55104. MAINE: Bigelow 4646. NEW YORK: Kauffman & Smith, Adirondack Mts., Sept. 1914, North Elba, Sept. 1914. OREGON: Smith 27326, 27400, 27797, 27799, 27886, 27897, 27952, 28003, 31072, 48497. WASHINGTON: Smith & Bigelow 48491, 48826, 62126; Stuntz F513. FRANCE: Geesteranus 12654 (ex-Herb. Leiden). AUSTRIA: Moser, Sept. 29, 1952 (Hesler 24130).

OBSERVATIONS—The darker colors of the pileus and gills, and lack of a fibrillose veil should distinguish it from *H. purpurascens.* Moser (1955) gives the spores 7–10 × 3.5–5 μ. Hongo (1958a), reporting this species from Shiga-Prefecture, Japan, says *H. purpureobadius* Imai is a synonym.

212
Hygrophorus erubescens (Fr.) Fr. var. **erubescens**
Epicr. Myc., p. 322. 1838

> *Agaricus erubescens* Fr., Syst. Myc., p. 32. 1821.
> *Limacium erubescens* (Fr.) Wünsche, Die Pilze, p. 117. 1877.

Illustrations:
> Fig. 110.
> Bresadola, Icon. Myc., tab. 306.
> Smith and Hesler, Lloydia 2, pl. 19.
> Juillard-Hartmann, Icon. Champ., pl. 49, fig. 5.

Pileus (2)5–8 cm broad, convex, becoming umbonate plane, disc "Vandyke red" to "Hessian brown," elsewhere whitish to "flesh pink" or "orange vinaceous," fading, a pink tinge often pervading the entire pileus, margin incurved and minutely tomentose, often with drops of moisture, even, surface glutinous or viscid, streaked with fibrils, finally with spot-like scales over the disc. Context white, often staining yellowish where bruised, thick on disc, thin on margin, soft; odor and taste not distinctive.

Lamellae adnate becoming decurrent, "pale pinkish buff," or flushed "shell pink," soon spotted or stained pinkish red, close to subdistant, medium broad, narrowed in front, edges stained "purplish-vinaceous," even or eroded.

Stipe 4–7 cm × 6–12 mm, dry, base attenuated, scaly, becoming beaded with drops of moisture above, appressed-fibrillose to scabrous, becoming scurfy below, apex white, elsewhere "pale brownish vinaceous," at times yellowish when bruised, base whitish, solid or stuffed. Veil none.

Spores 7–10(11.5) × 5–6 μ, ellipsoid, smooth, pale yellow in Melzer's reagent, white in mass. Basidia 53–64 × 6–9 μ, 4-spored. Pleuro-

Fig. 110. *H. erubescens* var. *erubescens*

cystidia and cheilocystidia none. Gill trama of divergent hyphae 4–10 μ broad. Cuticle of repent, gelatinous, narrow (2–4 μ) hyphae, at times some with free ends which are erect or ascendant. No hypodermium differentiated. Pileus trama loosely interwoven, hyphae more or less radial. Toward the base of the pileus trama there is a zone of periclinal, parallel hyphae resembling an hypodermium, a structural feature not observed in any other species. Clamp connections present in the cuticle and gill trama.

HABIT, HABITAT, AND DISTRIBUTION—Gregarious under conifers, especially pine and spruce, Tennessee, Michigan, Idaho, Colorado, New Mexico, Wyoming, California, Oregon, and Canada, June–December; also Europe.

MATERIAL STUDIED—CALIFORNIA: Smith 8338, 8396, 8567, 8603, 8703. COLORADO: Baxter, Tolland, Aug. 30 and Sept. 4, 1920; Cotner, Tolland, Aug. 26, 1929; Smith 52368, 52479, 52491, 52615, 52692, 52791, 52941, 52988. IDAHO: Smith 46126, 53498, 59170, 59286, 59786, 59970, 60014, 60092, 60191, 60239, 60354, 60602; Smith & Bigelow 44292, 46255. MICHIGAN: Bailey 179; Smith 34057, 38058, 43703, 43871. NEW MEXICO: Barrows, Aug. 1955. OREGON: Sipe 486; Smith 3521, 3530, 8025, 8139, 26898, 55407; Smith & Gruber 19260. WYOMING: Solheim, North French Creek, Aug. 11, 1950; Smith 35709. TENNESSEE: Hesler 17293. CANADA: (Ontario) Macral 45049; (Quebec) Hoare, Oct. 6, 1952.

OBSERVATIONS—The Tennessee specimens, both when fresh and

dried, are darker than the western collections; otherwise there is close agreement. In color, the pileus of the Tennessee collection approaches *H. capreolarius*, but the lamellae become spotted or stained pinkish red which is characteristic of *H. erubescens*. Smith has collected a form (No. 59170, from Idaho) which has a bitter taste. Nüesch (1922) says that *H. rubescens* Schröter is a synonym.

213
Hygrophorus erubescens var. gracilis Sm. & Hes.
Lloydia 2: 48. 1939
Illustration:
    Fig. 111.

Pileus 2–3 cm broad, plane with a decurved margin, sometimes slightly umbonate, "Vandyke red" on the disc, "flesh pink" toward the margin, the margin at first white pruinose. Context white, unchanging, soft; odor and taste mild.

Lamellae adnate, becoming decurrent, white or flushed grayish pink, staining reddish, distant, narrow.

Stipe 6–10 cm long, 4–8 mm thick, whitish, becoming purplish red in age, upper portion with white-fibrillose scales, or coarsely fibrillose-pruinose, lower portion appressed-fibrillose, dry, equal, base somewhat pointed.

Spores 8–11 × 5.5–6(7) μ, ellipsoid, smooth, yellowish in Melzer's reagent. Basidia 43–62 × 7–10 μ, rarely 2-spored, usually 4-spored. Pleurocystidia and cheilocystidia none. Gill trama divergent, hyphae 3–7 μ broad. Cuticle a gelatinous zone 175–250 μ thick, hyphae pale fuscous, narrow (2.5–4 μ). Hypodermium present, of parallel, periclinally disposed hyphae, not conspicuous. Pileus trama interwoven, radially disposed. Special hypodermial zone at the base of the pileus, as found in *H. erubescens* var. *erubescens*, absent. Clamp connections present in the cuticle, the gill trama, and the subhymenium (at the base of the basidia).

HABIT, HABITAT, AND DISTRIBUTION—Gregarious under pine, Oregon, Washington, and Tennessee, October–December.

MATERIAL STUDIED—OREGON: Sipe 922; Smith 3564 (type, from Florence, Nov. 20, 1935), 27990. WASHINGTON: Smith 49341. TENNESSEE: Hesler 24618.

OBSERVATIONS—This variety is related to *H. erubescens* var. *erubescens* in the same way that the slender form of *H. olivaceoalbus* is related to that species. There seems to be a series of slender variants in this subgenus. The variety (*gracilis*) differs from var. *erubescens* in its more distant gills, lack of yellowish stains when fresh, in general stature, and in the pileus trama structure. Smith has collected this variety (No. 49341) from Washington, observing that the stipe is white above, vinaceous below, stains vinaceous, and that the odor is faintly fragrant.

Fig. 111. *H. erubescens* var. *gracilis*

SERIES FULVENTES (Fr.) stat. nov.

Subsection Fulventes I. flavi Fr., Hymen. Eur., p. 408, 1874.
Subsection Fulvoincarnati Sm. & Hes., Lloydia 2: 36. 1939.
Characters as given in key to series, page 309.
Type species: *H. arbustivus* Fr.

KEY TO SPECIES

1. Spores (9)10–14 μ long 2
1. Spores 5.5–10 μ long 6
  2. Pileus pink to orange; odor not distinctive 3
  2. Pileus variously colored; odor distinctive 4
3. Spores 12–15 × 7–9 μ; pileus pink becoming pinkish buff ....
  ....214. *H. goetzii*
3. Spores 9–12 × 5–7 μ; pileus orange becoming nearly ferruginous ....
  ....215. *H. pseudolucorum*
  4. Taste disagreeable; stipe pink pruinose; lamellae pale pinkish cin-
    namon ....216. *H. vinicolor*
  4. Taste mild 5
5. Disc of pileus rusty brown; lamellae yellowish at first ....
  ....217. *H. pacificus*
5. Disc of pileus pale alutaceous but soon flushed vinaceous; lamellae
  whitish at first ....218. *H. monticola*
  6. A fibrillose veil present 7
  6. Lacking any kind of a veil 8
7. Pileus pale pink: spores 5.5–7 × 3.5–4 μ ....219. *H. velatus*
7. Pileus yellow to Isabella color; spores 8–10 × 4–5 μ ...220. *H. siccipes*
7. Pileus orange-yellow; spores 9–12 × 6–7 μ ....215. *H. pseudolucorum*
  8. Taste bitter; odor of raw potatoes; disc of pileus tawny ....
    ....221. *H. tennesseensis*
  8. Not as above 9
9. Lamellae dark reddish brown to pale buff or grayish 10
9. Lamellae essentially white 18
  10. Pileus yellow at least on disc 11
  10. Pileus not truly yellow 12
11. Stipe rufescent, not staining yellow, 8–16 mm thick ....222. *H. paigei*
11. Stipe staining yellow; 4–6 mm thick ....192. *H. tenax*
  12. Pileus and gills vinaceous-ferruginous ....223. *H. kauffmanii*
  12. Not as above 13
13. Odor distinctive in some way 14
13. No appreciable odor 15
  14. Lamellae pale bright pinkish cinnamon to ochraceous-cinnamon ..
    ....190. *H. saxatilis*
  14. Lamellae merely pinkish buff to clay color ....194. *H. subpungens*
15. Pileus pale dingy tan; base of stipe soon lemon yellow ....
  ....224. *H. sublutescens*
15. Not as above 16

214

Hygrophorus goetzii, sp. nov.

*Pileus 2–5 cm latus, late convexus, glutinosus, albidus demum pal-
lide alutaceus; lamellae subdistantes vel distantes, pallidae, late adnatae; stipes 3–6 cm longus, 3–8 mm crassus; sericeus, siccus, subalbidus;
sporae 12–15 × 7–9 μ. Specimen typicum lectum prope Mt. Hood, Oregon, July 7, 1957, Christel and Donald Goetz 6.*

Pileus 2–5 cm broad, obtuse to broadly convex, expanding to
broadly convex or nearly plane, at times slightly depressed, surface glabrous, slimy-viscid, rosy pink when young, fading out to cream color in
age but drying a grayish pinkish-buff. Context thin, pallid to cream
color, unchanging when bruised, odor and taste mild.

Lamellae subdistant to distant, broadly adnate, broad in age, one
tier of lamellulae, pallid to cream color drying almost concolorous with
the pileus, edges even.

Stipe 3–6 cm long, 3–8 mm thick, equal or nearly so, entirely
cream color and drying almost concolorous with pileus, surface dry,
apex silky and smooth, base hairy-strigose.

Spores 12–15 × 7–9 μ, elliptic to ovate in face view, obscurely in-equilateral in profile, yellowish hyaline in Melzer's solution, smooth, thin-walled. Basidia 4-spored, 50–80 × 10–12 μ, reddish in sections mounted in Melzer's solution. Pleurocystidia and cheilocystidia none. Gill trama of divergent hyphae from a central strand. Epicutis of pileus a thick layer of gelatinous, branched, flexuous hyphae 2–4 μ in diameter intricately interwoven, the layer pinkish red in Melzer's reagent. Clamp connections present.

HABIT, HABITAT, AND DISTRIBUTION—Mt. Hood, Oregon, near Timberline Lodge, under hemlock. July 7, 1957. Christel and Donald Goetz No. 6. This species is named in honor of Goetz.

This species is obviously closely related to *H. avellaneifolius* and *H. sublutescens* but is at once distinguished from both by its giant spores on 4-spored basidia.

215
Hygrophorus pseudolucorum Sm. & Hes.
Sydowia 8: 311. 1954

Pileus 1–3.5 cm broad, obtuse to nearly plane with an incurved margin, expanding to plane or shallowly depressed, with or without a low umbo, color near "apricot orange" or disc pinker and margin yellow, in age sometimes nearly ferruginous on the disc, surface viscid but soon dry, at first appearing as if covered by a very faint fibrillose coating. Context thin, pallid, yellowish, no color change on bruising; odor and taste none.

Lamellae decurrent, pallid when young, yellowish in age, subdistant to distant, broad, edges even.

Stipe 3–5 cm long, 3–5 mm thick, white or whitish at first, gradually lutescent especially where handled, dry, with a thin, fibrillose veil leaving an inconspicuous apical zone which soon vanishes, silky above the zone.

Spores 9–12 × 6–7 μ from deposits, when revived in KOH 8–11 × 5–6.5 μ, obscurely inequilateral in side view, in face view elliptic or nearly so, smooth, hyaline, yellowish in Melzer's reagent. Basidia 50–75 × 8–9 μ, 4-spored, pedicels flexuous. Pleurocystidia and cheilocystidia none seen. Gill trama of divergent hyphae (4–8 μ broad) from a central strand. Cuticle a narrow zone of repent, gelatinous hyphae. Pileus trama of interwoven hyphae. Clamp connections present.

HABIT, HABITAT, AND DISTRIBUTION—Gregarious under mixed hardwoods and larch, Michigan, October.

MATERIAL STUDIED—MICHIGAN: Smith 38943 (type, collected by Kent McKnight, North Lake, Washtenaw County, Oct. 25, 1951).

OBSERVATIONS—The thin, white, fibrillose veil, dry stipe, large spores, decurrent gills, the orange to pinkish color of the pileus and yellow stains on the stipe are distinctive. When old the fruiting bodies bear some resemblance to those of faded specimens of *H. speciosus*, but that species has a slimy veil. The same objection holds for *H. nitidus* Fr. as well as *H. lucorum* Kalch., although Nüesch's interpretation of the latter seems very close to *H. pseudolucorum*. However, Kalchbrenner's original description pretty well excludes any dry-stiped *Hygrophorus*. In addition, the spores from a deposit measure larger than given anywhere for *H. lucorum*.

The mycorrhizal association is very likely with larch. *H. lucorum* is said to have a dry stipe by Kühner and Romagnesi (1953), but the spore size as given by them is too small for our species. *H. laricinus* Pk. is close to *H. pseudolucorum* but differs in tawny red color and smaller spores.

216
Hygrophorus vinicolor, sp. nov.

Illustration:
    Fig. 112.

Pileus 2.5–5 cm latus, subviscidus, cito siccus, colore variabilis, disco "wood brown," "vinaceous buff" prope marginem; odore aromaticus, gustu ingratus; lamellae decurrentes, paene "pale pinkish cinnamon," distantes, latae; stipes 3–5 cm longus, 10–20 mm crassus, albus, siccus, rosaceo-pruinosus; sporae 10–14 × 6–8 μ, ellipsoideae. Specimen typicum in Herb. Univ. Mich.; lectum in Cape Horn Summit, Sawtooth Mts., Idaho, Aug. 25, 1954, A. H. Smith 47116.

Pileus 2.5–5 cm broad, obtuse with an inrolled margin, becoming pale or nearly so, color variable, "wood brown" on disc and "vinaceous buff" toward margin, margin rather pink in age at times, surface slightly viscid but soon dry. Context white or vinaceous near cuticle; taste disagreeable, odor aromatic, as in *H. agathosmus*, no color changes when bruised.

Lamellae decurrent, near "pale pinkish cinnamon," distant, broad.

Stipe 3–5 cm long, 10–20 mm thick, white throughout, dry, surface minutely pruinose at first and the pruina developing a pinkish tone, solid.

Spores 10–14 × 6–8 μ, ellipsoid, smooth, thin-walled, hyaline in KOH, yellowish hyaline in Melzer's reagent. Basidia 50–70 × 6-9 μ, 4-spored, pedicels flexuous. Pleurocystidia and cheilocystidia none. Gill trama of divergent hyphae (young gills), in old gills appearing almost interwoven. Cuticle of pileus rather indistinct and only subgelatinous as

Fig. 112. *H. vinicolor*

revived in KOH. Pileus trama of floccose, interwoven hyphae broader than those of cuticle. Clamp connections present.

HABIT, HABITAT, AND DISTRIBUTION—Gregarious on a mossy bank, Idaho, August.

MATERIAL STUDIED—IDAHO: Smith 46714 (type, from Cape Horn, Aug. 25, 1954), 47116.

OBSERVATIONS—The two collections referred to here could possibly be only a variant of *H. monticola*. The characters which seem to distinguish *H. vinicolor* are the "pale pinkish cinnamon" gills (almost the color of those of *H. saxatilis*), the disagreeable taste, and the pink pruina of the stipe, which might be only a continuation of the change toward pink which both show in the pileus of old or drying specimens.

217
Hygrophorus pacificus Sm. & Hes.
Lloydia 2: 42. 1939

Illustration:
  Fig. 113.

Pileus 3–8 cm broad, convex, margin long remaining incurved, becoming plane and variously lobed, notched or wavy in age, colors evenly "russet" to "tawny" when young, at maturity "tawny" on the disc and "pinkish buff" on the margin, viscid, glabrous, margin faintly tomentose under a lens, usually plicate crenate when unexpanded. Context whitish, rather thin and rigid; odor strong, penetrating and aromatic, taste mild.

Lamellae bluntly adnate or decurrent by a tooth, edges even, "marguerite yellow" to "cream-buff" when young, "cream color" in age, distant, broad (1 cm), often forking near the margin of the pileus, thickish.

Stipe 4–7 cm long, 8–15 mm thick, concolorous with the lamellae or whitish, equal above a narrowed base, solid or sometimes hollowed at the apex, dry, evenly fibrillose-pruinose over upper half with whitish fibrils, glabrous and unpolished below.

Spores 10–14 × 5.5–7.5 μ, ellipsoid, smooth, pale yellowish in Melzer's reagent. Basidia 50–82 × 7–9 μ, 2- and 4-spored, sterigmata stout.

Fig. 113. *H. pacificus*

Pleurocystidia and cheilocystidia none. Gill trama divergent, hyphae 3–8 μ broad. Cuticle an ixotrichodermium, hyphae more or less erect and tangled, 2.5–5 μ broad, at times finally repent and then resembling an ixocutis. No hypodermium differentiated. Pileus trama of radial hyphae. Clamp connections on the hyphae of the cuticle and gill trama. Lactifers present in the gill trama.

HABIT, HABITAT, AND DISTRIBUTION—Densely gregarious under spruce, Idaho, California, and Washington, November; also Canada.

MATERIAL STUDIED—CALIFORNIA: Smith 8518, 8581, 8732 (type, Fort Dick, Nov. 14, 1937), 9054, 9485. IDAHO: Smith 54790. WASHINGTON: Kauffman, Lake Quinault, Nov. 3, 1925. CANADA: (Nova Scotia) Harrison Kings Co., Sept. 21, 1955.

OBSERVATIONS—During the season of 1937 this species was very abundant in the vicinity of Fort Dick, California. Kauffman collected it in Washington in 1925. The large spores, dry stipe, russet to tawny colors, mild taste, and strong aromatic odor distinguish it. Kauffman tentatively referred it to *H. agathosmus* as a variety. It does resemble that species in having an odor and a dry stipe, but the colors of both the pileus and gills, and the large spores amply distinguish it. It is apparently very closely related to the little known *H. aromaticus* (Sow.) Berk. The latter apparently differs in its narrow, white to pink gills, and the flesh which is said to turn blackish when bruised.

218
Hygrophorus monticola, sp. nov.

Pileus 2–5 cm latus, convexus, alutaceus, vinaceo-coccineo tinctus, viscidus; odore amygdalino; lamellae decurrentes, albido demum tinctae, "pinkish buff," distantes, latae, interdum subintervenosae; stipes 3–6 cm longus, 3–25 mm crassus, albus demum concoloratus cum pileo; sporae 10–14 × 5.5–7.5 μ. Specimen typicum in Herb. Univ. Mich. conservatum; lectum prope Payette Lakes, Idaho, Sept. 9, 1956, A. H. Smith 53239.

Pileus 2–5 cm broad, broadly convex with an incurved margin, becoming plane or slightly depressed, color cinnamon-buff on disc and flushed vinaceous red, in age with salmon to vinaceous tones extending to margin, margin often irregular in age, viscid but soon dry. Context thick, firm, buffy white, unchanging, wormholes not darkened at borders appreciably; odor of cherry pits, taste mild.

Lamellae decurrent, whitish, in age becoming flushed with color of cap but paler, near "pinkish buff," not spotting, many forked halfway to margin, thickish, distant, broad, interveined (almost poroid or lacunose at times).

Stipe 3–6 cm long, 3–25 mm thick at apex, white at first, a few flushed with color of cap in age, not darkening to more than pale salmon-buff around wormholes, dry, narrowed below or equal, no veil.

Spores 10–14 × 5.5–7.5 μ, ellipsoid, smooth, yellowish in Melzer's reagent. Pleurocystidia and cheilocystidia none. Basidia 56–82 × 7–11 μ, 4-spored. Gill trama divergent, hyphae 4–10(14) μ broad. Cuticle an ixocutis, hyphae 3–5 μ broad, occasionally more or less erect, slightly gelatinous. No hypodermium differentiated. Pileus trama of interwoven hyphae, disposed both radially and periclinally. Clamp connections on the cuticular and gill trama hyphae.

HABIT, HABITAT, AND DISTRIBUTION—Gregarious on soil and moss, in coniferous woods (larch, spruce, fir), Idaho and Canada, August–November.

MATERIAL STUDIED—IDAHO: Smith 23537, 53239 (type, from Payette Lakes, Sept. 9, 1956), 53297, 53444, 53454, 53540, 60524, 60539. CANADA: (Nova Scotia) Kenneth A. Harrison 2049; (Quebec) Smith 61556, 61839.

OBSERVATIONS—This species is distinctive in appearance in its buff to brownish pileus which is flushed vinaceous and becomes fibrillose-streaked, its broad, distant, decurrent gills, its large spores, and its large basidia. The flesh has the odor of bitter almonds, or cherry pits. In one collection (Smith 60524) the odor is lacking. In this collection, the carpophores appear abnormal, somewhat as if slightly parasitized; the lamellae are rather narrow compared to other collections of *H. monticola;* many of the basidia are slender and sterile; and the spores are relatively few. If these are normal carpophores, which is doubtful, this would be an odorless form of *H. monticola.* In another variant (Smith 61839), although the spores measure up to 13.5 μ long, most of them are 9–11 μ in length. In *H. vinicolor* the gills are distinctly colored when young, and the stipe has a pruinosity which becomes pink.

219

Hygrophorus velatus, sp. nov.

Pileus 1.5–3 cm latus, convexus, pallido-rubicundulus, glaber, viscidus, margine aequo; caro albida, odore et gustu mitis; lamellae decurrentes, pallidus ochraceae, paene subdistantes, modice latae; stipes 3–5 cm longus, 4–6 mm crassus, pallidus demum pallido-ochraceae, albo-fibrillosus superne, siccus, aequalis; velum albo-fibrillosum, plenum; sporae 5.5–6(7–8) × 3.5–4 μ, ellipsoideae demum sub-ellipsoideae. Specimen typicum in Herb. Univ. Mich.; lectum prope Burgdorf, Idaho, Aug. 13, 1958, A. H. Smith 59968.

Pileus 1.5–3 cm broad, convex, more or less expanding, very pale pinkish, glabrous, viscid, margin even. Context whitish, medium thin; odor and taste not distinctive.

Lamellae decurrent, pale buff, rather close to subdistant, medium broad, edges even.

Stipe 3–5 cm long, 4–6 mm thick, pallid to pale buff, white-fibrillose above the veil-remnants, dry, equal. Veil white-fibrillose, copious.

Spores 5.5–6(7–8) × 3.5–4 μ, ellipsoid to subellipsoid, smooth, yellow in Melzer's reagent. Basidia 42–54 × 6–8 μ, 2- and 4-spored. Pleurocystidia and cheilocystidia none. Gill trama divergent, hyphae 4–9 μ broad. Cuticle a zone, 180–300 μ broad, composed of colorless, loosely interwoven, gelatinous hyphae. Clamp connections present on the cuticular and gill trama hyphae. Cuticular hyphae of the stipe are nongelatinous and have clamps.

HABIT, HABITAT, AND DISTRIBUTION—On soil, under conifers, Idaho, August.

MATERIAL STUDIED—IDAHO: Smith 59968 (type, from northeast of Burgdorf, Aug. 13, 1958).

OBSERVATIONS—This species is clearly related to *H. purpurascens*, but the pileus lacks the red fibrils, and the lamellae are not reddish-spotted. Consequently, we place it here.

220
Hygrophorus siccipes Sm. & Hes.
Sydowia 8: 312. 1954

Illustration:
    Fig. 114.

Pileus 2–3 cm broad, convex, margin incurved, expanding to plane or the margin elevated slightly and the disc depressed, "Isabella color" with a "warm buff" margin, disc becoming tinged with cinnamon and then more or less "sayal brown," glutinous and appearing fibrillose-streaked beneath the gluten. Context odor and taste not distinctive.

Lamellae decurrent, "ivory yellow" becoming "warm buff," narrow, distant.

Stipe 4–6 cm long, 3–6 mm thick at apex, concolorous with gills, equal or narrowed downward, dry, with a median fibrillose zone from the partial veil.

Spores 8–10 × 4–5 μ, nearly elliptic in face view, smooth, hyaline in KOH, yellowish in Melzer's reagent. Basidia 38–50 × 8–9 μ, 4-spored. Pleurocystidia and cheilocystidia none seen. Gill trama divergent. Cuticle a well-defined zone 200–300 μ thick, of fuscous, gelatinous hyphae, 2–3.5 μ broad, more or less erect, loosely tangled (no palisade), an ixotrichodermium. Hypodermium indistinct or none. Pileus trama of radially disposed hyphae. Clamp connections present.

HABIT, HABITAT, AND DISTRIBUTION—Gregarious in a pine barren, Oregon, October.

MATERIAL STUDIED—OREGON: Smith 25005 (type, from Rhododendron, Oct. 27, 1946).

OBSERVATIONS—When collected, the specimens were in perfect condition, but no evidence of a gelatinous veil over the stipe was present, nor were there any indications that such a veil had ever been present. In all other characters the fungus appears to be *H. hypothejus,* and it is worthy of note because of the number of "parallel species" of the kind in the subgenus *Hygrophorus.* There is *H. variicolor* Murr. and *H. bakerensis* Sm. & Hes. from the Cascades, which form a similar pair. Since the subgenus *Hygrophorus* has been divided on the basis of the presence or absence of a universal glutinous veil, it is interesting to see how closely related species can become widely separated in such a classification. However, if one places primary emphasis on color of pileus, one still encounters the same problem (see *H. pudorinus* f. *subcinereus*). *H. lucorum* sensu Kühner & Romagnesi may belong here, but the color of the pileus as given is too pale and certainly not fibrillose-streaked as in *H. hypothejus.*

Fig. 114.
   H. siccipes

221

Hygrophorus tennesseensis Sm. & Hes.
Lloydia 2: 40. 1939

Illustration:
Fig. 115.

Pileus (2)6–12 cm broad, convex then expanded, becoming depressed, marginal portion whitish to "clay color" or "tawny-olive," central portion "tawny" to "fawn color," viscid or glutinous, pellicle separable to disc, glabrous, margin even or substriate, involute, floc-cose-fibrillose. Context white, thick (up to 8 mm) on the disc, thin on margin, compact; odor distinct in young and in fresh specimens, resembling that of raw potatoes, taste bitter.

Lamellae adnate becoming short-decurrent, white, linear, about 7 mm broad, subdistant, many lamellulae, venose at cap, edges even.

Stipe 6–10 cm long, 8–18 mm thick, whitish or dingy, dry, more or less flexuous, tapering downward, fibrillose-striate, upper portion floc-cose-scabrous, solid.

Spores (6)7–9 × 4.5–6 μ, ellipsoid, smooth, yellowish in Melzer's reagent. Basidia 38–54 × 7–9 μ, 4-spored, rarely 2-spored. Pleurocystidia and cheilocystidia none. Gill trama of divergent hyphae, 4–9 μ

Fig. 115. *H. tennesseensis*

broad. Cuticle of gelatinous, colorless or nearly colorless hyphae, 3–5 μ broad, repent or more or less erect and tangled, an ixotrichodermium (no palisade). No hypodermium differentiated. Pileus trama of radial, slightly interwoven hyphae. Clamp connections on the hyphae of the cuticle and the gill trama.

HABIT, HABITAT, AND DISTRIBUTION—Gregarious on soil, under conifers, Tennessee, North Carolina, Kentucky, Massachusetts, and California, September–February.

MATERIAL STUDIED—KENTUCKY: Stevenson 16579. CALIFORNIA: Rea 917, 361. MASSACHUSETTS: Bigelow 8387, 8616, 8640, 8686, 8731. NORTH CAROLINA: Hesler 12371, 16438, 17147, 19386, 21006, 23479. TENNESSEE: Hesler 4443, 10922 (type, from Cades Cove, Great Smoky Mts. National Park, Oct. 17, 1937), 13077, 16578, 18157, 18285, 19471, 19477, 20201, 22420 (the last forming a fairy ring 15 feet in diameter).

OBSERVATIONS—The odor, taste, colors, dry stipe, and resemblance to *H. pudorinus* in stature are the distinctive features of this species. In its colors it closely resembles *H. variicolor* Murr. The dry stipe and bitter taste distinguish it readily from *H. pudorinus*. *H. arbustivus* Fr. sensu Nüesch (1922) is also closely related but differs in its virgate pileus and mild odor and taste. In addition other investigators have usually described the pileus of the latter as more reddish or incarnate tan.

222
Hygrophorus paigei Pammel
Iowa State Coll. Journ. Sci. 2: 115. 1928

Pileus 3–10 cm broad, expanded plane, frequently repand and irregular, egg yellow, viscid, not virgate. Context thick, firm, pallid, thin on the margin; odor none, taste mild.

Lamellae arcuate-decurrent, yellowish, thick, subdistant, pruinose, attenuate at both ends.

Stipe 3–8 cm long, 8–16 mm thick, rufescent, at first with an appressed, glaucous silkiness, glabrescent, innately fibrous, dry, shining, equal or tapering downward, attenuated at the base, often curved, rigid, solid.

Spores 7–9 × 4 μ, narrowly ellipsoid-lanceolate, or ovoid, smooth, white.

HABIT, HABITAT, AND DISTRIBUTION—On soil, among fallen leaves in deciduous woods, Iowa, October.

MATERIAL STUDIED—IOWA: Pammel (type).

OBSERVATIONS—The type at Iowa State College has a divergent

gill trama, and the pileus shows a viscid pellicle. It appears to be related to *H. gliocyclus* which has a viscid stipe.

223
Hygrophorus kauffmanii Sm. & Hes.
Lloydia 2: 44. 1939

Illustrations:
    Figs. 116 and 117.
    Smith and Hesler, Lloydia 2, pl. 17.

Pileus 2–11 cm broad, convex, turbinate to plane, at times not fully expanding, canescent, often with minute, spot-like scales, viscid to subviscid, "hazel" to "chestnut" when moist, usually appearing "pecan brown" or "vinaceous tawny," in age fading to "apricot buff," margin incurved and minutely tomentose. Context firm, thick on disc, thin on margin, "light pinkish cinnamon" or darker when moist; odor and taste mild.

Lamellae adnate, becoming slightly decurrent, "onion skin pink," becoming "Kaiser brown" to "orange-cinnamon," subdistant to nearly close, fairly broad, broadest behind, edges even.

Stipe 4–10 cm long, 5–20 mm thick, at times enlarged upward, not viscid, apex glabrous or at times subsquamulose, elsewhere fibrillose, "buff pink" at first, soon concolorous with the pileus or darker, canescent, solid.

Spores 7–9 × 4–5.5 μ, ellipsoid, smooth, pale yellow in Melzer's reagent. Basidia 48–62 × 6–7 μ, 4-spored. Pleurocystidia and cheilocystidia none. Gill trama divergent, hyphae 4–7 μ broad. Cuticle a narrow gelatinous zone of more or less erect hyphae, 100–210 × 2.5–4 μ, forming a loosely tangled turf (not a palisade). No hypodermium differentiated. Pileus trama of radially arranged hyphae. Clamps in the gill trama and the cuticle.

HABIT, HABITAT, AND DISTRIBUTION—Gregarious to scattered in open oak woods, Michigan and Tennessee, October–February.

MATERIAL STUDIED—MICHIGAN: Kauffman, Ann Arbor, 1912, 1926, 1936; Smith 6046 (type, Ann Arbor, Oct. 13, 1936), 6140, 33104, 51162, 62262. TENNESSEE: Hesler 11553, 13173, 14140.

OBSERVATIONS—Kauffman collected this species many years ago and in the *Agaricaceae of Michigan*, 1918, p. 188, described it under the name *H. leporinus*. Kühner (1936) states that *H. leporinus* of Kauffman is the same as *H. nemoreus*, as the latter is known in Europe. However, if the descriptions of *H. nemoreus* are carefully examined, it becomes apparent that the latter differs from *H. kauffmanii* in

Fig. 116. *H. kauffmanii*

Fig. 117. *H. kauffmanii*

certain important respects. Bataille (1910) described the gills of *H. nemoreus* as "blanches, puis creme, a reflet aurore." Bresadola (1928) figured a species which has the gill characters as Bataille described them. Nüesch (1922) also describes the gills of *H. nemoreus* as essentially pale ("blass cremfarbig bis rotlich ocherfarbig oder blassorange"). He also describes the stipe as whitish to pale ochraceous, colors strikingly different from the buff pink to chestnut color of the stipe of *H. kauffmanii.* Ricken's (1915) description and illustration are in accord with those mentioned above, and Rea's (1922) apparently applies to still a different species because of its spores. J. Lange (1923) describes a form he referred to *H. nemoreus* (as a variety) as having a white stipe, and the gills paler than the pileus. If descriptions can be relied upon, the dark reddish-brown gills of *H. kauffmanii* amply distinguish it.

In the Tennessee collections the lamellae, when dried, are somewhat paler than in the type; otherwise there is agreement between the collections. The color of the pileus is ferruginous to vinaceous-ferruginous.

224
Hygrophorus sublutescens, sp. nov.

Pileus 1.5–4 cm latus, convexus, viscidus, glaber, subfulvus; lamellae latae, confertae vel subdistantes, late adnatae, pallide subalutaceae; stipes 1–3 cm longus, 3–6 mm latus, siccus, deorsum luteus, sursum pruinosus; sporae 6–7.5 × 3.5–4.5 μ; hyphae fibulatae. Specimen typicum legit Wilderness State Park, Emmet County, Mich., Oct. 15, 1960, A. H. Smith 63330.

Pileus 1.5–4 cm broad, obtuse to broadly convex, surface viscid, glabrous, color a pale dingy tan (near "cinnamon-buff") on disc, grayer toward the margin (near avellaneous or a grayish-pinkish buff), the color duller than in *H. discoideus.* Context firm, pallid, odor and taste mild.

Lamellae broad, close varying to subdistant, broadly adnate to subdecurrent, dingy pinkish buff drying dingy pallid to grayish buff, edges even.

Stipe 1–3 cm long, 3–6 mm thick at apex, equal, dry, pubescent to fibrillose over lower half, pruinose-scurfy to silky above, typically becoming lemon yellow over basal part and any part of surface soon bright yellow when touched with KOH.

Spore deposit white. Spores 6–7.5 × 3.5–4.5 μ, subovoid, smooth, thin-walled, hyaline in KOH, yellowish hyaline in Melzer's solution. Basidia 4-spored, 36–48 × 5–7 μ, pedicels flexuous. Pleurocystidia and cheilocystidia none. Gill trama of divergent hyphae. Epicutis of pileus a tangled trichodermium of short, narrow filaments (1–2.5 μ wide) dingy yellowish as revived in KOH. Clamp connections present.

HABIT, HABITAT, AND DISTRIBUTION—Gregarious under white cedar and spruce. Wilderness State Park, Emmet County, Mich., Oct. 15, 1960.

MATERIAL STUDIED—MICHIGAN: Smith 63330.

OBSERVATIONS—The dry stipe often changing to yellow at the base, and spotting yellow in KOH, the dingy color and lack of an odor and taste are distinctive. It is related to *H. avellaneifolius*, but is not as soft and the gills are paler and dry paler.

225
Hygrophorus cinereipallens Sm. & Hes. var. cinereipallens
Sydowia 8: 309. 1954

Illustration:
    Fig. 118.

Pileus 1–3(4) cm broad, convex with an incurved margin, expanding to plane or nearly so, margin at times elevated in age, color avellaneous to dingy pinkish buff over disc, cinereous pallid over margin, in age a cinereous shade often pervading the entire cap, surface glabrous and viscid. Context thick but very soft, pallid to slightly cinereous; odor and taste not distinctive.

Lamellae adnate becoming decurrent, "avellaneous" or somewhat paler or darker, close to subdistant, moderately broad, edges even.

Stipe 3–5 cm long, 3–8 mm thick, more or less concolorous with the gills, equal, solid, soft, dry, densely pruinose above and at times over all except the mycelioid base. Veil none.

Spores 6.5–8 × 4.5–5 μ, oblong to ellipsoid, smooth, hyaline, yellowish in Melzer's solution. Basidia 42–50 × 6–8 μ, 2- and 4-spored. Pleurocystidia and cheilocystidia none. Gill trama divergent, hyphae 5–8 μ broad. Cuticle a well-defined gelatinous zone, 80–130 μ thick, with narrow (3–6 μ), loosely tangled hyphae. No hypodermium differentiated. Pileus trama interwoven, the hyphae radially disposed. Clamp connections present.

HABIT, HABITAT, AND DISTRIBUTION—Gregarious under conifers, Michigan, October.

MATERIAL STUDIED—MICHIGAN: Smith 43736 (type, Point Aux Chenes, Oct. 4, 1953).

OBSERVATIONS—The densely pruinose dry stipe, avellaneous gills which become cinereous like the pileus in dried material, small spores,

Fig. 118. *H. cinereipallens* var. *cinereipallens*

and dingy pileus when fresh distinguish it. It is similar to *H. subpungens;* but the stipe does not change where handled, the gills do not become clay color, and no pungent odor is present. Perhaps it is actually most closely related to *H. roseibrunneus* and *H. nemoreus,* but differs in the grayish colors.

226
Hygrophorus cinereipallens **var.** *fallax,* **var. nov.**

Pileus 1–3 cm latus, obtusus demum convexus, parum viscidus, glaber demum fibrillosus, disco obscure cinereo-rubicundo-coriaceus, margine pallidus; odore et gustu mitis (non proprius); lamellae brevi-decurrentes, latae, subdistantes, obscuro-pallidae mox avellaneae vel cinereae, deinde pallido-griseae; stipes 1–3 cm longus, 2.5–3.5 mm crassus, siccus, subcinereus, lente atro-brunneus deorsum, apice pruinosus, fibrillosus demum furfuraceus, squamulosus deorsum, oliveus in KOH; sporae 7–8 × 3–4.5 μ, suboblongae. Specimen typicum in Herb. Univ. Mich. conservatum; lectum in Wilderness State Park, Emmet County, Mich., Oct. 15, 1960, Smith 63323.

Pileus 1–3 cm broad, obtuse to convex, thinly viscid, appearing glabrous at first but soon fibrillose-streaked beneath the viscid layer, color a dingy grayish-pinkish buff on disc, margin pallid to pale cinereous, drying dingy cinereous, epicutis dingy olive to olive brown in KOH. Context soft, fragile, dingy pallid, odor and taste not distinctive.

Lamellae short decurrent, broad, subdistant, dingy pallid when very young but soon avellaneous or grayer and in age or when dried pale drab, edges even.

Stipe 1–3 cm long, 2.5–3.5 mm thick, equal, solid, dry, at first grayish pallid, slowly becoming dark brown below, surface hoary-fibrillose to furfuraceous with apex more or less pruinose, fibrils over lower part often rusty brown and arranged in minute squamules, surface quickly olive in KOH.

Spore deposit white, spores non-amyloid, 7–8 × 3–4.5 μ, thin-walled, oblong or nearly so, hyaline, smooth. Basidia 4-spored. Pleurocystidia and cheilocystidia none. Gill trama of divergent hyphae. Epicutis of pileus a tangled trichodermium of narrow (1.5–3 μ) gelatinous hyphae with dingy yellow-brown content in KOH. Clamp connections present.

HABIT, HABITAT, AND DISTRIBUTION—Gregarious under cedar (*Thuja occidentalis*), Wilderness State Park, Emmet County, Mich., Oct. 15, 1960.

MATERIAL STUDIED—MICHIGAN: Smith 63323.

OBSERVATIONS—No chemical reactions were obtained from the type variety so no comparisons on these characters can be made. Var. *fallax* differs from the type variety in the brown fibrils and squamules at the base of the stipe, and in the structure of the epicutis.

227

Hygrophorus avellaneifolius, sp. nov.

Pileus 3–5 cm latus, convexus demum obtusus deinde paene planus, glabrosus, glutinosus, "buckthorn brown" demum ochraceofulvus, interdum zonatus; desunt odor et gustus, immutabilis laesus; lamellae avellaneae, non insigniter mutantes, modice latae, subcrassae, adsunt una vel duae lamellularum ordines; stipes 4–6 cm longus, 9–18 mm crassus, infra constrictus, cinereo-pallidus, immutabilis tactus, siccus, nec pruinosus nec squamulosus; sporae 7–9 × 3.5–4.5 μ, ellipsoideae demum sub-oblongae. Specimen typicum in Herb. Univ. Mich. conservatum; lectum prope Seven Devils Mts., Idaho, Aug. 23, 1954, A. H. Smith 46584.

Pileus 3–5 cm broad, convex to obtuse when young, expanding to plane or nearly so, margin at first incurved, surface glabrous, glutinous, dark "buckthorn brown" to dingy dark-ochraceous tawny, gradually more or less clay color at least on the margin, at times zoned in age. Context brownish near the cuticle, grayish toward the stipe, unchanging when bruised; odor and taste none.

Lamellae broadly adnate to decurrent "avellaneous" or nearly so, not changing appreciably, moderately broad, subdistant, thickish, 1–2 tiers of lamellulae present.

Stipe 4–6 cm long, 9–18 mm thick at apex, narrowed below, solid, grayish-pallid, pale avellaneous within, unchanging when handled, lower portion drying more or less concolorous, dry at all stages, neither pruinose nor squamulose.

Spores 7–9 × 3.5–4.5 μ, ellipsoid to suboblong, smooth, yellowish in Melzer's reagent. Basidia 37–52 × 5–8 μ, 2- and 4-spored. Pleurocystidia and cheilocystidia none. Gill trama divergent, hyphae 3–7(8) μ broad. Cuticle a gelatinous zone (100–140 μ thick) of colorless hyphae, which are more or less erect, 2–3 μ broad, forming an ixotrichodermium. No hypodermium differentiated. Pileus trama of radial hyphae. Clamp connections on the cuticular hyphae.

HABIT, HABITAT, AND DISTRIBUTION—Gregarious, under conifers, Idaho, August–September.

MATERIAL STUDIED—IDAHO: Smith & Bigelow 46333, 46584 (type, from Pappoose Creek, Seven Devils Mts., Aug. 23, 1954), 47018, 47314, 53530.

OBSERVATIONS—This species is related both to *H. kauffmanii,* which has gills pinkish becoming brown to orange-cinnamon; and to *H. subpungens,* which has much paler colors. Our collections are from coniferous woods, Idaho, late summer and early autumn, all characterized by the avellaneous lamellae.

228
Hygrophorus bakerensis Sm. & Hes.
Lloydia 5: 88. 1942

Illustration:
Fig. 119.

Pileus 4–15 cm broad, obtuse when young, the margin incurved and cottony, in age becoming plane or nearly so, the margin sometimes elevated, margin whitish, disc "sudan brown" shading to "tawny-olive" or "amber brown" shading to "cinnamon-buff" toward the whitish margin (disc some shade of yellow-brown, paler toward the margin), surface glutinous when wet, merely viscid in age, appressed-fibrillose beneath the gluten. Context thick (1 cm near the stipe), tapering evenly to the margin, white, firm, unchanging when cut or bruised; odor heavy but fragrant and very characteristic, reminding one somewhat of almonds, taste perfectly mild.

Lamellae decurrent or soon becoming so, close to subdistant (56–88 reach the stipe, 2–3 tiers of short individuals), narrow but becoming broad in large caps (8–12 mm), creamy white, unchanging, edges even.

Stipe (4)7–14 cm long, 8–25 mm thick at the apex, white or pale pinkish buff, equal or narrowed downward, solid, firm, surface dry, cottony pruinose at apex when young, merely unpolished over all in age, not staining when bruised, in moist weather often beaded with hyaline drops of liquid.

Spores 7–9(10) × 4.5–5(6) μ, ellipsoid, smooth, yellowish in Melzer's reagent. Basidia 40–54 × 6–8 μ, 4-spored. Pleurocystidia and cheilocystidia none. Gill trama divergent, hyphae 4–8 μ broad. Pileus trama homogeneous. Cuticle, an ixotrichodermium, the gelatinous zone 100–250 μ thick, hyphae tangled as in *H. paludosus* but broader (4–8 μ), more conspicuously septate, and with an hypodermium of brownish, more or less parallel hyphae which are periclinally dis-

Fig. 119. *H. bakerensis*

posed. Pileus trama of radially disposed hyphae. Clamp connections present in the cuticle and gill trama.

HABIT, HABITAT, AND DISTRIBUTION—Scattered to gregarious, very common under conifers at elevations of 1000 to 4000 feet, Idaho, Washington, and Oregon, September–December.

MATERIAL STUDIED—IDAHO: Slipp 965; Smith 53621, 53883, 54056, 54391, 55016. OREGON: Gruber 708, 746; Sipe 766; Smith 18171, 19263, 20233, 26859, 26914. WASHINGTON: Bigelow 48887; Smith 16576, 17441, 17490 (type), 17528, 17695, 31351, 31631, 40179, 40954, 48740.

OBSERVATIONS—*H. bakerensis* bears the same relationship to *H. variicolor* that *H. piceus* bears to *H. eburneus;* it differs in having a dry stipe. Abundant material was collected under nearly all weather conditions, and the stipe was never found to be furnished with even a slight gelatinous veil. Dried specimens of both species appear identical. The caps have a dull red-brown color and the gills darken appreciably. The odor is easily missed if one has just a few fruiting bodies, but in large collections it is very distinct.

229
Hygrophorus laricinus Pk.
N.Y. State Mus. Mem. 3: 146. 1900

Illustration:
Peck, N. Y. State Mus. Mem. 3, pl. 51, figs. 1–12.

Pileus 12–25 mm broad, convex or nearly plane, reddish, tawny red or grayish red, viscid when moist. Context white, slightly yellowish under the adnate cuticle.

Lamellae adnate or slightly decurrent, distant, whitish.

Stipe 2.5–5 cm long, 4–6 mm thick, white, equal, firm, hollow.

Spores 7–8.5 × 3.5–4.5(5) μ, ellipsoid, smooth, yellowish in Melzer's reagent. Basidia 34–46 × 4–5 μ, 2- and 4-spored. Pleurocystidia and cheilocystidia none. Gill trama divergent, hyphae 3–8 μ broad. Cuticle of appressed, somewhat gelatinous hyphae. Clamps present.

HABIT, HABITAT, AND DISTRIBUTION—On soil, under tamarack trees, New York, October.

MATERIAL STUDIED—NEW YORK: Peck (type, from Davis Swamp, Warrensburg, October).

OBSERVATIONS—The description of microscopic characters given above is based on our study of the type.

Peck, in his original account, makes the following comments: "The larch *Hygrophorus* grows under tamarack trees in a gregarious manner and sometimes in great abundance. The cap in the young plant is very broadly conic or convex, but it expands with age till it is nearly or quite flat. It sometimes has a small central prominence or umbo. Under a lens the surface has a slightly silky appearance. The color is some shade of red and may be rusty red, tawny red or grayish red. The extreme margin is sometimes white, and in some specimens a reddish brown encircling line or narrow band is seen near the margin. Occasionally the margin is yellow. The flesh is white, slightly tinged with yellow under the inseparable cuticle. . . . The gills are white and not closely spaced side by side. They are broadly attached to the stipe or slightly decurrent on it. The stem is white, stuffed or hollow and rather short. It is 1 to 2 inches long and 2 to 3 lines thick. The cap rarely exceeds 1 inch in diameter. It has been found near Warrensburg only. It appears in October."

230

Hygrophorus subrufescens Pk.

N. Y. State Mus. Bull. 67: 23. 1903

> *Camarophyllus subrufescens* (Pk.) Murr., North Amer. Flora 9: 387.
> 1916.

Illustration:
> Peck, N. Y. State Mus. Bull. 67, pl. M., figs. 1–6.

Pileus about 2.5 cm broad, convex or nearly plane, pale pink or grayish red, dry, minutely floccose-squamulose. Context whitish faintly tinged pink; taste mild.

Lamellae decurrent, whitish, distant, medium-broad.

Stipe 4–8 cm long, 4–8 mm thick, white, equal, glabrous, solid.

Spores 5.5–8 × 4–5 μ, ellipsoid, smooth, non-amyloid. Basidia 52–68 × 6–8 μ, 2- and 4-spored. Pleurocystidia and cheilocystidia none. Gill trama divergent, hyphae 3–7 μ broad. Cuticle a trichodermium, the surface hyphae radial and more or less erect (not a palisade), septate, 3–10 μ broad, the terminal elements often cystidioid. No hypodermium differentiated. Pileus trama of radially disposed hyphae. Clamp connections present on the cuticle and gill trama.

HABIT, HABITAT, AND DISTRIBUTION—On soil, among fallen leaves, in woods, New York, August.

MATERIAL STUDIED—NEW YORK: Peck (type, from Port Jefferson, Suffolk County, August).

OBSERVATIONS—This species was thought by Peck (1903) to be a *Camarophyllus*, but the gill trama of the type is divergent. The description of microscopic characters given above is based on our study of the type.

231

Hygrophorus roseibrunneus Murr.

North Amer. Flora 9: 394. 1916

Illustrations:
Fig. 120.
Smith and Hesler, Lloydia 2, pl. 15.

Pileus 2–9 cm broad, convex, becoming broadly umbonate or sub-turbinate, sometimes flattened and with a decurved or elevated margin, "buff-pink," "light vinaceous cinnamon," to "vinaceous buff," at times, "pinkish buff" to "pale ochraceous salmon," at times "pinkish cinnamon," usually paler on the margin, subglutinous to viscid, appearing aggluti-nated-fibrillose near the cottony tomentose inrolled, even margin, somewhat streaked toward the disc. Context white, unchanging, soft,

Fig. 120. *H. roseibrunneus*

thick on disc, thin on margin; odor and taste mild.

Lamellae adnate, often becoming adnexed or decurrent, white, close to crowded, thin, moderately narrow, tapering either way, many short, edges even.

Stipe 3–9 cm long, 4–18 mm thick, white, equal or tapering slightly toward the base, stuffed-solid, dry or sublubricous when wet, densely pruinose to fibrillose-punctate, subglabrous toward the base, stuffed-solid, becoming yellow, base often curved. Partial veil slight, fugacious.

Spores (6)7–8(9) × 3.5–5 μ, ellipsoid, smooth, white in mass, yellow in Melzer's reagent. Basidia 36–58 × 5–8 μ, 2- and 4-spored. Pleurocystidia and cheilocystidia none. Gill trama divergent, hyphae 4–9 μ broad. Cuticle a broad (50–200 μ) gelatinous zone with repent, slender (3–4 μ) hyphae imbedded, an ixocutis. No hypodermium differentiated. Pileus trama of radially disposed hyphae. Clamp connections on the hyphae of the cuticle of the pileus and stipe, and the gill trama. The minute structure of the stipe is as follows: When viewed in longitudinal section, the stipe is seen to be composed of parallel to subparallel, vertically-disposed hyphae; when viewed in transverse section the component hyphae appear as a pseudoparenchyma. On the surface there are a few hyphae which may be regarded as epicuticular and which at times seem to be slightly subgelatinous; these hyphae, when wet, give a moist to sublubricous feel.

HABIT, HABITAT, AND DISTRIBUTION—Gregarious under oak, beech, fir, and pine, California, Michigan, Ohio, Tennessee, and Florida, October–March.

MATERIAL STUDIED—CALIFORNIA: Murrill 135 (type, from Jasper Ridge, near Stanford Univ., Jan. 11, 1912), 176, Feb. 8, 1912; Pusateri 100; Rea 114, 392, 1172; Smith, Santa Barbara, Feb. 21, 1939, 9234, 9432, 55639, 55988. FLORIDA: Hesler 21070. MICHIGAN: Kauffman, Ann Arbor, Oct. and Nov., 1926; Smith 6149, 15519. OHIO: Watters 189. TENNESSEE: Hesler 8643, 10110, 13020, 13171, 14142, 15212, 15531, 18865, 20065, 20628, 20759, 20761, 21616.

OBSERVATIONS—The following observations on the type have been recorded: Spores 6–8 × 3.5–4.5 μ, ellipsoid, smooth, pale yellow in Melzer's reagent. Basidia 28–43 × 4.5–5.5 μ. Pleurocystidia and cheilocystidia none. Gill trama divergent. Epicutis fibrillose. Clamps present on the cuticular hyphae.

Kauffman (1918) at first considered this to be a small form of *H. pudorinus*, but later in his notes indicated that he considered it distinct. The brownish to pinkish-brown virgate pilei with more or less tomentose margins when young, the stature, and the densely pruinose-punctate upper portion of the stipe all strongly point to a relationship with *H. arbustivus* Fr. sensu Quelét. The thin, close to crowded lamellae and possibly the dry stipe distinguish the American species, but a careful comparison of these two should be made.

232

Hygrophorus subisabellinus Sm. & Hes.
Lloydia 2: 40. 1939

Pileus 4.5–7 cm broad, hemispheric-convex then expanded, obtusely umbonate, "pinkish buff" to "cinnamon-buff," margin usually somewhat paler, glabrous but under a lens with a mat of closely woven fibrils, viscid, margin involute and downy. Context white, 10 mm thick on the disc, thin on the margin; odor and taste mild.

Lamellae adnate, becoming slightly notched, white, close, narrow, tapering at either end, edges even.

Stipe 4–9.5 cm long, 5–12 mm thick, white, dingy below (almost concolorous with pileus), dry, upper portion floccose-scabrous, flexuous, equal or tapering toward the base, solid.

Spores 5.5–7 × 3–4 μ, ellipsoid, smooth, very pale yellow in Melzer's reagent. Basidia 38–57 × 5–8 μ, 4-spored. Pleurocystidia and cheilocystidia none. Gill trama of divergent, hyphae 7–14 μ broad when fresh. Cuticle a gelatinous zone 75–200 μ thick, with slender, imbedded hyphae, the surface hyphae brownish, 3–5 μ broad, the subjacent hyphae colorless, some surface hyphae repent, many more or less erect and cystidioid forming more or less of a turf (not a palisade), an ixotrichodermium. No hypodermium differentiated. Pileus trama of radial hyphae. Clamp connections present on the hyphae of the cuticle.

Habit, Habitat, and Distribution—Gregarious on humus in mixed woods, Tennessee, February and May.

Material Studied—tennessee: Sharp 11427 (type, collected by A. J. Sharp, Knox County, May 26, 1938); Hesler (Feb. 22–29, 1939).

Observations—The mild odor and taste, the paler colors, and the mat of closely woven fibrils separate it readily from *H. tennesseensis*. It lacks the dense pruinose covering of the stipe of *H. roseibrunneus* as well as the pinkish tan colors of the dried specimens of the latter. The close gills and innate squamules over the upper part of the stipe distinguish it from *H. arbustivus* Fr. From pale forms of *H. pudorinus* it is readily distinguished in the dried condition by the lack of reddish-punctate points over the upper portion of the stipe. The dried pilei of the type of *H. subisabellinus* vary in color from "orange-cinnamon" to "cinnamon."

233
Hygrophorus leucophaeus Fr.
Epicr. Myc., p. 323. 1838

Illustration:
Lange, Flora Agar. Dan., pl. 163, fig. G.

Pileus 4–6.5 cm broad, campanulate-umbonate, remaining umbonate or becoming plane to slightly depressed, orange-buff to pale incarnate yellowish to pale yellowish brown, disc more brightly colored (reddish), surface slimy viscid, margin whitish and shimmering-fibrillose, occasionally creased, finally spreading, fleshy in the disc, margin thin-fleshed. Context pale buff, odor and taste not distinctive.

Lamellae adnate-decurrent, whitish to buff, 5–8 mm broad, distant. Stipe 5–10 cm long, 5–10(15) mm thick, pale buff to orange-buff, often narrowed below and rooting, straight or flexuous, fibrillose-rough, apex white-floccose, stuffed becoming hollow. Spores 6–8 × 4 μ, unequally elongate-elliptic. Basidia 26–42 × 6–7 μ.

HABIT, HABITAT, AND DISTRIBUTION—Only in beech woods, August and November, not rare, edible.

OBSERVATIONS—The description above is taken from Nüesch (1922). Notes following were made on Smith 52634, from Colorado, a collection which seems to be *H. leucophaeus:* Spores 5.5–8.5 × 3.5–4.5 μ, ellipsoid, smooth, yellowish in Melzer's reagent. Basidia 44–57 × 6–7 μ, mostly 4-spored, a few 2-spored. Pleurocystidia and cheilocystidia none. Gill trama divergent, hyphae 5–11 μ broad. Cuticle of the pileus a gelatinous zone 70–100 μ broad. Pileus trama of interwoven, more or less radial hyphae. Clamp connections present on the cuticular hyphae of both the pileus and stipe.

We believe that *H. leucophaeus* and *H. laurae* represent still another pair of similarly colored species in section *Hygrophorus* differing in the presence or absence of a universal veil. It must be remembered that *H. leucophaeus* is a species of the beech woods, and collections of what appear to be *H. discoideus* from under conifers but having a dry stipe should not be referred to *leucophaeus* without a very careful study.

234
Hygrophorus penarius Fr.
Epicr. Myc., p. 321. 1838

   Limacium penarium (Fr.) Wünsche, Die Pilze, p. 118. 1877.
Illustration:
   Lange, Agar. Flora Dan., pl. 164D.

Pileus 5–8 cm broad, convex, expanding to subumbonate, often viscid around the margin at first, soon dry, whitish to pinkish tan or stramineous on the center. Context white, compact; odor none, taste pleasant.

Lamellae slightly decurrent, pale, subdistant.

Stipe 4–6 cm long, 10–15 mm thick, white, apex white-furfuraceous, dry.

Spores 5–6(7.5) × 3.5–4 μ, ellipsoid, smooth, yellowish in Melzer's. Basidia 37–48 × 4–6 μ, 2- and 4-spored. Pleurocystidia and cheilocystidia none. Gill trama divergent, hyphae 4–5 μ (both narrow and broad hyphae abundant). Cuticle a gelatinous zone, 100–150 μ thick. Clamp connections on the cuticular hyphae.

HABIT, HABITAT, AND DISTRIBUTION—In woods, especially beech in Europe, Washington, September.

MATERIAL STUDIED—WASHINGTON: Kauffman, Rockdale, Sept. 18, 1915; Smith 62135. DENMARK: J. P. Jensen (Hesler 23970). FRANCE: Heinemann 1720.

OBSERVATIONS—We refer our collection (Smith 62135) to *H. penarius* with an awareness that descriptions of European material are not always in full agreement. Our collection agrees very well with a specimen from France, communicated by Dr. P. Heinemann, Gembloux, Belgium; and with a collection from Denmark, received from Mr. J. P. Jensen, Copenhagen. It is apparent that there is some variation in the width of the spores, and in the thickness of the stipe. Bresadola (1928) states that the odor is slightly butyric.

The problem is whether *H. penarius* and *H. sordidus* are actually different. A careful comparison of these two should be made with emphasis on chemical characters.

SERIES CAMAROPHYLLI (Fr.) stat. nov.

Section Camarophyllus Fr. (as "Tribus"). Epicr. Syst. Myc., p. 325. 1838.

Genus Camarophyllus (Fr.) Kummer, Führ. in Pilzk., p. 117. 1871.

Characters as given in the key to series, page 309.

Type species: *Hygrophorus camarophyllus* (Fr.) Kummer.

KEY TO SPECIES

1. Spores typically (10)11–13 μ or more long 2
1. Spores typically 6–10 μ long 5
   2. Pileus dry, fibrillose squamulose; stipe surface streaked with dark fibrils and dry .... 235. *H. inocybiformis*
   2. Pileus viscid when young and fresh 3

3. Odor strongly aromatic; stipe glabrous . . . . .236. *H. odoratus*
3. Odor not distinctive; stipe either fibrillose or colored or both in lower part 4
    4. Pileus glabrous; lamellae narrow; stipe brownish . .237. *H. nigridius*
    4. Pileus virgate; lamellae broad; stipe fibrillose below from a colored veil . . . . .238. *H. fuscoalboides*
5. Stipe apex distinctly scabrous-punctate, and the rough projections not staining gray 6
5. Stipe silky to pruinose above, or ornamentation may stain gray 7
    6. Spores 5.5–8 × 3–4.5 μ; growing under hardwoods . . . . .239. *H. albofuscus*
    6. Spores 8–11 × 5–6 μ; growing under spruce and fir . . . . (see 185. *H. pustulatus*, page 306; also 205. *H. pudorinus* var. sub- . . . .*cinereus*, page 338)
7. Odor of bitter almonds; stipe typically whitish at first . . . . .240. *H. agathosmus*
7. Not as above 8
    8. Odor of crushed flesh pungent-almost mephitic; growing under hardwoods . . . . .241. *H. camarophylloides*
    8. Not as above 9
9. Lamellae white to creamy but soon flushed delicate pink; stipe buffy brown; spores 5.5–8 × 4–5 μ . . . . .242. *H. calophyllus*
9. Lamellae white to grayish or some color other than pink 10
    10. Stipe 1–2.5 cm thick 11
    10. Stipe seldom over 10 mm thick 12
11. Pileus white to pallid to grayish or in age blackish . .199. *H. marzuolus*
11. Pileus fuscous to blackish when young . . . . .243. *H. camarophyllus*
    12. Lamellae avellaneous young 13
    12. Lamellae white or some color other than above 14
13. Pileus dark rusty brown .227. *H. avellaneifolius*
13. Pileus avellaneous to pinkish buff tinged gray . . . . .225. *H. cinereipallens* var. *cinereipallens*
    14. Spores 8–11 × 5–7 μ; stipe with yellowish stains . .244. *H. morrisii*
    14. Spores 7–9(10) × 4–5 μ; stipe not as above . . . . .see 183. *H. tephroleucus* var. *tephroleucus*, page 303; and . . . . .185. *H. pustulatus*, page 306

235

Hygrophorus inocybiformis Sm.
Mycologia 36: 246. 1944

Illustrations:
    Fig. 121; also 8f.

Pileus 3–6 cm broad, conic to obtuse when young, the margin in-curved and fringed with the remnants of a fibrillose veil, expanding to campanulate or obtusely umbonate, sometimes plane or the disc slightly depressed, dark gray ("drab") over all or with drab fibrils over a pallid background in age, dry, innately fibrillose to fibrillose-squamu-lose. Context whitish or tinged pallid gray near surface, unchanging

Fig. 121. *H. inocybiformis* (photograph by H. E. Bigelow)

when cut or bruised, thin except on the disc, soft and fragile; odor none, taste mild.

Lamellae short-decurrent or arcuate, pallid to grayish buff ("pale olive-buff"), broad, subdistant, rather thick and firm, edges even.

Stipe 3–6 cm long, 5–12 mm thick, streaked with dark grayish-brown fibrils, up to the zone left by the broken veil, white and glabrous to appressed silky toward the apex, white within, dry over all, subequal, the base at times slightly narrowed, solid, fleshy.

Spores 9–14 × (5)6–8 μ, ellipsoid, smooth, not amyloid. Basidia 62–84 × 10–12 μ, 4-spored. Pleurocystidia and cheilocystidia not differentiated. Gill trama divergent, hyphae 6–10 μ broad. Cuticle of chiefly radially arranged, repent, non-gelatinous hyphae, 10–15 μ broad, their contents smoky in color and the end-cells more or less pointed, often clustered to form squamules. No hypodermium differentiated. Pileus trama of radially disposed hyphae. Clamp connections abundant.

HABIT, HABITAT, AND DISTRIBUTION—Gregarious to scattered under spruce and balsam fir, California and Idaho, July–October.

MATERIAL STUDIED—CALIFORNIA: Gruber P17. IDAHO: Smith 15919 (type, collected by W. B. Gruber, from Lick Creek Summit, Idaho National Forest, Sept. 1943), 45462, 45995, 46078, 46086, 46759, 46730, 46897, 46959, 46981, 47010, 47067, 47139, 54760, 59327, 59882, 60104, 60728; Bigelow 47162; Smith & Bigelow 46729, 46930; Helen V. Smith, Aug. 1945.

OBSERVATIONS—Because of its fibrillose to squamulose pileus this fungus has somewhat the stature and appearance of an *Inocybe* or of a small species of the *Tricholoma terreum* group. Actually, the fungus is closely related to *H. pustulatus*, but is readily distinguished by its spores and by the fibrillose veil. *H. pustulatus* was found in the same area in 1943 and appeared to have a perfectly dry stipe. Previously (Smith, 1937b) reported a collection of *H. pustulatus* from California with a thin gelatinous universal veil. The latter was found during very wet weather, whereas the Idaho collection was made during dry weather. Since large numbers of carpophores were not available for study in either instance, the discrepancy is merely pointed out here in the hope that any who find *H. pustulatus* will pay particular attention to the presence or absence of a gelatinous veil. *H. olivaceoalbus* has both a glutinous sheath and one of fuscous fibrils beneath it. Consequently, *H. inocybiformis* might be considered closely related to it.

One collection (Smith 60104), when found, was very pale becoming gray, and staining ochraceous on the margin. Smith 54760 is a slender form, but it has the large spores typical of the species.

236
Hygrophorus odoratus Sm. & Hes.
Sydowia 8: 310. 1954

Illustration:
Fig. 122.

Pileus 2–4 cm broad, obtuse to broadly convex, expanding to almost plane or disc slightly depressed and margin arched, dark ashy gray over the disc, paler gray to pallid along the margin, when old with a faint ochraceous tinge pervading throughout, surface viscid, fibrillose-streaked to merely matted-fibrillose beneath the viscidity. Context soft, pallid; odor strongly aromatic (somewhat as in *H. agathosmus*), taste insipid. Lamellae decurrent, whitish when young, more creamy in age, distant, broad, unchanging when bruised.

Stipe 4–8 cm long, 3–6 mm thick at apex, pallid at first, unchanging when bruised but in drying developing an over all faint ochraceous tinge, equal or in some narrowed below, dry, glabrous, apex faintly silky.

Spores 11–14 × 6.5–8 μ, ovoid to broadly ellipsoid, smooth, hyaline, hyaline to yellowish in Melzer's reagent. Basidia 4-spored, 40–62 × 8–10 μ. Pleurocystidia and cheilocystidia not seen. Gill trama divergent, hyphae 5–8 μ broad. Cuticle a gelatinous zone, 180–300 μ broad, the hyphae repent, radially disposed, interwoven, 2.5–4 μ broad, an ixocutis (similar to *H. agathosmus*). Pileus trama chiefly radial. Clamp connections present in the gill trama and cuticular hyphae.

HABIT, HABITAT, AND DISTRIBUTION—Scattered on moist earth under conifers, Idaho and Oregon, October.

Material Studied—idaho: Smith 54516, 54581, 54605, 54781, 54945, 54997, 55136, 55187. oregon: Smith 28300, 28387 (type, from Paradise Park Trail, Mt. Hood, Oct. 28, 1957).

Observations—In the field this fungus was mistaken for slender specimens of *H. agathosmus,* but the large spores on 4-spored basidia make such a disposition untenable. *Hygrophorus lucandi* Gill. is usually described as having the field characters of *H. odoratus,* and one is tempted so to designate our collections. However, we have no reliable information on the spore size of Gillet's species and deem it best not to risk confusing a distinct American species with a European species which European authors have regarded as a synonym of *H. agathosmus.* Actually, *H. odoratus* appears to be related to *H. pacificus* Sm. & Hes., but differs in the gray pileus and faint tinge of yellow which is evident in age. In spore size, odor, and dry stipes they are similar. *H. hyacinthinus* Quél. appears to be closely related by virtue of its pale gray to white cap, and with spores 9–11.5 × 5–6 μ. The apex of its stipe is said to be silky. In a collection of Smith (54581) identified as *H. odorus* because of its pale coloration, the spores measure 9–11.5 × 5.6 μ.

Fig. 122.
H. odoratus

237

Hygrophorus nigridius Pk.

Torrey Bot. Club Bull. 22: 211. 1895

Pileus 2.5–5 cm broad, fleshy, convex, obtuse or subumbonate, glabrous, viscid, grayish brown, often a little darker in the center. Context white.

Lamellae decurrent, distant, rather narrow, white.

Stipe 2.5–5 cm long, 4–8 mm thick, rather slender, dry, solid, brownish, white at the top.

Spores (9)10–13 × (5.5)6–8 μ, ellipsoid, smooth, pale yellow in Melzer's reagent. Basidia 48–65 × 7–12 μ, 2- and 4-spored, sterigmata 4–10 μ long, stout. Pleurocystidia and cheilocystidia none. Gill trama divergent, hyphae 6–9 μ broad. Cuticle of radial, narrow (2.5–5 μ), gelatinous hyphae. No hypodermium differentiated. Clamp connections present on the cuticle, not abundant.

HABIT, HABITAT, AND DISTRIBUTION—In pine and fir woods, Prince Edward's Island, Canada, October–November.

MATERIAL STUDIED—CANADA: Peck (type, from Prince Edward's Island, collected by J. MacSwain, October and November).

OBSERVATIONS—Although the macroscopic characters given above are taken from Peck's account, the microscopic characters are based on our study of the type.

This species appears related to *H. morrisii* Pk. which, however, is characterized by a conic-umbonate pileus, adnate to subdecurrent, broad gills, and dingy-yellow stains at the base or nearly over all the stipe.

238

Hygrophorus fuscoalboides, sp. nov.

Pileus 5–7 cm latus, convexus demum planus, cinereus, viscidus; lamellae subdecurrentes, albae, subdistantes, latae; stipes 3.5–5 cm longus, 8–10 mm crassus, cinereus, siccus, fibrillosus; sporae 9–13 × 5.5–7 μ. Specimen typicum in Herb. Univ. Mich. conservatum; lectum prope Cape Horn Summit, Idaho, Aug. 25, 1954, Smith et Bigelow 46726.

Pileus 5–7 cm broad, conic, becoming more or less plane, gray, streaked, viscid. Context medium thick on the disc, thin on the margin; odor slight, taste mild.

Lamellae subdecurrent, white, subdistant, broad.

Stipe 3.5–5 cm long, 8–10 mm thick (apex), 20 mm (at base when clavate), clavate or equal, gray, white above, with a thin coating of gray fibrils below the line where the veil breaks, dry, glutinous in the button stage around the base from the gluten of the pileus.

Spores 9–13 × 5.5–7 μ, ellipsoid, smooth, yellowish in Melzer's reagent. Basidia 48–62 × 7–10 μ, 4-spored. Pleurocystidia and cheilocystidia none. Gill trama divergent, hyphae 4–10 μ broad. Cuticle a gelatinous zone, 120–200 μ thick, hyphae fuscous, 4–7 μ broad. No hypodermium differentiated. Pileus trama of interwoven, radially disposed hyphae.

HABIT, HABITAT, AND DISTRIBUTION—On soil, in woods, Idaho, August.

MATERIAL STUDIED—IDAHO: Smith & Bigelow 46726 (type, from Cape Horn Summit, Aug. 25, 1954); Smith 46904.

OBSERVATIONS—This species is distinguished from *H. fuscoalbus* by its dry stipe. It is closest to *H. limacinus* variety *intermedius* but lacks a gelatinous coating over the colored fibrils of the stipe.

239
Hygrophorus albofuscus, sp. nov.

> *Hygrophorus fuscoalbus* var. *occidentalis* Kauff., Agar. Mich., p. 187. 1918.

Pileus 2–5 cm latus, extensus convexus deinde planus vel depressus, livido-cinero-fuscus, demum albofuscus, nonnumquam disco subniger, viscidus, glaber, margine involutus et floccosus; lamellae adnatae demum decurrentes, cremeo-albae, subdistantes demum arctae, angustae; stipes 3–7 cm longus, 4–6 mm crassus, albus vel pallidus, aequalis vel deorsum se attenuans, siccus, apice floccoso-scabrosus, aliis locis floccoso-pruinosus, glabrescens; sporae 5.5–8 × 3–4.5 μ, ellipsoideae. Specimen typicum in Herb. Univ. Mich. conservatum; lectum Ann Arbor, Mich., Aug. 23, 1912, C. H. Kauffman.

Pileus 2–5 cm broad, convex-expanded, at length plane or depressed, livid grayish brown to brownish-ashy, sometimes blackish on disc, viscid when moist, glabrous, becoming fragile, margin at first involute and floccose-downy, even. Context white, rather thin, rather soft; odor and taste mild.

Lamellae adnate to decurrent, creamy white, subdistant to close, rather narrow venose, interspaces.

Stipe 3–7 cm long, 4–6 mm thick (rarely 10–12 mm), slender, rarely stout, white or pallid, equal or tapering downward, dry solid, straight, or curved at base, sometimes flexuous, rather fragile, apex floccose-pruinose, glabrescent.

Spores 5.5–8 × 3–4.5 μ, ellipsoid, smooth, colorless or only faintly yellowish in Melzer's reagent. Basidia 36–43 × 6–7 μ, 4-spored. Pleuro-cystidia and cheilocystidia none. Gill trama divergent, hyphae 3–6 μ broad. Cuticle of tangled, gelatinous hyphae, more or less erect, narrow (2–4 μ). No hypodermium differentiated. Pileus trama of parallel hyphae which are radially disposed. Clamp connections on the cuticular hyphae.

HABIT, HABITAT, AND DISTRIBUTION—Gregarious or subcaespitose, on the ground in oak woods, Michigan, October.

MATERIAL STUDIED—MICHIGAN: Kauffman (type, near Ann Arbor, Aug. 23, 1912); Smith 15517.

OBSERVATIONS—Kauffman commented as follows on this fungus in his unpublished notes: "Distinguished from its relatives by a rather slender, dry stem which is distinctly white floccose-dotted, and by the creamy gills and the spores. H. lividoalbus Fr., it is agreed, has distinctly larger spores. The European species, H. fuscoalbus, is generally said to grow in conifer forests. From H. fuscoalbus (sensu Ricken) it differs by the absence of the glutinous sheath on the stem.

"The change in color of the pileus during development and on drying out is rather marked. The pileus, in a very fresh or young condition (wet weather) is 'brownish olive' (R) or darker on the disc and 'olive-ochre' toward the margin. Under these conditions it is glutinous, shining and even. It dries out rapidly on exposure to a dryer atmosphere and the surface then becomes much paler, with shades of gray and with a dull lustre. The partial veil is very evanescent."

This species by virtue of its dry stipe and small spores is amply distinct from H. fuscoalbus Fr.

240
Hygrophorus agathosmus Fr.
Epicr. Syst. Myc., p. 325. 1838

> Agaricus agathosmus Fr., Obs. Myc. 1: 16. 1815.
> Agaricus cerasinus Berk., in Smith Engl. Fl. 5²: 12. 1836.
> Hygrophorus cerasinus (Berk.) Fr., Hymen. Eur., p. 410. 1874.

Illustrations:
> Fig. 123.
> Bresadola, Icon. Myc., tab. 319.
> Juillard-Hartmann, Icon. Champ., pl. 50, fig. 2.
> Lange, Flora Agar. Dan. 5, pl. 163F.
> Smith and Hesler, Lloydia 2, pl. 22.

Pileus (3)4–8(11) cm broad, convex to obtuse with an inrolled margin, becoming plane or with the disc slightly depressed in age, sometimes remaining slightly umbonate, evenly "light drab" or a dull ashy gray, glutinous to viscid, glabrous, margin very faintly tomentose,

Fig. 123. *H. agathosmus*

scarcely fading, sometimes with watery zones or spots near the margin. Context soft, whitish or watery gray; odor fragrant and very pronounced, of bitter almonds (occasionally the odor weak), taste mild.

Lamellae adnate, becoming adnate-decurrent, white becoming sordid grayish in age, close to distant (40–50 reach the stipe), moderately narrow, rather thin.

Stipe 4–8(10–16) cm long, 6–14(19–25) mm thick, whitish at first, pale ashy in age, equal or narrowed toward the base, solid, dry or moist but no gelatinous universal veil present, evenly fibrillose pruinose over all at first, glabrescent.

Spores (7)8–10.5 × 4.5–5.5 μ, ellipsoid, smooth, yellowish in Melzer's reagent. Basidia 48–65 × 6–8 μ, 4-spored. Pleurocystidia and cheilocystidia none. Gill trama divergent, hyphae 5–10 μ broad. Cuticle a broad (175–350 μ), gelatinous zone, with loosely interwoven, slender (1.5–4 μ), sparingly septate hyphae, an ixocutis, the surface hyphae fuscous. No hypodermium differentiated. Pileus trama of loosely interwoven hyphae which are radially disposed. Clamp connections found on the hyphae of the gill trama; none found in pileus trama nor in cuticle.

HABIT, HABITAT, AND DISTRIBUTION—Scattered under spruce and pine and in mixed woods, Colorado, Idaho, Oregon, Washington, Wyoming, California, Michigan, Maryland, and New Jersey, August–January; also Europe, and Africa (Bresadola, 1928).

MATERIAL STUDIED—CALIFORNIA: Smith 3891, 8519, 8580, 8720, 8790, 8952, 43647, 52032, 52488, 56381, 56477, 56679, 56733, 56748; Smith & Parks 3651. COLORADO: Kauffman, Leal, Aug. 18, 1917; Smith 51892, 52591, 52807, 52827. IDAHO: Smith 8912, 9117, 9320, 23586, 35605, 46532, 53497, 53939, 54803; Syce 594. MARYLAND: Kelly 325, 326. MICHIGAN: Smith 42911, 43827, 43830, 43884, 43983, 50908. NEW JERSEY: Ellis 907, N. A. Fungi (as *H. cerasinus*). OREGON: Smith 3406, 8156, 9320, 19186, 24115, 24116, 26653, 55476. WASHINGTON: Cooke 18683; Smith 3302, 3356, 17628, 24817. WYOMING: Kanouse & Kauffman, Medicine Bow Mts., Sept. 5, 1923. BAVARIA: Singer, München, 1932. NETHERLANDS: Bas 1105. DENMARK: J. P. Jensen (Hesler 23958). BELGIUM: Heinemann 2107.

OBSERVATIONS—Although in the western United States it has been found in dense conifer forests, this species is particularly abundant in pastures around scattered spruce trees. The large specimens collected in southern Oregon with caps 11 cm broad, and stipes 16 cm long and 2.5 cm thick were most unusual, but are nothing more than growth forms, and are not taxonomically significant. One must be continually on guard when collecting in this area not to allow oversized specimens to influence his concept of any species. The odor is variously described as of celery, anise, or bitter almonds. In some of our collections the odor was weak. In Europe the stipe is described as having pallid, yellowish, or fuscescent squamules. In California, a pale form (Smith 56477) was found. In it, the pileus was pallid, the disc cinereous, and the surface faintly zonate. A slender form (Smith 52032), also from California, has been collected.

Following the observations of Dennis (1948), we have listed *H. cerasinus* as a synonym of *H. agathosmus*. He studied the type of *H. cerasinus* and states that there is no adequate grounds for separating the two species. Nüesch (1922) also lists *H. cerasinus* as a synonym.

241

Hygrophorus camarophylloides, sp. nov.

Pileus 3–6 cm latus, turbinatus, glaber, viscidus, fuscus vel atrobrunneus; odor subpungens; lamellae confertae, angustae, decurrentes, crassae, albidae demum cinereae vel pallide brunneae; stipes 3–6 cm longus, 10–15 mm crassus, solidus, subaequalis subfuscus, siccus, glaber; sporae 6.5–8 × 4.5–5 μ, ellipsoideae. Specimen typicum prope Milford, Mich., Nov. 16, 1951, legit Ruth Dawson (Smith 60807), in Herb. Univ. Mich. conservatum.

Pileus 3–6 cm broad, turbinate, color dark gray to bluish-fuscous or finally blackish brown ("mummy brown"), surface glabrous and moist, slightly viscid from a thin gelatinous pellicle, in age finally slightly squamulose, margin at times rimose in age. Context gray to pallid; odor of crushed flesh and the taste strong and resembling that of *Clitocybe nebularis* (Fr.) Quél.

Lamellae decurrent, whitish becoming cinereous, finally brownish in age, thick, waxy, close, narrow to moderately broad, intervenose.

Stipe 3–6 cm long, 10–15 mm thick, concolor with pileus above, paler (pallid) at the base, equal to narrowed downward, surface dry, glabrous, naked, solid.

Spores 6.5–8 × 4.5–5 μ, ellipsoid, hyaline. Basidia 36–47 × 6–7 μ, 4-spored, flexuous, hyaline in KOH. Pleurocystidia and cheilocystidia none. Gill trama of divergent hyphae. Pileus with a gelatinous epicutis of appressed narrow hyphae. Clamp connections present.

HABIT, HABITAT, AND DISTRIBUTION—Scattered on low ground at edge of a swamp in a beech-maple forest (no conifers near by, larch 50 yards away), Michigan, November.

MATERIAL STUDIED—MICHIGAN: Smith 60807 (type, from Proud Lake Recreation Area, near Milford, collected by Ruth Dawson, Nov. 16, 1958).

OBSERVATIONS—This species is obviously a segregate of *Hygrophorus camarophyllus*, but we have never found the latter to have the odor and taste of *Clitocybe nebularis* and to grow under hardwoods.

242
Hygrophorus calophyllus Karst.
Bidr. Finl. Nat. Folk 3: 375. 1876

Hygrophorus camarophyllus var. *calophyllus* (Karst.) Konr. & Maubl., Icon. Selectae Fung. 6: 431. 1924–1937.
Hygrophorus caprinus var. *calophyllus* (Karst.) Quél., Ench. Fung., p. 51. 1886.

Illustrations:
Fig. 124.
Bresadola, Icon. Myc., tab. 323.

Pileus 5–11 cm broad, convex, obtuse or with a low umbo and a decurved margin, nearly flat in age, glutinous to viscid, glabrous beneath the gluten, "raw umber," "dresden brown" or "olive brown" over all or slightly paler near the margin. Context thick, whitish, unchanging, odor faintly fragrant, taste mild.

Lamellae evenly flushed pale pink ("pale pinkish buff") or at times white (in Smith 59650, pale salmon when young), not spotted, subdistant to distant, narrow, decurrent.

Stipe 6–10(12) cm long, 10–15 mm thick, equal or slightly enlarged above, solid, flesh whitish and unchanging, surface dry, glabrous and unpolished or the apex slightly fibrillose pruinose, "buffy brown" up to an abruptly paler zone at the line of gill attachment, somewhat uneven below, the basal buried portion gray and watery but not viscid.

Spores 5.5–8 × 4–5 μ, ellipsoid, smooth, pale yellowish in Melzer's reagent. Basidia 40–60 × 6–8 μ, sterigmata stout, 2- and 4-spored. Pleurocystidia and cheilocystidia none. Gill trama divergent, hyphae 3–7 μ broad. Cuticle a well-defined, gelatinous zone, 100–200 μ thick, of tangled, fuscous, narrow (2–4 μ) hyphae, at times many hyphae more or less erect, almost forming a palisade (an ixotrichodermium). Hypo-

Fig. 124. *H. calophyllus*

dermium rather distinct. Pileus trama of hyphae which are disposed radially. Clamp connections present on the cuticular and gill trama hyphae.

HABIT, HABITAT, AND DISTRIBUTION—Singly, under fir and pine, California, Colorado, Idaho, Oregon, and Washington, Canada; also Europe, August–November.

MATERIAL STUDIED—CALIFORNIA: Smith 8326, 8632, 8665, 9445. COLORADO: Kauffman, Tolland, Aug. 24 and Sept. 4, 1920. IDAHO: Smith 8209, 27492, 28117, 53561, 59650, 60016, 60071. WASHINGTON: Smith 17622, 17808, 49181. CANADA: (Quebec) Jackson, Oct. 1952. AUSTRIA: Moser, Oct. 10, 1948 (Hesler 24127).

OBSERVATIONS—This species has been made a variety of *H. caprinus* by some authors, but is now generally regarded as distinct. Both *H. calophyllus* and *H. camarophyllus*, because of their divergent gill trama, are properly included in the section *Hygrophorus*.

Although the lamellae color varies from pinkish or rosy to white, the pileus colors are generally umber to gray-brown. However, Smith has one collection, No. 59650, from Idaho in which a salmon tint was observed in the young pileus, the flesh, and young lamellae.

243

Hygrophorus camarophyllus (Fr.) Dumée, Grandjean, et Marie
Bull. Soc. Mycol. France 28: 292. 1912

> *Agaricus camarophyllus* Fr., Syst. Myc. 1: 99. 1821.
> *Hygrophorus caprinus* Fr., Epicr. Syst. Myc., p. 326. 1836.
> *Camarophyllus caprinus* (Fr.) Karsten, Hattsvamp., p. 224. 1879.
> *Limacium caprinum* (Fr.) Singer, Ann. Myc. 34: 327. 1936 (*L. caprinum* Kühner).
> *Hygrophorus burnhami* Pk., N. Y. State Mus. Bull. 116: 56. 1907.
> *Camarophyllus burnhami* (Pk.) Murr., North Amer. Flora 9: 389. 1916.

Illustrations:
> Fig. 125.
> Bresadola, Icon. Myc., tab. 324 (as *H. caprinus*).
> Pomerleau, Mushrooms of Eastern Canada and the U. S., fig. 18A (as *H. caprinus*).
> Ricken, Die Blätterp., pl. 7, fig. 4 (as *H. caprinus*).
> Smith, Mushrooms in their Natural Habitats, Reel 11, No. 76.
> Smith and Hesler, Lloydia 2, pl. 23 (as *H. caprinus*).

Pileus 4–7(13) cm broad, obtuse, convex to turbinate, occasionally either plane or with a slight umbo, evenly "fuscous" over all, surface subviscid when wet, soon dry, appearing virgate with lighter and darker streaks or patches but glabrous under a lens, margin downy pubescent to pruinose at first. Context thick, white, fragile; odor very slight, reminding one of coal tar, taste mild.

Lamellae adnate, becoming short decurrent, whitish or faintly tinged cinereous, close, sometimes subdistant, moderately broad, thin.

Stipe 3–8(13) cm long, 10–20 mm thick, pallid fuscous or concolorous with the pileus, color ceasing abruptly at the line of gill attachment, equal or tapering downward, solid, flesh pale cinereous, dry over all, appressed silky or faintly pruinose above, nearly glabrous toward the base.

Spores 7–9 × 4–5 μ, ellipsoid to subellipsoid or drop-shaped, hyaline, smooth, non-amyloid. Basidia 44–50 × 7–8 μ, 2- and 4-spored. Pleurocystidia and cheilocystidia none. Gill trama of divergent hyphae, 5–10 μ broad. Cuticle a cutis of repent (a few more or less erect), medium broad hyphae (3–7 μ), non-gelatinous, not strikingly differentiated from the pileus trama. No hypodermium differentiated. Pileus trama of subparallel hyphae disposed radially. Clamp connections on the cuticular hyphae.

HABIT, HABITAT, AND DISTRIBUTION—Gregarious under pine and spruce, Canada, Maine, Massachusetts, New York, Michigan, Idaho, Wyoming, Oregon, Washington; also Europe; July–November.

MATERIAL STUDIED—IDAHO: Smith 53306, 53329, 53892, 54055, 55185, 60208. MAINE: Parlin 15487. MASSACHUSETTS: Boston Myc. Club 1448. MICHIGAN: Smith 3879A, 38535, 51029, 58217. NEW YORK: Kauffman, Ithaca, Oct. 24, 1902; Peck (type of *H. burnhami*, West Fort Ann, Washington Co.). OREGON: Gruber 683, Mt. Hood National Park, Oct. 15, 1942; Smith 18158, 19990, 26813, 27195. WASHINGTON: Smith 3263, 17493, 17601, 17694, 17919, 17920, 17980, 28843, 48631; Smith & Bigelow 48778, 49130. WYOMING: Smith 34455; Thiers 99. CANADA: (British Columbia) Beebe, Vancouver Island, Nov. 30, 1942; (Ontario) Cain 30812; Jackson & Smith 4800. FRANCE: Tourillon, Oct. 1938. SPAIN: Salardir, Sept. 1936.

OBSERVATIONS—The virgate almost dry pileus and the gills which become grayish in age clearly distinguish it from the closely related but distinct *H. calophyllus* Karst. The latter is glutinous when wet, and distinctly viscid at other times besides being evenly colored, having white to pale-pink gills and mild taste. There was a slight difference in the spore size as well, but it does not appear to be significant.

Notes on the type of *H. burnhami* Pk.: Spores 7.5–10 × 4.5–5.5 μ, ellipsoid, smooth, pale yellowish in Melzer's reagent. Basidia 44–55 × 5–7 μ, 4-spored. Pleurocystidia and cheilocystidia none. Gill trama divergent, hyphae narrow, 3–5 μ broad. Cuticle of appressed hyphae; no gelatinous pellicle. Clamps present on the cuticular hyphae. A note in the box (marked Type), signed by Dearness, Jan. 1931, states that he fails to find any specific difference in the micro-features of this and the

Fig. 125. *H. camarophyllus*

plant that Kauffman, Atkinson, and Peck have labeled *Hygrophorus caprinus*. Smith and Hesler (1942, p. 85) state that it is properly referred to *H. caprinus*, which, along with *H. burnhami*, is a synonym of *H. camarophyllus*. Murrill (1922) has reported it from Massachusetts. The difference in width of the hyphae of the gill trama between *H. burnhami* and *H. camarophyllus* we do not regard as significant; it could easily be due to the type of *H. burnhami* being immature as far as hyphal expansion is concerned.

244
Hygrophorus morrisii Pk.
Torrey Bot. Club Bull. 26: 64. 1899

Illustration:
    Fig. 126.

Pileus 1.5–4(5) cm broad, convex, obtusely conic, at times more or less umbonate, expanding plane with a conic umbo, at first pallid or grayish brown or dark brown over all, developing an obscure yellowish

Fig. 126.
H. morrisii

tone in places, glabrous, viscid to glutinous, pellicle separable. Context whitish, becoming cinereous at least under the cuticle; odor and taste not distinctive.

Lamellae adnate then short-decurrent, white, yellowish near cap in one, grayish there in an old one, not staining appreciably, subdistant, broad, edges often eroded or uneven.

Stipe 3–9(11) cm long, 3–9 mm thick, white, pallid, or brownish, in age with dingy-yellow stains below or nearly to apex, equal or narrowed below, solid, furfuraceous-flocculent, straight or flexuous.

Spores 8–11 × 5–7 μ, ellipsoid, smooth, yellowish in Melzer's reagent. Basidia 44–62(74) × 6–9 μ, 2- and 4-spored. Pleurocystidia and cheilocystidia none. Gill trama divergent, hyphae 5–9(12) μ broad. Cuticle a broad zone, 100–300 μ thick, of gelatinous, repent, hyphae, which are 2–4 μ broad. No hypodermium differentiated. Clamp connections present on the cuticular hyphae. Surface hyphae of stipe gelatinous and with clamp connections.

Habit, Habitat, and Distribution—On soil, under conifers, Massachusetts, Michigan, Idaho, California, and Canada (Quebec), November–December.

Material Studied—california: Smith 56616. idaho: Smith 53937, 59445. massachusetts: Davis, Stow, Oct. 14, 1911; Morris (type, from Waltham, Nov. 1898), also Nov. 1899 and 1906; Kauffman 711. michigan: Bailey 94; Smith 60800. canada: (Quebec) Smith 61861.

Observations—The description of microscopic characters above is based on our study of the type. The description of macroscopic characters above is adapted from Peck's original account. His comments follow: "This species is closely related to *H. pustulatus* Fr., but differs from it in the entire absence of pustules or papillae from the uniformly colored pileus and in having a solid stem which, though somewhat scurfy, is not rough or scabrous with black points. The presence of concolorous papillae on the pileus and of black points on the stem of *H. pustulatus* is given by Fries special emphasis in his description of this species. In Icones he describes the lamellae as very entire (*integerrimae*) which character is not applicable to our plant. These differences seem to me too important to be disregarded and I take pleasure in dedicating this interesting American species to Mr. George F. Morris, who sent me numerous specimens of it in fine condition."

Murrill (1916) reduced *H. morrisii* to synonomy with *H. hypothejus,* but it seems closer to *H. tephroleucus.* Spore size suggests that *H. morrisii* and *H. fuscoalbus* are also related.

Bibliography

ATKINSON, G. F. 1900. Mushrooms, Edible, Poisonous, etc., pp. 1–275.

———. 1902. Preliminary notes on some new species of fungi. Jour. Mycol. 8:110–119.

BATAILLE, FREDERIC. 1910. Flore monographique des Hygrophores. Mem. Soc. d'Emulation du Doubs. 4(1909):131–191.

———. 1912. Deux champignons comestibles peu connus. Bull. Trimestr. Soc. Mycol. France 28:131–135.

———. 1948. Les reactions macrochimiques chez les champignons, suivies d'indications sur la morphologie des spores. Bull. Trimestr. Soc. Mycol. France 63(Supple.):1–172.

BAUCH, ROBERT. 1926. Untersuchungen uber zweisporige Hymenomyceten. I. Haploide parthenogenesis bei Camarophyllus virgineus. Zeitschr. Bot. 18(7):337–387. 2 pl., 7 fig.

BECKER, G. 1954. Un nouvel Hygrophore: Hygrophorus (Limacium) barbatulus. Schweiz. Zeitschr. für Pilzkunde 32:91–92.

BEELI, M. 1928–1933. Contribution a l'etude de la flore mycologique du Congo belge. Fungi Goossensiana, 5, 6, 7, 8, 9, 10. Bull. Soc. Roy. Bot. Belgique 60(2):153–171. 3 pl.; 61(1):78–103. 4 pl. 1928; 62(1):56–66. 1 pl. 1929; 63(2):100–109. 3 pl. 1931; 64(2):206–219. 3 pl. 1932; 66(1):14–28. 3 pl.

BERKELEY, M. J. 1836. *In* Smith's The English Flora 52:1–386; 1–32.

———. 1860. Outlines of British Fungology, pp. 1–442.

——— AND M. A. CURTIS. 1859. Centuries of North American fungi. Ann. Mag. Nat. Hist. III. (4):284–296.

——— AND C. E. BROOME. 1871. The fungi of Ceylon. Jour. Linn. Soc. Bot. 11:494–567.

BIGELOW, HOWARD E. 1959. Interesting fungi from Massachusetts. Rhodora 61:127–136.

——— AND MARGARET E. BARR. 1960. Contributions to the fungus flora of northeastern North America. Rhodora 62:186–198.

BÖHME, CHR. FR. 1942. Norsk Soppbok, pp. 5–125. J. W. Cappelens Forlag, Oslo.

BOHUS, G. 1939. De Limacio arbustivo et var. mesotephro. Borbasia 1(3/7):91–93. 1 pl., 2 fig.

BOUDIER, J. L. E. 1911. Icones Mycologicae, ou iconographie des champignons de France.

BREBINAUD, P. 1931. Révision de quelques Hyménomycètes. Bull. Trimestr. Soc. Mycol. France 45(1):89–105.

BRESADOLA, G. 1881–1900. Fungi tridentini novi, vel nondum delineati Vols. 1 & 2.

———. 1899. I Funghi Mangerecci e Velenosi dell'Europa Media, pp. 1–136. Pls. 1–112.

———. 1928. Iconographia Mycologica. 7:Tab. 301–350; 8:Tab. 351–400.

BRITZELMAYER, M. 1899. Revision der Diagnosen zu den von M. Britzelmayer aufgestellten Hymenomyceten-Arten. IV. Folge. Botanisches Centralblatt 80:116–126.

CEJP, KAREL. 1958. Houby. Vol. I (495 pages) and II (407 pages). Czechoslovakian Academy of Science. Prague.

CHRISTIANSEN, M. P. 1941. Studies in the larger fungi of Iceland. Botany of Iceland.

CLEMENTS, F. E. 1893. *Mycena acuto-conica* Clements, Nebr. Bot. Survey 2:38.

COKER, W. C. 1929. Notes on Fungi. Elisha Mitchell Sci. Soc. Jour. 45:164–178.

———. 1948. Notes on some higher fungi. Elisha Mitchell Sci. Soc. Jour. 64:135–146. 10 pl.

COOKE, M. C. 1881–1891. Illustrations of British Fungi (Hymenomycetes), plates 1–1198.

COOKE, WILLIAM BRIDGE. 1955. Fungi of Mount Shasta. Sydowia 9:94–215.

CORNER, E. J. H. 1934. An evolutionary study in agarics: *Collybia apalosarca* and the veils. Trans. Brit. Mycol. Soc. 19:39–88.

———. 1936. Hygrophorus with dimorphous basidiospores. Trans. Brit. Mycol. Soc. 20:157–184. 8 fig.

———. 1947. Variation in size and shape of spores, basidia and cystidia in Basidiomycetes. New Phytol. 46:195–228. 4 fig.

DENNIS, R. W. G. 1948. Some little-known British species of Agaricaceae. Trans. Brit. Mycol. Soc. 31:191–209.

———. 1953. Some West Indian collections referred to Hygrophorus Fr. Kew Bull. 2:253–267.

———. 1961. Fungi venezuelani: IV. Kew Bull. 15:67–156.

———, P. D. ORTON, AND F. B. HORA. 1960. New check list of British agarics and boleti. Trans. Brit. Mycol. Soc. (Vol. 43) Suppl., pp. 1–225.

DODGE, C. W. 1927. *Hygrophorus constans* of central Europe. Rhodora 29:238–239.

DONK, M. A. 1949. Nomenclatorial notes on generic names of agarics (Fungi: Agaricales). Bull. Bot. Gard. Buitenzorg 18(3):271–402 (especially pp. 371–376).

DOUGLAS, GERTRUDE E. 1918. The development of some exogenous species of agarics. Amer. Jour. Bot. 5:36–54.

DUFOUR, LEON MARIE. 1891. Atlas des champignons comestibles et vénéneux, pp. 1–80.

DUMÉE, P., M. GRANJEAN, ET R. MAIRE. 1912. Sur la synonymie et les affinités de l'*Hygrophorus marzuolus* (Fr.) Bres. Bull. Trimestr. Soc. Mycol. France 28:285–298.

EARLE, F. S. 1909. The genera of the North American gill fungi. New York Bot. Garden Bull. 5:373–451.

EKLUND, OLE. 1943(1944). Weitere Beiträge zur Pilzflora des Scharenarchipels SW-Finnlands. Memoranda Soc. Fauna et Flora Fennica 19:212–216.

ELLIS, J. B. 1876. New fungi found at New Field, New Jersey. Torrey Bot. Club Bull. 6:75–77.

FARLOW, W. G. 1929. Icones Farlowianae, pp. 3–120, pl. 103.

FAVRE, JULES. 1955. Les champignons superieurs de la zone Alpine de Parc National Suisse, pp. 3–212 (Hygrophoracees, pp. 33–36).

———. 1957. Agaricales nouvelles ou peu connues II. Schweiz. Zeitschr. für Pilzkunde 35:117–122.

———. 1960. Catalogue descriptif des champignons supérieurs de la zone subalpine du Parc National Suisse. Soc. Helvétique des Sciences Naturelles, Band 6:325–610, pls. 1–8.

——— ET C. POLUZZI. 1947. *Hygrophorus (Limacium) karstenii* Sacc. & Cub.-*Hygrophorus bicolor* Karst., non Berk. & Br. Schweiz. Zeitschr. für Pilzkunde 25:168–170.

——— ET CHARLES POLUZZI. 1948. Unsere Pilze. Vita Helvetica, pp. 71–76.

FAYOD, V. 1889. Prodrome d'une historie naturelle des Agaricines. Ann. Sci. Nat. VII (9):181–411.

FRIES, E. M. 1821. Systema Mycologicum 1:1–520.

———. 1835. Corpus florarum provincialum Sueciae. I. Florum scanicam scripsit Elias Fries.

———. 1838. Epicrisis Systematis Mycologici, pp. 1–610.

———. 1857 and 1863. Monographia Hymenomycetum Sueciae 1:1–484; 2:1–355.

———. 1860–66. Sveriges ätliga och giftiga svampar.

———. 1874. Hymenomycetes europaei sive Epicriseos systematis mycologici, pp. 1–755.

GILLET, C. C. 1874–78. Champignons (Fungi, Hyménomycètes) qui croissent en France, pp. 1–828.

GROVES, J. WALTON, SHEILA C. THOMSON, AND MARIA PANTIDOU. 1958. Notes on fungi from Northern Canada. III. Amanitaceae, Hygrophoraceae, Rhodophyllaceae, and Paxillaceae. The Canadian Field-Naturalist 72:133–138.

GÜSSOW, H. T. AND W. S. ODELL. 1927. Mushrooms and Toadstools, pp. 7–274.

HALLER, R. 1951a. *Hygrophorus nitiosus* Blytt. Schweiz. Zeitschr. für Pilzkunde 29:179–182.

———. 1951b. Bemerkungen zur Nomenklatur von Hygrophorus amoenus (Lasch) und Hygrophorus calyptraeformis Berk. Schweiz. Zeitschr. für Pilzkunde 29:182–183.

———. 1952. *Hygrophorus quietus* Kühner, Schürsporiger Saftling. Schweiz. Zeitschr. für Pilzkunde 30:180–183.

———. 1953. *Hygrophorus conico-palustris* nov. spec. (Hygrocybe conico-palustris.) Schweiz. Zeitschr. für Pilzkunde 31:141–145.

———. 1954. Beitrag zur Kenntnis der schweizerischen Hygrophoraceae. Schweiz. Zeitschr. für Pilzkunde 32:81–91.

———. 1955. Contribution a l'étude du genre Hygrocybe. Schweiz. Zeitschr. für Pilzkunde 33:169–172.

———. 1956. Beitrag zur Kenntnis der Schweitzerischen Hygrophoraceae. Schweiz. Zeitschr. für Pilzkunde 34:177–180.

——— UND G. MÉTROD. 1955. Beitrag zur Kenntnis der schweizerischen Hygrophoraceae. Schweiz. Zeitschr. für Pilzkunde 33:33–38.

HEIM, ROGER. 1947. Deux hygrophores nouveaux du Jura. Bull. Trimestr. Soc. Mycol. France 63:126–132.

HEIM, ROGER. 1957. Hygrophacées. Les Champignons d'Europe, Tome II, pp. 195–220.

HEINEMANN, P. 1951. Quelques récoltes mycologiques intéressantes de 1950. Nat. Belges Bull. Mens. 32:160, 161.

———. 1952–53. Les Hygrophores. Nat. Belges Bull. Mens. 33:125–128; 34:2–6; 25–28.

HERINK, JOSEPH. 1959. Species Famileae Hygrophoracearum. Acta Musei Bohemiae, Septentr. Liberecensis 1:53–86. Taf. 1–11.

HONGO, TSUGUO. 1951a. Larger fungi of the Provinces of Omi and Yamashiro. II. Acta Phytotax. et Geobot. 14(3):72–76. Illus.

———. 1951b. Notes on Japanese larger fungi. Jour. Jap. Bot. 26:23–26.

———. 1951c. Notes on Japanese larger fungi (2). Jour. Jap. Bot. 26:141–146.

———. 1952a. Notes on Japanese larger fungi (3). Jour. Jap. Bot. 27(5):159–164. Illus.

———. 1952b. Larger fungi of the Provinces of Omi and Yamashiro. Jour. Jap. Bot. 27:189–194.

———. 1952c. Notes on Japanese larger fungi. IV. Jour. Jap. Bot. 27(12):368–372. Illus.

———. 1952d. Interesting fungi of Omi. I. Kenkyu-Ronshu 1:93–95.

———. 1953. Interesting fungi of Omi. II. Kenkyu-Ronshu 2:48–50.

———. 1954. Two new agarics from Omi. Acta Phytotax. et Geobot. 15(4):102–104. Illus.

———. 1955a. Notes on Japanese larger fungi (6). Jour. Jap. Bot. 30(3):73–79. Illus.

———. 1955b. Notes on Japanese larger fungi (7). Jour. Jap. Bot. 30(7):215–222. Illus.

———. 1957. Notes on Japanese larger fungi (11). Jour. Jap. Bot. 32(7):208–214.

———. 1958a. Studies on the Agaricales of Japan. 1. The genus *Hygrophorus* in Shiga-Prefecture (1). Jour. Jap. Bot. 33(4):97–103.

———. 1958b. Studies on the Agaricales of Japan (1). The genus *Hygrophorus* in Shiga-Prefecture (2). Jour. Jap. Bot. 33(5):134–141.

HORA, F. B. AND P. D. ORTON. 1955. Three new British agaric records. Trans. Brit. Mycol. Soc. 38:400–404.

HOWE, E. C. 1874. New fungi. Torrey Bot. Club Bull. 5:43.

IMAI, SANSHI. 1938. Studies on the Agaricaceae of Hokkaido I. Jour. Fac. Agri. Hokkaido Imperial Univ. 43:1–178.

———. 1939. Studia agaricacearum Japonicarum. I. Bot. Mag. (Tokyo) 53:392–399.

———. 1941. Studia agaricacearum Japonicarum. II, III. Bot. Mag. (Tokyo) 55:444–452; 514–520.

JACQUIN, N. J. VON. 1778–81. Miscellanea Austriaca ad Botanicum, Chemiam et Historiam Naturalem Spectantia, vols. 1–2.

JENNINGS, O. E. 1936. Algae and fungi of Southampton Island. Memoirs Carnegie Mus. 12:1–4, pl. 29.

JOSSERAND, M. 1933. Notes critiques sur quelques champignons de la région lyonnaise (1ʳᵉ Série). Bull. Trimestr. Soc. Mycol. France 49:340–376.

———. 1937. Notes critiques sur quelques champignons de la région lyonnaise (2ʳᵉ Série). Bull. Trimestr. Soc. Mycol. France 53:175–230.

————. 1943. Notes critiques sur quelques champignons de la région lyonnaise. (3ᵉ Série). Bull. Trimestr. Soc. Mycol. France 59:5–34. Illus.

————. 1959. Notes critiques sur quelques champignons de la région lyonnaise. Bull. Trimestr. Soc. Mycol. France 75:359–404.

JUILLARD-HARTMANN, G. 1919. Iconographie des Champignons Superieurs, vols. I–V.

KALCHBRENNER, KAROLY. 1873–77. Icones Selectae Hymenomycetum Hungariae, pp. 1–66, pls. 1–40.

KANOUSE, BESSIE B. 1950. A study of *Peziza bronca* Peck. Mycologia 42:497–502.

KARSTEN, P. A. 1879. Rysslands, Finlands, och den Skandinaviska halföns Hattsvampar. Bidr. Finl. Nat. Folk 32:1–571.

KAUFFMAN, C. H. 1906. Unreported Michigan fungi. Mich. Acad. Sci. Rept. 8:26.

————. 1918. Hygrophorus. *In* The Agaricaceae of Michigan, pp. 172–203. Lansing, Mich.

————. 1922. The mycological flora of the higher Rockies of Colorado. Papers Mich. Acad. Sci., Arts and Letters 1:101–150.

————. 1926. The fungus flora of Mt. Hood with some new species. Papers Mich. Acad. Sci., Arts and Letters 5:115–148.

———— AND ALEXANDER SMITH. 1933. Agarics collected in the vicinity of Rock River, Michigan in 1929. Papers Mich. Acad. Sci., Arts and Letters. 17:153–200.

KAWAMURA, SEIICHI. 1930. The Japanese Fungi, pl. 244 (in color).

KONRAD, P. 1929. Notes critiques sur quelques champignons du Jura. Quatrième série. Bull. Trimestr. Soc. Mycol. France 45:35–77.

————. 1936. Notes critiques sur quelques champignons du Jura. Sixième et dernière série. Bull. Trimestr. Soc. Mycol. France 52:35–53.

KOPS, JAN, F. W. VANEEDEN, AND L. VUYCK. Flora Batava. Afbeelding en Beschrijving der Nederlandische Gewassen. Aflevering 396e–299e. Pls. 1977–1992.

KRIEGER, LOUIS C. C. 1927. New or otherwise interesting Agaricaceae from the United States and Canada. Mycologia 19:308–314, pls. 31–36.

————. 1936. The Mushroom Handbook, pp. 11–538.

KÜHNER, R. 1936. Contribution a l'étude des Hyménomycètes et specialement des Agaricacés. Le Botaniste 17:5–224.

————. 1949. *Hygrophorus piceae* sp. nov., champignon méconnu des sapinières de montagne, voisin de H. eburneus. Bull. Mens. Soc. Linneenne Lyon 18:179–182.

———— ET HENRI ROMAGNESI. 1953. III. Hygrophoracées. *In* Flore Analytique des Champignons Supérieurs, pp. 49–62.

KUMMER, PAUL. 1871. Der Führer in die Pilzkunde, pp. 1–146.

LANGE, JAKOB E. 1923. Studies in the agarics of Denmark. V. Dansk Botanisk Arkiv. 4(4):1–56.

————. 1935–40. Flora Agaricina Danica. 1–5. 200 col. pls.

LANGE, MORTEN. 1948. The agarics of Maglemose. A study in the ecology of the agarics. Dansk Botanisk Arkiv. 13:9–141.

————. 1954. *Coprinus insignis* and *Hygrocybe schulzeri* in Denmark. Bot. Tidsskr. 50:175–179.

LANGE, MORTEN. 1955. Macromycestes. II. Greenland Agaricales Meddel. Grönland 147(11):1–69. Illus. map.

———— AND ERIK BILLE HANSEN. 1949–50. Notes on Danish fungi. Friesia 4(1/2):61–65.

LARSEN, POUL. 1931–32. Fungi of Iceland. The Botany of Iceland, II, III.

LASCH, WILHELM GOTTFRIED. 1829. Enumeratio Hymenomycetum pileatorum marchiae brandenburgicae, nondum in floris nostratibus nominatorum, cum observationibus in cognitos et novorum descriptionibus. Linnaea 4:518–553.

LUNDELL, SETH. 1932. Bidrag till Uppsalatraktens hymenomycetflora. I. Vardsatra naturpark. K. Svenska Vetenskapsakad. Skrifter i Naturskyddsärenden 22:1–35.

MAIRE, R. 1902. Recherches cytologiques et taxonomiques sur la Basidiomycetes. Bull. Trimestr. Soc. Mycol. France (separate issue) 18:1–212.

————. 1910. Some new and interesting British Hymenomycetes gathered at the Baslow fungus foray, 1909. Trans. Brit. Mycol. Soc. 3(part 3): 170.

————. 1926. Remarques sur les causes de divergences entre les auteurs au sujet des dimensions des spores. Bull. Trimestr. Soc. Mycol. France 42:43–50.

————. 1928. Diagnoses de champignons inédits de l'Afrique du Nord. Bull. Trimestr. Soc. Mycol. France 44:37–56.

MALENCON, G. 1930. Hygrophorus laetus (Pers.) Fr. Bull. Trimestr. Soc. Mycol. France 45:atlas, pl. 37. 1 col. pl.

————. 1953. L'origine des revêtements piléiques chez les champignons supérieurs. Bull. Trimestr. Soc. Mycol. France 69:425–428.

MASSEE, GEORGE E. 1892. Some West Indian fungi. Jour. Bot. 30:161–164.

MÉTROD, G. 1938a. Hygrophorus tephroleucus (Fries et Persoon) sensu Bresadola. Bull. Trimestr. Soc. Mycol. France 54:70–72.

————. 1938b. Descriptions de quelques Agarics peu communs. Rev. Mycol. 3:148–156.

————. 1941. Hygrophores cystidiés. Rev. Mycol. 6:102–107. 4 fig.

MICHAEL, EDMUND. 1904. Führer f. Pilzfreunde, vol. 2.

MÖLLER, F. H. 1945. Fungi of the Faeröes. I, p. 295. Copenhagen.

————. 1958. Fungi of the Faeröes. II, p. 286. Copenhagen.

MORGAN, A. P. 1883. The mycologic flora of the Miami Valley, O. Cincinnati Soc. Nat. Hist. Jour. 6:173–199.

MOSER, MEINHARD. 1950. Neue Pilzfunde aus Tirol. Sydowia 4:84–123.

————. 1955. Hygrophoraceae. In Kleine Kryptogamen-flora, Band II b. pp. 36–46.

MURRILL, W. A. 1910. Illustrations of fungi—VII. Mycologia 2:159–163. Plate 27, figs. 1–10.

————. 1911. The Agaricaceae of tropical North America—III. Mycologia 3:189–199.

————. 1912a. The Agaricaceae of the Pacific Coast. Mycologia 4:205–217.

————. 1912b. New combinations of Tropical agarics. Mycologia 4:331–332.

————. 1913. The Agaricaceae of the Pacific Coast—IV. New species of Clitocybe and Melanoleuca. Mycologia 5:206–223.

————. 1916. *Hydrocybe, Camarophyllus* and *Hygrophorus*. North Amer. Flora 9:376–396.

————. 1922. Hygrophorus caprinus. Mycologia 14:48–49.

————. 1938. New Florida agarics. Mycologia 30:359–371.

————. 1939a. Some Florida gill-fungi. Elisha Mitchell Sci. Soc. Jour. 55:361–372.

————. 1939b. Oligocene island fungi. Torrey Bot. Club Bull. 66:151–160.

————. 1940. Additions to Florida fungi. III. Torrey Bot. Club Bull. 67:145–154.

————. 1941. More Florida novelties. Mycologia 33:434–448.

————. 1942. New fungi from Florida. Lloydia 5:136–157.

————. 1943. Some southern novelties. Mycologia 35:422–433.

————. 1944. More fungi from Florida. Lloydia 7:303–327.

————. 1945. New Florida fungi. Florida Acad. Sci. Proc. 7:107–127.

NÜESCH, EMIL. 1922. Die Weissporigen Hygrophoreen. Heilbronn a. Neckar.

ORTON, P. D. 1960. New check list of British agarics and boleti. III. Notes on genera and species in the list. Trans. Brit. Mycol. Soc. 43:159–439.

PAMMEL, L. H. 1928. A new species of *Hygrophorus*. Iowa State Coll. Jour. Sci. 2:115.

PARKER-RHODES, A. F. 1951. The Basidiomycetes of Skokholm Island. VI. Observations on certain uncommon species and varieties. Trans. Brit. Mycol. Soc. 34:360–367.

————. 1954. The Basidiomycetes of Skokholm Island. XI. Intramycelial variation in Hygrocybe turunda var. lepida. New Phytol. 53:145–154.

————. 1957. Some phenological observations on basidiomycetes. New Phytol. 56:193–206.

PATOUILLARD, NARCISSE. 1883–89. Fabulae Analytical Fungorum, vols. 1–2.

————. 1909. Quelques champignons de l'annam. Hygrophorus erinaceus n. sp. Bull. Trimestr. Soc. Mycol. France 25:10.

PEARSON, A. A. 1952. New records and observations. V. Trans. Brit. Mycol. Soc. 35:97–122.

PECK, CHARLES H. 1874. Report of the Botanist. N. Y. State Mus. Ann. Rept. 26:35–91.

————. 1878. Report of the Botanist. N. Y. State Mus. Ann. Rept. 29:29–82.

————. 1879. Report of the Botanist. N. Y. State Mus. Ann. Rept. 28:31–88. Pl. 1.

————. 1884. Report of the Botanist. N. Y. State Mus. Ann. Rept. 35:125–164.

————. 1887. New species of New York fungi. N. Y. State Mus. Bull. 1(2):5–24.

————. 1895a. New species of fungi. Torrey Bot. Club Bull. 22:198–211.

————. 1895b. New species of fungi. Torrey Bot. Club Bull. 22:485–493.

————. 1897. New species of fungi. Torrey Bot. Club Bull. 24:137–147.

————. 1898a. New species of fungi. Torrey Bot. Club Bull. 25:321–328.

————. 1898b. Report of the State Botanist. N. Y. State Mus. Ann. Rept. 51:267–321.

————. 1899. New species of fungi. Torrey Bot. Club Bull. 26:63–71.

PECK, CHARLES. 1901a. Report of the State Botanist on edible fungi of New York. N. S. State Mus. Mem. 3:131–234.

————. 1901b. Report of the State Botanist. N. Y. State Mus. Ann. Rept. 53:823–864.

————. 1901c. Report of the State Botanist. N. Y. State Mus. Ann. Rept. 54:131–195.

————. 1902a. New species of fungi. Torrey Bot. Club Bull. 29:69–74.

————. 1902b. Report of the State Botanist (1901). N. Y. State Mus. Bull. 10:929–984.

————. 1902c. Report of the State Botanist. N. Y. State Mus. Bull. 54:931–982.

————. 1903. Report of the State Botanist (1902). N. Y. State Mus. Bull. 67:23.

————. 1906. New species of fungi. Torrey Bot. Club Bull. 33:213–221.

————. 1907. New York species of *Hygrophorus*. N. Y. State Mus. Bull. 116:45–67.

————. 1909. Report of the State Botanist. N. Y. State Mus. Bull. 131:5–190.

PEYRONEL, B. 1922. Nuovi casi di rapporti micorizici tra basidiomiceti e fanerogame arboree. Boll. Soc. Bot. Ital. 1922:7–14.

PHILLIPS, WILLIAM. 1878–79. *Hygrophorus foetens* nov. spec. Grevillea 7:74.

POMERLEAU, RENE. 1951. Mushrooms of Eastern Canada and the United States, pp. 7–302.

QUÉLET, LUCIEN. 1872–75. Les Champignons du Jura et des Vosges. 1:1–320; 2:321–424; 3:1–128.

RAMSBOTTOM, JOHN. 1953. Mushrooms and Toadstools, pp. 1–306. Collins, St. James Place, London.

REA, CARLETON. 1922. British Basidiomycetae. Cambridge.

———— AND J. RAMSBOTTOM. 1929. Some fungus forays in America. Trans. Brit. Mycol. Soc. 14:293–299.

REID, DEREK A. 1955. New or interesting records of British Hymenomycetes. Trans. Brit. Mycol. Soc. 38:387–399.

REIJNDERS, A. F. M. 1948. Études sur le développement en l'organisation histologique des carpophores dans les Agaricales. Rec. Trav. Bot. Néerland. 41:213–396. 30 pl.

REUTER, ENZIO. 1944/45. Rättelse och tillägg angående tvenne svampfynd. Memoranda Soc. Fauna et Flora Fennice 21:16.

RICK, J. 1938. Agarici Riograndenses. Lilloa 2:251–316.

RICKEN, A. 1915. Die Blätterpilze. Leipzig.

RIDGWAY, ROBERT. 1912. Color Standards and Color Nomenclature. Washington, D. C.

ROZE, ERNST. 1876. Eassai d'une nouvelle classification des agaricinées. Bull. Soc. Bot. France 23:45–54.

SASS, JOHN E. 1929. The cytological basis for homothallism and heterothallism in the Agaricaceae. Amer. Jour. Bot. 16(9):663–701. 4 pl., 6 figs.

SCHAEFFER, JACOB CHRISTIAN. 1762–74. Fungorum qui in Bavaria et Palatinatu circa Ratisbonam nascuntur icones, vols. 1–4, pls. 1–330.

Schweinitz, L. D. de. 1822. Synopsis Fungorum Carolinae Superioris. Schr. Nat. Ges. Leipzig. 1:20–131.

Scopoli, J. A. 1772. Flora Carniolica, ed. 2. Vols. 1–2.

Singer, R. 1931. Pilze aus dem Kaukasus II. Ein Beitrag zur Flora Swanetiens und einiger angrenzender Täler. Beih. Bot. Centralbl. Abt. 248(3): 513–542.

———. 1936. Das System der Agaricales. Ann. Mycologici. 34:286–278.

———. 1940. Notes sur quelques Basidiomycètes. Rev. de Mycologie 5(n.s.):1–13.

———. 1943a. Type studies on Basidiomycètes. II. Mycologia 35:142–163.

———. 1943b. Das System der Agaricales. III. Ann. Mycologici. 41:1–189.

———. 1950. Type studies on Basidiomycètes. IV. Lilloa 23:147–246.

———. 1951. The "Agaricales" (mushrooms) in modern taxonomy. Lilloa 22:1–768.

———. 1952. The agarics of the Argentine Sector of Tierra del Fuego and limitrophous regions of the Magallanes Area. Sydowia 6:165–240.

———. 1955. Type studies on Basidiomycetes. VIII. Sydowia 9:367–431.

———. 1957. Fungi mexicani, series prima—Agaricales. Sydowia 11:354–374.

———. 1958. Fungi mexicani, series secunda—Agaricales. Sydowia 12:221–243.

——— y Antonio P. L. Digilio. 1951. Prodromo de la flora Agaricina Argentina. Lilloa 25:5–461.

Smith, Alexander H. 1934a. Unusual agarics from Michigan. Papers Mich. Acad. Sci., Arts and Letters 19:205–216.

———. 1934b. Investigations of two-spored forms in the genus Mycena. Mycologia 26:305–330.

———. 1935. Unusual agarics from Michigan II. Papers Mich. Acad. Sci., Arts and Letters 20:171–183.

———. 1937a. Unusual agarics from Michigan IV. Papers Mich. Acad. Sci., Arts and Letters 22:215–223.

———. 1937b. Notes on agarics from the western United States. Torrey Bot. Club Bull. 64:477–487.

———. 1939. Studies in the genus Cortinarius I. Contr. Univ. Mich. Herb.

———. 1941. New and unusual agarics from North America I. Contr. Univ. Mich. Herb. 5:1–73.

———. 1944. New North American agarics. Mycologia 36:242–262.

———. 1947. North American Species of Mycena. 521 pp. 99 pl., 56 fig. Univ. Michigan Press, Ann Arbor.

———. 1949. Mushrooms in their Natural Habitats, pp. 1–626. 231 color stereo-photographs. Sawyer's Inc., Portland, Oregon.

———. 1953. New and rare agarics from the Douglas Lake Region and Tahquamenon Falls State Park, Michigan, and an account of the North American species of Xeromphalina. Papers Mich. Acad. Sci., Arts and Letters 38:53–88. Illus.

——— and L. R. Hesler. 1939. Studies in North American species of Hygrophorus—I: The subgenus Limacium. Lloydia 2:1–62. 24 pl.

——— and L. R. Hesler. 1940. New and unusual agarics from the Great Smoky Mountains National Park. Elisha Mitchell Sci. Soc. Jour. 56:302–324. 6 pl., 2 fig.

SMITH, ALEXANDER H. AND L. R. HESLER. 1942. Studies in North American species of *Hygrophorus*. II. Lloydia 5:1–94. 18 pl.

———— AND L. R. HESLER. 1954. Additional North American Hygrophori. Sydowia 8:304–333.

———— AND ROLF SINGER. 1958. New species of Galerina. Mycologia 50:469–489.

STORDAL, JENS. 1952. Notater om storsop i Våle, Vestfold. Friesia 4:267–295. Illus.

SUMSTINE, DAVID R. 1941. Notes on some new or interesting fungi. Mycologia 33:17–22.

VELENOVSKY, J. 1926. Nové druhy agaricinef. Mykologia 3:70–72.

VITTADINI, CARLO. 1832–35. Descrizione dei Funghi Mangerecci piu Communi dell'Italia, pp. 1–364.

WAKEFIELD, ELSIE M. AND R. W. G. DENNIS. 1950. Common British Fungi, pl. 13–290.

WILLIAMS, E. M. 1899. Three edible species of *Hygrophorus*. Asa Gray Bull. 7:14–17.

WÜNSCHE, O. 1877. Die Pilze. Leipzig.

ZELLER, S. M. 1922. Contributions to our knowledge of Oregon fungi.—I. Mycologia 14:173–199.

Index